Youth

FUNDING GUIDE

Denise Lillya

Contributors:

Jessica Carver
Amy Rosser
John Smyth
Tom Traynor

DIRECTORY OF SOCIAL CHANGE

Published by
Directory of Social Change
24 Stephenson Way
London NW1 2DP
Tel. 08450 77 77 07; Fax 020 7391 4804
email publications@dsc.org.uk
www.dsc.org.uk
from whom further copies and a full books catalogue are available.

Directory of Social Change Northern Office
Federation House, Hope Street, Liverpool L1 9BW
Policy & Research 0151 708 0136

Directory of Social Change is a Registered Charity no. 800517

First published 1997
Second edition 2002
Third edition 2009

ISBN 978 1 906294 29 8

British Library Cataloguing in Publication Data
A catalogue record for this book is available from the British Library

Cover design by Kate Bass
Text designed by Kate Bass
Typeset by Marlinzo Services, Frome
Printed and bound by Page Bros, Norwich

Contents

Foreword

If we are going to change the world we need to start with the young people. Young people, in my experience, rarely let you down. I have spent a lifetime involved with them in many different guises but so often I come across a 'they'll never do that' attitude amongst many folk who should know better.

I recently ran a project involving ballet and 'disadvantaged' teenagers – I now do talks called 'It Can't Be Done'. Not only did they 'do it' but it has transformed lives, spawned new projects and, in its own way, changed the world.

Inevitably this requires funding but, if we truly believe in the cause, funding can be found. It is never easy but putting the individual young person at the centre of any appeal or bid will create a focus for success. This guide will steer you through the minefield of possibilities so that they, the young people, can change the world.

Good luck!

Keith Horsfall
Chief Executive
Leaps & Bounds Trust

Introduction

The third edition

'No one is born a good citizen; no nation is born a democracy. Rather, both are processes that continue to evolve over a lifetime. Young people must be included from birth. A society that cuts off from its youth severs its lifeline.'

Kofi Annan – Ghanaian diplomat, seventh secretary-general of the United Nations, recipient of the 2001 Nobel Peace Prize.

It's fair to say that most of us want the best for young people and are gratified when they learn, gain confidence, achieve, flourish and contribute in a positive way to society. However, some young people don't have the best of starts, have perhaps received little encouragement so far in their lives and have to work especially hard to have confidence, self-respect and respect for others. This book hopes to help these young people, their youth leaders and mentors, to access funding through various means and hopefully to gain a better understanding of funding for the voluntary sector in general.

Young people aspire, even if sometimes they are not confident enough to voice their aspirations and, given encouragement and help, have the potential to work to fulfil them. We should empower them to achieve their full potential – they can do great things.

Fundraising can be a long, slow process and is often frustrating, but patience, determination and keeping in mind the rewards at the end for the people you are working for is what good fundraisers are all about. Remember, it's important not to leave your fundraising until you desperately need the money – make it a regular agenda item and plan ahead.

Why publish a youth funding guide?

There is now more funding than ever available for organisations working with children and young people and in producing this guide we want to enable charities working with them to access sustainable and broad based sources of revenue and become more effective agents for social change.

Recent research on giving by grant-making trusts, companies and central government to the voluntary and community sector, published by DSC in *The Funders' Almanac 2008*, found that children and young people is the most popular beneficiary group to be specified by grant-making charities – this is a positive indicator of the help available for youth groups (see page 133 for more details on grant-making charities).

There have recently been major changes in statutory funding, with central government focusing more on national projects and organisations, often under contract. Local authorities and other local public bodies are beginning to exercise increased authority over their budgets, with local strategic partnerships aiming to influence funding allocations. Also, grantmaking has commonly been replaced by procurement, with service providers being selected through competitive tendering processes. More information on this can be found in chapters 11 and 12.

In recent years the voluntary or 'third' sector has been high on the political agenda and government is now a major funder for voluntary organisations. According to *The Funders' Almanac 2008* the voluntary sector is currently funded by central government grant programmes totalling £1.4 billion, although the overall amount of statutory income into the sector is estimated at around £10.5 billion (*The UK Civil Society Almanac 2008*, NCVO), highlighting the significance of locally administered funds.

Children and young people are a priority and an example of this in practice is the government programme, Every Child Matters: Change for Children, a new approach to the wellbeing of children and young people from birth to age 19.

The government's aim is for every child, whatever their background or circumstances, to have the support they need to:

- be healthy
- stay safe
- enjoy and achieve
- make a positive contribution
- achieve economic wellbeing.

This guide brings together information available on funding from various sources including central and local government, grant-making charities, the public, companies and the National Lottery, together with help and advice on how to access it.

The reach of the book

This third edition, as with the second, generally covers England only, as funding arrangements are very different in Northern Ireland, Scotland and Wales, (although some grantmakers listed will give throughout the UK and overseas). It aims to highlight a wide range of funding sources for young people and focuses on the work of organisations, not individuals.

We have listed the main grantmakers, funding programmes and partnerships and have also provided examples of success stories in the hope that youth leaders and fundraisers can see what can be achieved.

For anyone to keep absolutely up to date with funding developments, web access is essential and those groups that are not fortunate enough to have their own computers will be able to access, free of charge, those at a local library or perhaps make arrangements with another group to use theirs.

The research for the guide has been carried out as fully and carefully as possible, but there may be funding sources that have been missed and some information may be incomplete or will become out of date. If any reader comes across omissions or mistakes in the book, please let us know so that they can be rectified in future editions. Please call the Research Department of the Directory of Social Change (0151 708 0136) or email: research@dsc.org.uk.

Acknowledgements and thanks

Many people have been generous in giving their time, expertise, insight and encouragement and I am very grateful to all those who have contributed to this guide. To name everyone would be impossible but special thanks to Keith Horsfall, Chief Executive of Leaps & Bounds for the inspirational work of that organisation and for writing the foreword for this guide, May de Silva, Chief Executive of Women into Politics in Northern Ireland for her expertise in European funding and her contribution to that chapter and to Kate Welham of Bradford University for her knowledge of funding for young people and her helpful contributions.

I hope this book is useful to you in your search for funding and the development of your organisation.

Working with young people has its own rewards, so enjoy what you do and you'll never work another day in your life – pass it on.

How to use this guide

The first six chapters of this guide give you the basic tools to start fundraising and to increase your chances of success. Chapters 7 to 13 outline the funding sources with details of those that support work with young people. Chapter 14 gives information on charitable status, the legal implications of becoming a registered charity and how to register your group with the Charity Commission. Chapter 15 deals with tax and VAT.

The main sources of funding and support are:

Grant-making charities

These charities exist to give money to other charities. Some are particularly interested in children and young people; others in general welfare or education; others in certain geographical areas. Most support salaries and project costs for up to three years; others give small one-off grants for equipment or individuals.

For further information, see Chapter 8 *Raising money from grant-making charities.*

The National Lottery

This supports good causes through its distribution boards. Some of these give mainly capital grants (building, equipment, etc.); others give revenue grants as well (i.e. salaries and running costs).

For further information, see Chapter 9 *The Big Lottery Fund.*

Members, friends, the local community and the public

Many youth organisations survive on membership subscriptions and fundraising from the general public. The public is still one of the largest funders of youth work through sponsored events, buying raffle tickets and contributing to collections and subscriptions. This funding tends to come with fewer strings attached. There is a list of useful addresses and sources of information at the end of the guide.

For further information, see Chapter 7 *Raising support from the public.*

Local authorities

Support for project costs, programme development, equipment, salaries and so on can still be raised from your local authority. Each will be different and there are guidelines for making your approach. Contractual arrangements are increasingly entered into with local authorities for the provision of services, and the nature of this funding has both increased and become more dependent on conditions.

For further information, see Chapter 11 *Raising money from local authorities.*

Central and regional government

Support for youth organisations is available through various government departments which can help with project costs that meet their clearly defined priorities (for example, regeneration, rural development, social inclusion).

For further information, see Chapter 12 *Raising money from government.*

European money

There is a variety of schemes available from Europe, and young people are often a focus area of the programmes. Programmes usually require matching funding from other sources, and many are tied to geographical areas, economic outcomes or capital projects. Some are aimed specifically at young people (for example, Youth in Action).

For further information, see Chapter 13 *Raising money from Europe.*

Companies

Company support is extensive and varied and is not just about cash. Links with a company can secure donations, gifts in kind, professional advice and expertise, profile-raising and sponsorship.

For further information, see Chapter 10 *Winning company support.*

1 Getting started in fundraising

Background

This chapter explains the main challenges facing organisations that are looking for funding and provides suggestions on how to meet them.

Fundraising today

Every organisation needs money to meet its running and project costs – to pay staff salaries and office overheads, to maintain any buildings or vehicles and, importantly, to develop programmes for the future.

Given the short-term nature of most current grant regimes, many organisations find themselves continually involved in fundraising, whether by holding fundraising events or making formal applications to other organisations.

Part of the challenge of being involved with a charity – whether as a member, volunteer, member of staff or trustee – can be the fundraising aspect, with charity workers involving the public in their enthusiasm and commitment by holding events designed to publicise the charity's aims, vision and work and to involve the public in its goals. These events can be productive in ways other than financial gain and can show the public the charity's successes, imagination and creativity.

Fundraising by application to grant-making bodies, companies or other organisations is much less fun and requires a more formal and structured approach.

Fundraising in general has become more difficult in the competition between charities for donations and grants. New statutory regulations following the Charities Act 2006 impose further requirements on charity trustees to ensure the integrity of their fundraising methods and the protection of charity funds.

1

It is important for charity trustees in their fundraising to be aware of, and sensitive to, public opinion and to manage and control their fundraising by adopting the highest standards to protect the monies raised and the integrity of their charity and the sector as a whole.

It is also important for fundraisers to be accurate and truthful when applying for funds, whether by way of appeal, collection box or application to grant-making bodies. They also need to decide on, and make known, the contingency provisions if the money raised is insufficient for the purpose or if there is a surplus.

A planned budget with regular forecasting is a necessary management tool to show the amount of money you plan to spend, the amount already raised or promised and the extra you will need to meet your outgoings for the year.

You should monitor your progress in fundraising by keeping records of all money received or promised, and by preparing and discussing management accounts at regular management meetings. If your income isn't coming in as planned, then you will need to take some sort of action – step up your fundraising programme, find and develop new sources of funds, cut costs, defer planned projects or agree to subsidise the deficit out of your reserves.

Creating a viable and sustainable organisation

Fundraising is about helping to create or maintain a viable and strong organisation which is able to sustain itself in the future.

There are many ways of doing this. One is to build a substantial and active donor base – getting people to support you who sympathise with your aims and who will continue to give their support over a long period. Other ways include:

- organising fundraising events (which can create a regular and continuing source of income)
- creating capital within your organisation, such as a capital fund for buildings or equipment (especially when this reduces your need for running costs or can help you generate an income)
- developing income generating schemes for the organisation itself.

Many organisations are addressing long-term needs – for example, through community development, which will not yield immediate results, or in looking after young people with disabilities where there is a continuing commitment to provide care well into the future.

You need to create an organisation that is financially strong in the long as well as the short term, rather than one that is unstable and running in crisis mode from year to year or month to month. Financial concerns can affect the morale of the whole organisation. Crisis fundraising is time consuming and increasingly difficult – and in the end you will find you run out of goodwill. You need to find ways of strengthening the financial position of your organisation and this means developing a sensible fundraising strategy for the future.

Your supporters

Your supporters are a very useful resource to you. They may provide financial help or attract financial support from other sources. Importantly, they can volunteer or by their efforts and enthusiasm encourage friends who are also willing to support you. They provide an indication of the level of support that your organisation is attracting and therefore can add extra resources for your organisation and strength to any lobbying and campaigning work.

You need to think about what kind of supporters you would like to attract and who your work will appeal to: they might be from a particular type of business or profession, perhaps students or activists, women, people from minority backgrounds or perhaps retired people with some spare time to give. You will need to think about how best to identify them, the sort of message they will respond to and in what format this should be.

Reducing dependency

Many organisations are funded by only one or a handful of donors or funders. If one of the grants is withdrawn or sponsorship ceases, this can create a financial crisis. It may also be difficult to determine your own agenda if you are constantly having to adapt to the priorities or terms and conditions of a key donor or funder.

Broadening your fundraising base can reduce this dependency. You need to decide whether your organisation is too dependent on any one source. You might then see if you can build some stability by developing alternative sources of income. See 'Developing independent sources of funding' on page 11.

Key principles

Asking for money

When asking for money you need to be clear about exactly what you want, while being aware of what that particular donor may be able and/or willing to give. You must also make it as easy as possible for the donor to respond.

The personal approach

The general rule is that the more personal you can make your approach, the more effective you will be. Consider the following methods of approach, starting with the most effective:

- Ask someone face to face.
- Telephone someone to ask for support.
- Write a personal letter to someone asking for support.
- Give a presentation to a group of people.
- Organise a meeting at your project where the prospective donor/s can see your work and meet some of the beneficiaries.
- Put out a request on your website (the people who visit it are likely to be interested in what you are doing).
- Ask someone with a high profile who has already given, such as a business leader or expert in the field, to make the approach on your behalf. This can be more effective than a request from your fundraiser or project leader as it shows that someone with a reputation to maintain endorses what you are doing.
- Send an appeal to lots of people. Many fundraisers prefer to send letters asking for support and this is sometimes the only way to reach a large group. However, this is not the most effective way of asking.

Understanding the donor's viewpoint

The funder or donor will have their own set of criteria by which your application or appeal is assessed. The larger grant givers will have the responsibility of dealing with charitable or public funds and need to ensure that these are used in line with their own purposes. They are accountable and need to be able to demonstrate transparency in their giving. They also need to be confident that there is a good chance of the project succeeding in its aims and outcomes. They will use their own set of criteria – who and where they want to benefit, the financial procedures they require an organisation to have in place, procedures for how you will monitor and evaluate your project, and what the outcomes are expected to be, etc.

A donor may have personal reasons for wanting to give. They might support a drama project for young disadvantaged people because they themselves were at one time helped through this sort of group, or a cancer charity because a relative has benefited from a similar organisation. They may feel strongly about an issue – such as the environment – and want to do something about it.

In supporting your cause they are also supporting *their* cause, doing something they feel needs doing and that they want to see done. You need to recognise this and try to discover what will trigger a positive response from the person/ organisation you are asking.

Fundraising is all about people

People give to help other people or because they want to create a better world and your job as a fundraiser is to show how you can help them to achieve this. One way of doing this is through case studies – illustrating your work with examples of who you have been able to help, how you have been able to change their lives and the difference that a donation has made.

Another way is to focus your fundraising on particular aspects of your work: the drama project you are planning and how it will improve young people's lives or the YouthBank UK programme that enables young people to act as grantmakers to other young people in their local community. By focusing on specific projects rather than the overall work of the organisation, it makes it easier to excite and enthuse your donors.

Fundraising is selling

Fundraising is a two-stage process. It is about showing people why your work is important and effective and only then persuading them to give. You should demonstrate that there is a need for the work you are undertaking and that you can do something useful to address it given their support. If they agree with you that the need is there and that your organisation is capable of doing something to make a difference, then provided you meet their criteria, they will want to support you – your success is their success.

Credibility and communication

People prefer to give to organisations and causes they have heard about and think well of. Your organisation's credibility and reputation are important. Media coverage of your work, making known your successes in the newsletters you send to supporters and getting endorsements about the quality of your work from experts and prominent figures can all help give people confidence that you are doing a worthwhile and successful job. This then makes it much easier for you to ask for support.

How to ask a donor

There are various ways of asking for money and you might want to consider some of the following:

- Ask for a specific sum to cover a particular item of expenditure (for example, £500 to purchase learning toys for younger children with disabilities).
- Give a shopping list of different items at different prices (for example, if you are equipping music workshops, you can list all the items you will need to purchase, put a price against each and ask a donor to contribute to one or more). The price does not have to be just the direct cost of buying the item, but can include a reasonable overhead allocation.
- Show the cost per client in your user group as a unit cost, and ask the donor to support one or more units (for example, at a homework club, show how much it costs for a child to attend for a week or a term, and ask a supporter to sponsor a child for a week, a term or a year).
- Give examples of gifts already received.
- Provide a 'shopping list', breaking down your appeal total into numbers of gifts of different sizes that you need if you are to reach your target. This technique is commonly used in major capital appeals.

Case study

Richard House Children's Hospice

Sample shopping list

Richard House Children's Hospice is a registered charity and has been providing care and support for life-limited and life-threatened children and their families since 2000.

'We accompany them during the child or young person's journey through life to death, creating positive experiences along the way which become good memories for the future.'

This sample shopping list is taken with kind permission from Richard House's website:

Shopping list

Richard House Children's Hospice depends on voluntary donations. Without your support the hospice could not offer its vital services to children, young people and their families.

Below is a partial shopping list, showing what your donation could be used for:

- A memory book £3.50
- A set of finger paints £5
- A session in the multisensory room £47
- A day trip out, including staff costs £60
- One fortnight in family flats £250
- Care – one day session £514
- Care – one day and night £1,028
- Laundry service £3,000
- Care team uniforms £3,500
- Care – five days and nights £5,140
- Medical cover (after-hours GP) £6,000
- Disposable and medical equipment £8,000
- Physio and occupational therapy £9,000
- Salary of one play and care worker £20,620*
- Salary of a respite and palliative care nurse £28,945*
- Cost to run Richard House – one day £7,814
- Cost to run Richard House – one week £54,846

The cost of keeping Richard House open for one year is currently £ 3.1 million of which we need to raise £1.8 million through voluntary donations.

*Including pension and national insurance, but not unsocial hours pay.

Saying thank you

Saying thank you is extremely important. It recognises and values the donor's generosity, it makes the donor feel better about your organisation and it might also encourage them to give again.

Telephoning or writing to your donors saying how thrilled you were to receive their gift and how it is to be used makes the donor feel that they or their organisation are doing a good job and that their money will have a real impact. This is a very personal approach to thanking your supporters and may not be something you are practically able to do. However, even if you can't show your appreciation for every gift made, you should make sure you thank your donors periodically – at least once or twice a year.

Long-term involvement and commitment

What you really want are people who will give to you regularly and substantially. The effort you make in finding a donor and persuading them to give will be most effective if they continue to give over a few years, maybe increasing their level of giving over time. To achieve this means getting them involved with the work of your organisation and committed to its success by:

- saying thank you immediately and telling them what you plan to do with their money
- regular reporting back, showing them what you have achieved with their contribution
- sharing your ideas and hopes for the future
- encouraging them to visit you and meet some of the people they have been helping
- inviting them to meet with the staff and volunteers who are actually doing the work.

Accountability and reporting back

When you accept a donation from somebody, you are responsible for seeing that the money:

- is spent on the purposes for which it was raised – failure to do this is a breach of trust
- is well spent and actually achieves something
- follows an audit trail.

You should always report back to the donor to show them that you have used their money effectively, and that their support has made a difference. You can do this by telephoning, sending a personal letter, a project report or a newsletter, by post or by email. This is not only polite, it is good fundraising practice – an enthusiastic donor who has seen the money make a difference may consider becoming a more committed supporter.

You should be aware that with the growing variety of methods and media used by charities to fundraise from their existing supporters and the general public, such as face-to-face 'clipboard' fundraising, emails and SMS, the accountability and transparency of charities is essential.

Different approaches to fundraising

Besides funding the work, you will also need to fund the organisation and its future. There are several factors to consider.

1) Capital developments

Capital developments, such as acquiring new buildings or IT systems, can have an impact on future fundraising needs in four ways. On the plus side:

- they can reduce operating costs
- they can generate income from fees and charges (for example, from letting out space)
- they can generate a greater capacity to fundraise (for example, when organising a major appeal you will be building a database of important contacts which you can utilise later on for further support).

On the minus side:

- they may increase your revenue costs if they require extra people to run them.

2) Endowment

Many organisations want to develop an endowment – that is, a capital reserve which can be invested to produce a regular income for the organisation. Some approach major donors for contributions to this fund; others set aside some of their income each year. They feel that this will give them greater financial security, remove some of the fundraising pressure or act as a reserve in times of unexpected difficulties. However, most trusts and companies will prefer to fund your work directly rather than have their money tied up as an investment.

Case study

Successful endowment fundraising

The Christopher Edwards Endowment Fund for Sport

During his time as Vice Chancellor, Christopher transformed the University's relationship with the local community and the region as a whole. He was committed to raising aspirations in the city, taking an active role in creating employment and helping to combat feelings of disengagement amongst our young people, as well as improving accessibility to the University campus.

Under Christopher's guidance, a number of areas of excellence have been created within the University, and pioneering research has led to recognition on an international stage, particularly through facilities such as our Institute for Ageing and Health, and the North East England Stem Cell Institute.

To celebrate Christopher's achievements in his term as Vice Chancellor, an appeal to establish the Christopher Edwards Endowment Fund for Sport has been launched. This is a particular area of interest for Christopher, who supported the development of sporting activities throughout his tenure.

Since the introduction of Performance Sport two years ago, Newcastle has climbed from nineteenth position in the national British Universities Sports Association (BUSA) rankings in 2004/5 to ninth in 2006/7: an outstanding achievement.

Building on our flourishing reputation for sport, Christopher also oversaw the construction of the University's new Centre for Physical Recreation and Sport, which opened in July 2005; the establishment of our 'Sports Concession' scheme (which allows student athletes up to ten days' leave of absence when representing the University in key national events); and the employment of our first full-time rowing coach.

By raising £250,000 the Christopher Edwards Endowment Fund for Sport will be used to help continue the integration of sport, fitness, physical activity and wellbeing into life at Newcastle University.

Development and Alumni Relations Office, Newcastle University, Newcastle upon Tyne

It takes a lot of hard work and time to raise an endowment and there may be other, more suitable ways of fundraising for your organisation, to raise the money you need.

3) Developing independent sources of funding

There is a fundamental difference between an organisation that receives all its money from one source, and an organisation that receives money from several or many sources, each contributing towards the total requirement. Over-reliance on one source might give that donor too much influence over what the organisation should be doing and where it should be going. It creates a risk of failure – which the organisation will not be able to survive if the grant is cut back or withdrawn.

You need to decide whether your organisation's funding base is too narrow and, if it is, how you can broaden it. You will need to think about all the possible sources of income, and decide which are the most sensible for your organisation to develop.

On the other hand, although it is good to have a broad base of support, there is a danger of taking this principle too far and having so many small-scale donors that all your fundraising energies go into servicing them without being able to develop your fundraising further.

4) Developing a membership and a supporter base

A strong membership or supporter base helps create financial independence by:

- creating a constituency of support (the number of people who support you adds to your credibility as an organisation and gives you lobbying power)
- building a local base for your organisation (your relationship with your local community will be much closer if the funding is drawn from it rather than obtained externally)
- creating opportunities for further fundraising. Each donor can be asked to give regularly and more generously, to recruit other donors, to volunteer their time and skills, to donate items of equipment, or even to leave a legacy. The more people who are supporting you, the more opportunities you will have for developing your fundraising.

Some key issues

Before deciding who to approach there are some more general issues to think through.

- **Be cost conscious.** You need to monitor the money you spend carefully. Someone has to pay. Many charities exist to provide a service to beneficiaries that is free or highly subsidised. This means that the amount raised determines the volume of work that can be undertaken. However, you may be able to charge for your services and you need to decide if that is appropriate for you and your users. Alternatively, in the current contract culture, statutory bodies may be able to pay for the services you deliver. Either way, you must cost what you do carefully and accurately. Someone has to pay for it – your funders, your sponsors, your donors or your users.

- **Avoid risks.** The cash that you spend on your fundraising is intended to generate money to spend on your work. You shouldn't be speculating with it on high-risk fundraising schemes where there is a real possibility that it might be lost. Fundraisers must minimise risk. You might need to pilot or test a new fundraising idea. You should identify the worst case scenario and take whatever action you can to avoid it, insure yourself against it or even scrap it if it looks set to fail.

- **The long-term approach.** You can simply concentrate on getting cash now, or you can devote some of your fundraising resources to ensuring the longer-term flow of funds into your organisation. For example, committed giving by individuals and appeals for legacies have high costs in the short term, but their long-term value usually far outweighs that of casual giving.

- **The multiplier approach.** A good way to maximise fundraising results is to 'cascade'. A sponsored run can bring your organisation to the attention of a large number of people. Every runner will sign up sponsors, and some of these may subsequently become interested in becoming a member or a regular donor (rather than in simply sponsoring a friend). This cascade effect will multiply the number of people supporting you and the amount you raise.

- **Sustainability.** In an ideal world, your organisation would be structured so as to minimise the need for permanent fundraising. Even if this seems ambitious to you in your current situation, there are a number of ways of making yourself more sustainable and therefore financially more secure:
  - Develop a range of income-generating activities.
  - Develop partnerships with larger bodies capable of giving larger sums – government, for example.
  - Raise an endowment fund.

continued...

- Recruit volunteers and get support donated in kind.
- Develop income sources that continue over many years, such as a membership.
- Organise events that are repeatable, so that if they work they can be done again and again with less cost – and be even better next time.

■ **Time.** You need to be realistic about how long things will take. To go from £0 to £100,000 a year from grant-making trusts may require years of patient fundraising effort. To land your first major company sponsorship requires professionalism and good relationships that you may not yet have. To get your first 1,000 supporters is far harder than getting the next 1,000. Everything can take longer than you expect and there is a danger of being over-optimistic.

Accounting for fundraising

The following extract is taken directly from CC20 – Charities and fundraising on the Charity Commission website:

The costs of fundraising are a legitimate matter of public interest. Trustees should ensure that these costs are shown properly in the accounts. They include publicity costs associated with fundraising or raising the profile of the charity. They do not include costs of purely educational material produced by the charity as a way of achieving its purposes.

For those charities producing accruals accounts the Accounting and Reporting by Charities: Statement of Recommended Practice *(SORP 2005, revised July 2008) provides more detailed guidance.*

Appeals for funds
Whatever type of appeal is chosen by trustees to raise funds there are certain points that trustees should bear in mind:

■ *The purpose of the appeal should be clearly expressed. Where the appeal is for general funds then any specific project mentioned in the appeal document should be clearly identified as an example of the charity's work. Care needs to be taken so as not to mislead donors into thinking that their money will only be used for a particular project identified in the appeal literature where this is not the case.*

■ *If the appeal is for a specific project then it is very important that there are plans to deal with any unspent money and that these are reflected in the fundraising document. This will enable trustees to deal with any surplus funds that are raised over the appeal target or if the appeal fails to apply the money which was raised.*

We recommend that any funds raised for a special appeal be accounted for separately. One way to do this is to arrange for a separate bank account.

■ *All contributions, as far as possible, need to be made directly to the charity and be under the control of the trustees.*

■ *Where possible set an end date for the appeal.*

[Further information explaining in detail what to do if insufficient or surplus funds have been raised and plans have not been made is given on the Commission's website.]

Registered status to appear on certain documents

Trustees of registered charities with a gross income of £10,000 or more in the last financial year are required by section 5 of the 1993 Act to state, on a range of official documents, that the charity is a registered charity. The documents on which the statement must appear include notices, advertisements, material placed on websites, and other documents issued by or on behalf of a charity intended to persuade the reader to give money or property to the charity. This includes the solicitation of membership subscriptions.

If your club or organisation is not a registered charity, it is still prudent to follow the advice provided by the Charity Commission, as donors, supporters and sponsors will still expect accountability and transparency.

2 Developing a fundraising strategy

It is essential to spend time before undertaking any fundraising exercise to develop a strategy: some forms of fundraising can be costly and it is important to be sure that the costs will be justified in terms of a realistic return. The strategy will need to cover the following points.

- **The level of funding:** are funds required for a special project or part of the charity's rolling programme of work? How much is needed? Would it be possible to collaborate with other charities operating in the same field to meet the need?

- **Possible sources of funding:** for example, grants from local or central government, grant-making charities or companies.

- **The resources available to support fundraising:** fundraising costs money. Costs can range from producing appeal literature to employing a professional fundraiser and organising fundraising events.

- **The proportion of gross receipts that will be left after fundraising costs have been met:** the trustees should agree in advance the likely proportion of the gross receipts that will be spent on the costs of fundraising. Actual performance needs to be monitored against that target and the trustees should satisfy themselves that the expenditure is justified.

Strategy is about organising your ideas to produce a viable plan to take you forward beyond the current year. If you just need a small amount for equipment, for example, all you may need to do is approach an individual or business sympathetic to your cause or organisation. This would not need a strategic plan. However, if you have wider hopes and new projects to fund, you will need to spend some time and be creative in developing a sustainable fundraising strategy.

Your fundraising strategy is an integral part of your business plan and it should indicate where your organisation is expected to be in a specified number of years. Business plans should be flexible and should be updated every year to incorporate changes and new ideas. You will also need to revise your strategy every two to three years.

There are few quick fundraising fixes: getting funding for a project takes time. It can take nine months or more to prepare, apply for and receive a grant from one of the larger funders. It may take years to build up to a really big event. Be realistic from the start about both how much time you have and how much time it will take.

Planning your approach

Spending time on planning your fundraising strategy is a good investment: forward planning can save time and resources and prevent difficulties later. It is also a sign of a proactive charity and this is attractive to funders.

The starting point for your fundraising strategy should be to define the needs of the organisation. This can be done at three levels.

To continue at the current scale of operation

For the organisation to continue at its present level, how much funding do you need? How much is already in place or assured and how much do you need to raise to meet spending requirements?

Expanding to meet a growing need

Most organisations would easily be able to target and benefit more beneficiaries if they had the resources. They often face a growing problem, which means there is a wish to expand the organisation to meet the need.

It might be helpful to ask yourself the following questions.

- What is the current level of unmet need?
- What will happen if nothing is done?
- How and why are the needs growing and what changes do you foresee over the next few years?
- What should your organisation be doing to respond to the challenges of the future?
- Who else is tackling the need?
- How does your plan fit in with what others are doing?
- Is your idea an effective way of addressing the need?
- Could or should you be providing solutions to the problem rather than simply addressing the need?
- Are there ways of collaborating with others that could combine efforts and resources to save money and make a greater impact?

- Is it just a case of expanding what you are already doing or do you need to develop new mechanisms to address the problem?
- Will staff or volunteers need further development and training?

Expanding and developing your organisation's work

Organisations need to be flexible and forward thinking if they are to meet the needs of their beneficiaries and develop in order to meet changing needs. For example, changes in demographics caused by immigration into a particular area or the closure of industries resulting in people moving away from an area will require changes in the organisation's services.

It may be necessary to extend your work, evaluate your impact, undertake research, experiment, innovate and perhaps campaign. This all requires extra money and the resources to raise it.

Fundraising for projects

It is far easier to raise money for something specific than to appeal for administrative costs or general funds. Donors prefer that their money is going to fund something they are genuinely interested in and specific, such as buying specialist equipment for children with disabilities to use or providing a minibus for a young people's centre.

Many funders say they won't fund organisations, only their individual projects, and this is one reason to think of your work in project terms. The project should include the core costs necessary to run it, but it is discrete from the organisation's general funds.

It is easier to design, develop, market, monitor and control a specific project with its own budget and set outcomes than an entire organisation.

You should simply focus on a particular piece of work or activity instead of the whole organisation. A fundable project should be:

- **specific**, an identifiable item of expenditure or aspect of your work
- **important**, both to your organisation and to the need it is meeting – long-term impact is an added bonus
- **realistic and achievable**, giving the funder confidence that you will be able to deliver the intended targets and outcomes
- **good value**, so that it stands out in a competitive funding environment
- **topical**, looking at current issues and concerns

- **relevant to the donor**, meeting their known interests and priorities
- **a manageable size**, so that it won't overload the organisation.

To cost a project properly, you need to include all the direct and indirect costs that can reasonably be attributed to the running of the project; for example, an appropriate percentage of management salaries, the cost of occupying the building, using the phone, photocopying and so on. This is known as full cost recovery.

Projection of financial need

The next step is to make a financial projection of the resources you will need to undertake your planned programme of work over the next three to five years. This must take in all planned expenditure and all probable income. It should show you two things: the funding gap that needs to be met, and possible fall-back options if funding is not received. This is best illustrated by the following example.

Example of a funding projection for a small organisation

Source of income	Current year	Next year	Two years' time	Three years' time
Current local authority grant	10,000	10,000	5,000	nil
Grant from charitable trust	2,500	2,500	nil	nil
Membership subscriptions	250	250	250	250
Total committed income	**12,750**	**12,750**	**5,250**	**250**
Reserve at start of year	500	2,050	2,050	2,050
Current operational costs	10,000	12,500	15,000	15,000
New project costs	1,200	3,500	5,000	5,000
Projected fundraising target	**nil**	**3,250**	**14,750**	**14,250**

The example shows that the funding position for the current year is good, and that there is a small target to meet next year which is a realistic goal for fundraising. However in two years' time, as the major grants run out, these will need to be replaced or new ways developed to fund the organisation

Six key points to consider in your fundraising strategy

Most donors, whether they are big trusts, major companies or individual members of the public, receive many more requests each year than they can hope to respond favourably to. How are you going to construct your case so that it stands out from the others? Before you start to fundraise, you need to ask yourself:

■ **Who are you?** Are you reliable and professional, with a strong track record of good work successfully completed?

■ **What is the need that you intend to meet?** This should not simply be an emotive statement, but should include factual evidence about, for example, whether the situation is local or national; how many people it affects; why it is urgent.

■ **What is the solution that you offer?** This is where you can describe what you intend to do, the results you expect to obtain and how these will be monitored and measured. You may want to use examples of how similar projects have worked.

■ **Why should you do it?** This is where you establish your credibility. What other work have you done? Have you had good publicity for this? Do you involve volunteers and/or beneficiaries in your work? Do you have a good track record in attracting funding?

■ **How much do you need?** You need to have a clear idea of the total, who you intend to approach for the money, and how the total could be broken down for donors who want to contribute but could not possibly fund the whole thing.

■ **What future do you have?** If you can show that you have thought ahead and have attempted to achieve long-term stability, funders will be more inclined to support you.

Once you have the answers to these key questions, you will be able to use them in your fundraising, when you write an application to a trust or company or when you appeal to the public.

Measurement and control of fundraising

Your fundraising strategy should be flexible and you should update it from time to time to take account of changes, both inside and outside your organisation. You should aim to review that strategy each year and rewrite it every three to five years.

The first step with a new or revised strategy must be to ensure that all your committee members, staff and key volunteers understand it and accept it. It will not be possible for everyone to be involved in producing the strategy document, so before you finalise it, make sure that all the issues have been widely discussed. This process of consultation will help everyone feel more committed to the outcome.

Monitoring progress

Without a strategy and a detailed plan, it is hard to monitor how you are getting on.

Why monitoring is important
- To check your overall returns.
- To compare the effectiveness of different aspects of your fundraising.
- To justify the level of investment the charity is making.
- To help assess your fundraising performance.

You will need to keep a particularly close eye on:
- costs incurred by each fundraising method
- cash received
- pledges of future support received
- offers of help and support in kind received.

Monitoring is often easier for a small organisation. It can be surprisingly difficult for many larger organisations if their financial systems have not been designed to produce the information that fundraisers require.

To compare the effectiveness of each fundraising initiative, the fundraiser needs to know exactly how much time and money is being spent on it and what income it is producing.

Sample monthly monitoring sheet

Source	Income this month	Income this year	Budgeted income for the year	Direct costs	Indirect costs	Cost ratio
Collections						
Postal appeal						
Sponsored event						
General income						
Total						

Detailed measurement of fundraising

You can measure the effectiveness of your fundraising in a number of ways, although not all measures are appropriate to all situations. The most common measures are the cost ratio and the profit. You might find the sample table above useful when making your calculations.

The cost ratio is calculated by taking the direct income generated and dividing it by the total costs that can be attributed to that activity (including an estimate of the indirect costs). This is then expressed as a ratio (for example, 5:1) or a percentage (for example, 20%). The main problem is that it does not tell you how much you have raised.

For example, you may discover that your public speaking to a wide range of local groups and appealing for support raised £2,380 and cost only £340 (a ratio of 7:1 or 14%). On the other hand, you raised £17,200 from trusts at an estimated cost of £6,500 (a ratio of 2.6:1 or 38%). This makes the latter look less successful and can be misleading. You may have exhausted all the local speaking possibilities and so you cannot repeat your success, even if this has been your most cost-effective method of fundraising.

The cost ratio is an important management tool for controlling costs, but on its own it is not a sufficient measure of fundraising success. There are other measures which you can use.

If you are using the telephone to fundraise, you need to know how cost effective this method is. The first indicator is the response rate to your request (divide the number of successes by the total number approached). This method can similarly be used in postal appeals and payroll giving campaigns.

Knowing how many people have responded is not enough, you also need to know how they have responded and how much they have given. It may be good to get 10 people in 100 saying yes; but if they only give £5 each, this has not been cost effective in terms of time and money spent. You can then try to increase both the response rate and the average donation. For example, when you ask a supporter to renew their membership, why not suggest that they increase the level of their giving? When organising a sponsored event, you can ask people to sponsor by the minute rather than by the hour, and they are then likely to give more. If you ask a supporter to pay monthly contributions, you are likely to receive more than if you ask for quarterly or annual contributions.

Another measure is the yield. This is the income received divided by the number of people approached. Thus, if you mail 1,000 people and receive £550 in donations, the yield would be 55p per donor mailed.

Finally, you will need to have some way of measuring the impact of long-term or open-ended commitments. Your fundraising commitments have gained you a donor; you can measure the donation they have made, but many of them will go on to give further support, and the costs of getting this further support will be much lower than the costs of getting the first donation. A very few may even go on to make a major gift or leave you a legacy.

Another measure you can use is lifetime value. This is a useful measure because it helps you justify a higher level of initial expenditure on promotion and fundraising. For example, you mail 1,000 people and get 20 responses and a total of £550 in income. You predict that those 20 people on average will each make two further donations of the same amount. The total income you expect to receive from these donors is £1,650. The total cost is the cost of the initial mailing to 1,000 people plus the additional cost of further mailings to your 20 new supporters. From this you can calculate the lifetime value of these 20 donors and demonstrate that the costs of acquiring them, in this instance, were very reasonable.

Selecting appropriate measures to assess your fundraising is extremely important. It enables you to manage the process better – to control costs, to try to generate more income and more supporters, and to retain these supporters for longer periods. It enables you to see what works and what doesn't work, to develop new and better fundraising techniques, and to test out new ideas. It is important that you succeed in generating the money you have committed to raise and that you do this within your agreed budget. It is also important that you continue to improve your fundraising skills.

Useful tips for a fundraising strategy paper

- Review of the current position, including:
  - strengths and weaknesses
  - past fundraising experience
  - existing fundraising resources.
- Who will undertake the fundraising.
- Projection of fundraising needs.
- Overall funding strategy.
- Proposed new sources of income.
- Suggested methods to meet fundraising targets.
- Resources needed to do this.
- Timeline for implementation.

3 The fundraiser

It is very important to get the person with the right attitude, commitment and skills to undertake fundraising for your organisation. In theory, anyone can be a fundraiser – they don't have to belong to a professional body, have formal qualifications or even have had vast experience in fundraising. They do, however, require exceptional skills. This chapter looks at those skills and the procedures the organisation should have in place when employing a fundraiser.

Please note that there is a difference in this chapter between 'fundraiser': a person who has been given the job of fundraising and 'professional fundraiser': a person who carries on a business for gain (see further details on page 25).

Who should fundraise?

This is one of the first considerations when developing a fundraising strategy and there are several options to consider.

The trustees

The people who are legally responsible for the administration and management of the charity and protecting its funds (the managing trustees, committee of management, board of directors, etc.) are required to ensure that the fundraising is carried out efficiently and effectively and to bear in mind all the legal requirements and best practice. They can carry out fundraising themselves, although this is more likely to happen with smaller charities.

The chair

In larger charities the chair, with the chief executive or manager, may be involved in meetings with businesses or larger grant-making charities in trying to secure funding. The chairs of smaller organisations will often undertake much of the fundraising themselves.

The chief executive or manager

The chief executive or manager is in the unique position of having a good knowledge both of the charity and its workforce and the legal requirements and responsibilities of the trustees. They are usually good networkers and often aware of other charities' events and sometimes their fundraising plans, and of the latest funding possibilities. They are also in a senior position and are able to make decisions on behalf of the trustees within certain parameters. They are, however, often very busy and if they are to manage a fundraising project will need administrative and other support.

A member of staff

Often, where fundraising is a high priority, charities may create a post of fundraiser to ensure that fundraising is ongoing rather than for one-off projects or events that happen from time to time.

Fundraising, whether by appeal, events or making applications to grantmakers, requires specific skills, imagination, creativity and a good knowledge of the charity and of the legal requirements surrounding fundraising. Members of staff employed to fundraise should be required to give frequent progress reports in order to ensure they have adequate support to meet their target goals.

Volunteers

Volunteers often have direct knowledge of the beneficiaries of the charity and the commitment and enthusiasm necessary for successful fundraising. They may have more time to give but will probably need support from the staff and trustees. Very often volunteers will be given responsibility for one aspect of a fundraising strategy. Targets should be set and agreed and regular monitoring should be in place to ensure they are adequately supported.

A professional fundraiser

The following definition is taken from the Charity Commission website:

> A **professional fundraiser** is any person (apart from the charitable institution or a company connected with such an institution) who carries on a fundraising business for gain which is wholly or primarily engaged in soliciting or otherwise procuring money or other property for charitable purposes; or any other person who solicits for reward money or other property for charity apart from:
>
> ■ any charity or connected company
>
> ■ any officer or employee of a charity or connected company

- *any charity trustee*
- *any public charitable collector – other than promoters*
- *people who solicit funds on TV or radio*
- *any commercial participator.*

In addition, the definition of professional fundraiser does not apply if the fundraiser receives £500 or less by way of remuneration in connection with a particular campaign or £5 per day or £500 or less per year where there is no specific venture.

*A **commercial participator** is any person who carries on a business for gain, and which is not for fundraising, but who in the course of that business engages in any promotional venture (i.e. any advertising or sales campaign or any other venture undertaken for promotional purposes) in the course of which it is represented that contributions are to be given to or applied for the benefit of a charity.*

When employing a professional fundraiser or consultant you should consider whether the charity can afford their fee and consequent administration costs and whether their employment will increase the resources of the organisation in a significant way. Not many organisations are able to acquire sponsorship for a professional fundraiser and so their costs have to be met from funds they generate. It may be that you consider that it is necessary to employ them as no one else within the organisation has the time or the skills and expertise to take on the task and that without a dedicated person the organisation will not have the capacity to raise the income necessary to continue. However, you should be extremely selective in the recruitment process in order to achieve your aims cost-effectively and find the right person for the job.

People prefer to give to organisations and causes they have heard about and think well of. Your organisation's professionalism, credibility and reputation are important and your fundraiser is, in effect, an ambassador for your group.

Recruiting a fundraiser

If you decide to recruit a fundraiser you should circulate information about the job opportunity to your staff, supporters and volunteers and advertise in all the usual press, journals and recruitment services or via the Institute of Fundraising.

Once you have decided to recruit a fundraiser, you should consider the following objectives and skills required.

Objectives

What are the objectives for the fundraising post? Is it to:

- develop alternative sources of funds to replace grants that are coming to an end?
- launch an expansion programme?
- run a major capital appeal?
- develop independent and local funding?
- create a large and active membership?
- develop corporate support?
- organise high profile events that will raise awareness as well as money?

You need to be clear about your objectives. This will help you to write a job description and a person specification so that you recruit someone with the experience and ability to do a good job. The objectives must be realistic: they should recognise your need for money, the opportunities that exist to raise it and a reasonable timetable for doing this which is achievable.

There is always a learning process at the very start when the fundraiser is undertaking background research and developing contacts (and getting familiar with the work of the organisation if you have recruited externally). It is important, nonetheless, that results begin to flow reasonably quickly.

The skills required in a fundraiser

For whomever undertakes the role of fundraiser there are a number of key skills and qualities required to achieve success.

Commitment and enthusiasm

These are two important qualities for the job of fundraiser. They must believe in the organisation's work and the cause it is addressing. Some people have the ability to raise significant amounts through their enthusiasm, personality and commitment to the group's beneficiaries and will encourage others to support them and add to the fundraising effort.

Stamina and persistence

Fundraising can be a hard and dispiriting business and many fundraisers will give up too soon. If your application or appeal is based on a worthwhile project, with realistic outcomes and where there is need in that area, it is worthwhile trying to persuade people of your belief in the organisation's ability to succeed and the positive contribution they could make.

Funders or donors want to be involved with projects that meet their own aims and which have a good chance of success. If the fundraiser feels that a potential funder would benefit from giving you money, it does no harm to persuade them of this even if the initial approach has been turned down (this is of course assuming that your project meets their criteria).

Truthfulness and realism

It is essential for fundraisers to be truthful and not exaggerate the need or promise outcomes that can't be delivered. The fundraiser should present a truthful case, making it attractive and powerful enough to persuade donors to give and using sensitivity and honesty.

There can be a temptation to present the beneficiaries as victims, which is patronising and not appropriate for people who are trying to reach their potential, often despite disadvantage.

There can also sometimes be a temptation to promise unrealistic outcomes in order to get money, or to say what you think the donor wants to hear in order to illicit sympathy or to meet criteria. This is not a good idea: even if you get the money this time, the organisation will not be able to meet the targets set, budgets will be problematic, monitoring and evaluation will be very difficult and outcomes will not be met. The funder will be reluctant to trust your organisation again and this will discredit your organisation. The fundraiser should raise money for what you want and for what you know you can deliver.

Knowledge

This can range from the detail of a current project – what the targets are and who will benefit – to the overall aims and mission of the organisation. The fundraiser should also have a good knowledge of the organisation's finances; for example, how much is spent on administration and what the staffing costs are. When talking to potential donors, the fundraiser must be able to answer their questions.

Contacts and networking

The fundraiser should be aware of who they should be in contact with in your local area and who it might be useful to know. They should find out about local umbrella charities, councils for voluntary service, community foundations and which groups these organisations support. It would be helpful to attend local events and find out about other organisations, their difficulties, their successes and who has funded them.

Training courses or conferences run by the Directory of Social Change or the Institute of Fundraising are both informative and useful for the fundraiser and a place where they will meet people in similar situations.

Good social skills

A good fundraiser needs confidence, patience, tact and diplomacy. Any appeal needs to be compelling and this requires confidence when dealing with questions from potential donors. They should be confident in the success of your group's appeal and the aims of your organisation. They will require patience, tact and diplomacy when asking for donations face to face – they are representatives acting on your behalf and need these skills to reflect the professionalism of your organisation.

Good organisational skills

Good organisational skills are essential for achieving success in any job and when fundraising it is equally important to keep accurate financial records, copies of all correspondence and appeal literature and notes of all meetings held in connection with the fundraising project. It is also important that clear and detailed records are kept of every donation given (where possible), so that no act of generosity is forgotten or unrecorded. This is good customer care and ensures transparency with public funds.

Imagination and creativity

The good fundraiser should aim to present your work in an imaginative and creative way. Your appeal needs to stand out from the others to inspire existing supporters and catch the attention of potential donors. Your organisation will be constantly evolving and the fundraiser can use these changes to identify new approaches. They should try not to rely on what has been done in the past, but to use fresh and innovative ideas to encourage people to think about and want to support your organisation's aims.

Opportunism

The good fundraiser makes things happen. For example, the difference between an adequate event and a really successful one could be the fact that a person of real standing in the community or a 'celebrity' is invited. This gives the event a higher profile and prestige and makes it much easier to market.

You should, however, be very selective in who you approach. Your invited special guest would need to have views sympathetic to your cause and be someone who you would want your organisation to be associated with.

Employing a fundraiser

Once you have a fundraiser in position you must provide the structure, guidance and resources they need to do their job.

Setting targets and monitoring progress

Targets should be agreed with the fundraiser rather than imposed and progress should be monitored regularly. It may not be the fundraiser's fault if targets are not being met – you or they may have been overly optimistic, or one large donation may have failed to materialise. Regular monitoring and adjustment of targets will help to ensure that any problems are addressed quickly.

The organisation should try to learn from past mistakes. You may want to create a small fundraising advisory group that will take a particular interest in the fundraising and with or to whom the fundraiser can discuss issues or refer problems.

Keep track of the time and effort put into each fundraising initiative. Too much time can be spent chasing after marginal or unlikely sources and too little developing those central to your future. Fundraising events can take up a lot of time for little financial return. Time is usually your most expensive asset, so your fundraiser must use it effectively.

Budget

Your fundraiser will need to be provided with a budget for equipment, operational costs and promotional activity. Without such a budget they will be unable to do their job properly. The box on the following page gives a list of headings that you will probably need to include.

Budget headings (employing a fundraiser)

- Recruitment and training
- Salary, national insurance and pension contribution
- Computer and printer
- Mobile phone
- Stationery, printing and photocopying
- Share of office overheads
- Travel
- Subscriptions to professional organisations, magazines, etc.
- Purchase of directories or CD ROMs, etc.
- Design and print of leaflets and a presentable annual report
- Mailing costs

Equipping a fundraising office

Some items and pieces of equipment are essential for a fundraiser; others are extremely useful. The main items that should be made available are as follows.

- **Annual reports and brochures** If you are a registered charity you have to produce an annual report by law. However, it is also an important fundraising document, as many funders will want to see your report and accounts. They do not need to be expensively produced but should be well prepared and presented. You may also need a small range of information leaflets for the public that include reply coupons to encourage a direct response.

- **Books and websites** Books or websites on fundraising, sources of funding and technical information on tax are all very valuable. Directories of trusts and companies that list the major givers and provide information on their grant policies are essential (visit www.dsc.org.uk for information on DSC's range of publications and subscription websites).

- **Cash collection facilities** You must have a bank account so that you can pay in donations. If you expect to have large sums on deposit for any length of time you should have a high interest account. If you plan to do door-to-door or street collections you will need to have the appropriate envelopes or collecting boxes. You will also need to be aware of new regulations regarding this following the Charities Act 2006. Please refer to the Charity Commission website – see *Useful contacts and sources of information* on page 371.

31

- **Computer** A computer together with a basic software package such as Microsoft Office (or OpenOffice.org, which is free) will help you produce high-quality letters and proposals as well as storing your database of supporters and perhaps your budget and financial records. You will also need a good printer, and as part of your start-up package you may be offered a scanner, which can be useful when producing material such as publicity leaflets.

- **Display equipment** Fairs, exhibitions and shop windows can be good ways of gaining more interest in your work. You will need attractive (not necessarily expensive), informative display material.

- **Email and the internet** More and more information is sent by email, and most funders now have websites. You may want to have a second telephone line for a fax. All sorts of package deals are now available from telecoms companies and internet service providers (ISPs).

- **Fax** From time to time you may need to fax a document. You can get a fax machine that will also do small volumes of photocopying.

- **Letterheads** Most organisations will need stationery such as letterheads, compliments slips, business cards and reply envelopes. Letterheads need to include certain information (name and address, website, logo, legal status and charity registration number, etc.). The design of your letterhead is important; it is the first point of contact for many people. You can also spread your message through a strapline explaining your aims or mission.

- **Photocopier** This will help you to prepare large volumes of printed material for circulation to supporters. If you don't have access to a photocopier, try to make arrangements with your local copy shop and ask them to give you a good price.

- **Telephone** This is absolutely essential. Ideally you need a line for the fundraiser only, because of the volume and length of the calls, and to have it in a quiet place, so that calls can be made in privacy. Fundraisers are often out of the office, so you need to ensure either that someone is there to answer the calls or that there is a voicemail facility. You should also be able to track the cost of calls in order that you can compare this with the budget.

Setting up an office can be expensive. You may be able to borrow some of the equipment from friendly organisations or supporters; other equipment you might get cheap or second hand. You can also try to get equipment donated (local companies often have surplus equipment or furniture), or ask local suppliers for a good discount.

You could also use a recycling scheme or check to see if a Freecycle scheme operates in your area. If you are a member of NCVO (National Council for Voluntary Organisations), you can take advantage of discounts it has negotiated on a range of products and services for its members.

You might want to prepare a shopping list of your needs and present it to a major funder as an investment package. It is in the funder's interest to help you set up a fundraiser's post – it will reduce your dependency upon them.

Keep your donors committed

Remember, getting money is only the start of the process. First-time donors are more likely to give again if your project is a success and you can back this up with the targets you have met, i.e. the people you have benefited. Your fundraiser should keep your donors or funders informed of how you are progressing and how the quality of your beneficiaries' lives is improving as a result.

4 How much do we need?

A guide to basic budgeting

Success in raising money depends upon research, showing evidence of that research, planning and presentation. All of these are involved in drawing up a budget for a project. You want to be confident that what you are asking for is realistic in terms of what the funder can give, but also that you have asked for enough to meet your project's needs. Surprisingly, funders often say that projects have been under-costed and applicants should have asked for more – the required amount to achieve success. An under-costed budget is as unlikely to succeed as an over-priced one: both show that the budget has been poorly planned.

A budget will help your organisation with:

- planning
- accountability
- setting objectives
- directing funders
- raising money for core costs.

Who should draw up the budget?

There are undoubtedly people who cope with figures more confidently than others and hopefully there is at least one person in your organisation who has this expertise. However, the process of budgeting should also involve those who will actually carry out the work, as they are likely to have an idea of what will be involved and they will carry the burden of an under-funded project if the costing is not realistic. Consultation also encourages accountability. Where people have been involved in drawing up estimates for income and expenditure they will have a better idea of what resources are really available and why they should keep to their forecasts.

What needs to be included in the budget?

How much a project really costs

Before looking at any income that will come to the project, you need to look first at how much the project will cost to run. There are obvious costs and other costs that are hidden. Some items such as equipment may seem easier to fund than others. Don't leave less attractive elements out as these are part of the real cost of running the project. This is an opportunity to apportion core costs to a project and raise money for salaries, running costs and depreciation.

Some organisations are nervous about this approach, worrying that funders may be scared off by large amounts that seemed to have been 'smuggled in'. Don't be. Full cost recovery was endorsed in *The Role of the Voluntary Sector in Service Delivery: A Cross Cutting Review* (HM Treasury, 2002), which states:

> *All voluntary and community organisations have fixed or overhead costs. There is a strong view within the voluntary and community sector (VCS) that funders are often unwilling to finance these costs and a common perception by funders that other sources of finance are already being used for this purpose.*

> *But there is no reason why service providers should not include **the relevant portion of overhead costs** within their bids for service contracts. These are part of the total costs of delivering a service. To do this, the VCS needs to be able to apportion overhead costs effectively. But there is no reason why service funders should be opposed in principle to the inclusion of relevant overhead costs in bids. Clearly, different providers will want the autonomy to decide how to structure individual bids and funders will want to award service contracts on a best value basis.*

The same principle applies when making applications to grant-making charities – you should ask for the full cost of delivering your project, or your organisation or club may struggle to meet your targets.

Funders who have a feel for the business of sifting applications will recognise a realistic project costing when they see one. (If you are applying to funders whom you suspect may not appreciate this approach you can explain your figures more fully, or simply present a shopping list of items for them to choose from.)

If you ask for too little you may not be able to run the project at all, or if you do, benefit fewer beneficiaries and only run it half as well as you would have done if you had allocated costs properly.

One national foundation stated that applicants sometimes seemed to lack the confidence to ask for the full sum they needed. This didn't help their cases. If the proposal is well thought out and it needs £20,000 rather than £10,000 to see it through, applicants should apply for £20,000.

Having a realistic grasp of how much a project will cost means allowing for:

- any capital costs (machinery, equipment, buildings, etc.)
- running costs (salaries, rent, heating, depreciation, decoration, etc.).

Whether you are budgeting for a capital item or the running costs of the project, the processes will be the same.

Capital costs

If you are planning a capital project (an extension to your existing facilities, or a new building for the youth club, for example), you need first to list all your costs. These may include all or some of the following:

Land and buildings

- How much will it cost to buy the land?
- How much will it cost to provide access or facilities for people with disabilities?

Professional charges

- Accountant
- Architect
- Feasibility studies
- Quantity surveyor
- Solicitor
- Structural engineer

Building costs

- Site works before construction
- Construction cost (as on contractor's estimate)
- Furniture and fittings
- Security system
- Decoration
- Equipment

You should add to this list as necessary. However, these are only the costs of *building* your extension or new hall. They do not show how you will pay for the long-term costs (such as maintenance, heating, lighting, security and insurance). These ongoing costs should be included in your revenue budget, as shown on the following page.

No budget will be 100% accurate. It is your best estimate, with evidence if appropriate, at the time you are planning the project of how much money you will need. You may wish to put in a contingency for unforeseen costs, if you feel this is a sensible precaution.

If at a later stage it appears that your figures are no longer accurate, you can always revise your budget so that it reflects the financial situation as you then know it. Remember though, that you will probably not be able to get any extra money from your funder to cover this.

The above list also assumes that you will be paying for everything. In fact, it may be that a friend of the organisation who is an architect may reduce their fees as a donation; you may be able to get your members to paint the hall with donated paint from a local factory; and your furniture may be given by a firm that has recently had its offices refurbished. All this should be taken into account and your budget adjusted as necessary. It helps when applying to funders to show how much you have raised from your own resources. Gifts in kind (such as donated furniture or reduced solicitor's fees) should be costed and their financial value recorded.

Revenue costs

These are your main running costs and will include all or some of the following:

Premises
- Rent
- Rates
- Maintenance of the building, inside and outside
- Heating
- Lighting
- Health and safety measures
- Security
- Insurance
- Depreciation of equipment

Administration
- Salaries (including national insurance)
- Telephone
- Postage
- Stationery or printing
- Cleaning or caretaking
- Book-keeping, audit and bank charges

- Training courses
- Childcare
- Volunteers' expenses
- Miscellaneous (travel, tea, coffee, etc.)

Project costs

These are the costs of running individual activities or pieces of work that take place in the building or as part of your remit as a youth organisation. Where you can, split your work up into separate units that can be costed individually. You can then look at what a project costs, which includes capital items and revenue costs such as those listed previously.

By costing projects separately you can keep track of individual project costs and allocate some of your general running costs to projects when preparing funding applications. (See Chapter 5 *Fundraising for projects.*)

Drawing up a budget: estimating your income

Your budgeted costs set out what you need to spend. The other side of a budget needs to show where you intend the money to come from.

Look at each source of income you can expect (for example, your local community foundation, local authority, subscriptions, fundraising events) and list them as you did your expenditure. The project itself may produce an income and you should provide evidence of your research into this and how much is expected to be generated.

You will need to look at where this year's income came from and make a reasonable guess about what will happen next year. Most of this is common sense and an awareness of local issues. You can look at opportunities as well as threats to your funding. Is there a new source of trust support that has opened up? Do you have more members this year than you did last year? Do you have a new group of parents and helpers? Has your funding been affected by local government reorganisation?

Monitor your income frequently and carefully and allow for any shortfall in your expected income quickly. For example, if you had expected to raise £30,000 from the Big Lottery Fund to expand your support service for young homeless people but your application fails, you then have to make some decisions. Do you have reserves, and do you want to use them for this? Can you borrow the money and can you afford to? Can you raise money through cutting expenditure in other areas? Do you have time to find another funder? Should you abandon the scheme and, if so, what are the consequences for your beneficiaries?

When forecasting income it helps to list both definite and hoped for funds. For example:

Source of income	Budget	Certain	Probable	Possible
Local authority	£25,000	£25,000	–	–
Membership subs (i)	£2,000	£1,200	£600	£300
Grant-making charities (ii)	£5,000	–	£3,000	£2,000
Local companies (iii)	£250	–	£250	–

1) **Membership subs:** Say you have 100 members paying £12 each. You can enter £1,200 in the 'certain' column for next year. You estimate you can accommodate more (although you will have to work out any significant increases in expenditure that this will cause). You have a waiting list of around 50, and you predict that they are all likely to join, so enter £600 in the 'probable' column. You also hope that some publicity will bring in an extra 25, but you are not sure, so put £300 in the 'possible' column.

2) **Grant-making charities:** Your budgeted £5,000 can be entered in the 'probable' column if you are confident of the charity (for example, the grant is recurrent). You would put the figure in the 'possible' column if you know less about it and felt less hopeful.

3) **Local companies:** Similarly with companies, if you have a good relationship with local businesses or they are represented on your management committee, the £250 can go under 'probable'. Otherwise enter under 'possible'.

Income versus expenditure

Having listed your projected spending and income you will now have an idea of where you stand. This process can give an overview for the whole organisation but can also give the picture for individual projects. Try to make sure that you are not too optimistic about your sources of income and that you haven't missed some areas of expenditure or under-costed them.

If your income is below your projected spending you will need to look carefully at the reasons for this. Is the snapshot year you are looking at exceptional in some way? Do you have a large number of one-off start-up costs related to a big project (such as building work, feasibility studies, equipment costs, etc.) that will not be repeated in following years, or does the deficit come as a result of regular income failing to match routine expenditure? Wherever there is a shortfall you will have to do some planning immediately. What you should *not* do is ignore the problem.

You will need to think clearly and be realistic. Look carefully at the figures again and satisfy yourself that they are reasonable. Decide whether the shortfall is short-term or long-term.

Look at what you can afford to do, and decide whether you can manage the deficit by some cutting-back or whether you need to take more drastic action. You may need to scale some things down or wait a while longer to start other things. You will need to allow for time lapse if you are cutting expenditure; the effect will not necessarily be instant. You may have to cut some activities altogether or use successful projects to subsidise other under-funded ones.

Whatever you decide, make sure that it is realistic and that it is clearly understood within the organisation.

Cash flow predictions

The final phase of this part of budgeting is looking at your cash flow. This is where you try to forecast when the money will come in, and when it will go out. Will there be any significant changes in costs or income during the year? This is particularly important if you have a building project where large bills have to be paid. Will you have enough money to cover them?

Take all the different areas of expenditure that you have listed and work out in which month each will be paid. For example, salaries are paid evenly throughout the year; rent is paid quarterly; insurance is due in October; deposit for the residential activity week is to be paid in February; and the printing bill for the summer arts event is due at the end of June. Once you have done this, try then to allow for the events and items of expenditure that will be extra this year. If you have some flexibility, you may want to plan them in months where other expenditure is relatively low. Once you have done this, total up each month's expenditure.

You should now do the same with your expected income. Again, this may be erratic and difficult to predict. If you have a grant, payment is probably made on a fairly regular basis (provided your project is meeting its targets) and you will know when to expect it to be paid into the organisation's account;

membership subscriptions may be collected throughout the year; government · money for your employment skills project may be paid in a particular month; and your second year's funding from, say, the local community foundation is sent after its February trustees' meeting. These are the sources you can predict.

There may be others such as the various award schemes that change each year and make planning difficult. If you have a source of money such as a grant from the Youth Justice Board that is new to your organisation, you will have to become familiar with the timing of payments – phone them and ask.

By matching the expected monthly spending with the expected monthly income you will spot any gaps where there is little or no money to meet expected bills. You need to plan and take action for this. You may be able to renegotiate your payment terms for some items. You may need to arrange an overdraft facility. If you are hiring equipment you will want to schedule payments in months that have less expenditure.

Forecasting becomes particularly important if you are planning a large capital project. Some funders will award you your grant but will only pay in stages when work has actually been completed; you need to reach agreement with your builders over this. Funders will rarely consider applications for work that has already started, and before embarking on a large capital project you should apply for money for a feasibility study and surveys before you present with your application for the build.

Having worked out your budget you should have a good idea of how much you need, what you need it for and when you need it by and you will have evidence to support your figures. You are now in a position to approach funders.

When you are implementing your budget, review and monitor it regularly and try to stay within the budget headings. Where these change because of an anticipated over- or under-spend, and you think it best to modify, ask for approval from your funder and keep them informed of any changes before you implement them. Similarly, the management committee will need to be informed where money allocated under one heading is to be used to subsidise another.

Budgeting – a five step plan

Step 1 Estimate your costs (these are very often higher than you first think).

Step 2 Estimate your income (this is usually lower than you first think).

Step 3 Predict your cash flow.

Step 4 Make adjustments as necessary.

Step 5 Implement your budget, monitor it and make it work – reviewing the budget and forecasting should be a standard item at management committee meetings.

5 Fundraising for projects

Fundraising is about getting hold of enough money to meet the day-to-day and/or capital costs of your organisation, plus the resources required for future development. However, it is far easier to raise money for something specific than to appeal for administrative costs or general funds. This is because donors can then match the support they give to a specific piece of work that they are really interested in and for which they can see direct outcomes. This way they can see that their money is actually making a change and that they have made a real contribution.

Asking for money towards the upkeep of your youth club may (just) work with your local authority; it won't get very far with BBC Children in Need. They will only want to fund a particular project or part of your work, for example: your new work with children and young people who have not had the best start in life and who need help and support to mature and contribute to society.

Your members (or their parents) will also respond much better to an appeal for one specific item (such as a new piece of equipment) than for a generous contribution to your overall expenses.

Thinking of your work in project terms and designing projects that will attract support is the basis of successful fundraising.

Make your project sound exciting

One of the great advantages with project fundraising is that you can highlight particular areas of your work that will interest the person you are writing to. Make sure you do everything that you can to show that the work is worthwhile, worth funding and will be enjoyed and used by your members.

A fundable project should be:

- **specific** – an identifiable item of expenditure or aspect of the organisation's work
- **important** – both to the organisation and to the cause or need it is meeting. If there is some long-term impact that will be an advantage

- **effective** – there should be a clear and positive outcome
- **realistic** – the work proposed should be achievable
- **good value** – it should be a good use of the donor's money
- **topical** – it should be looking at current issues and concerns
- **relevant** – it should be relevant to the donor and the donor's particular funding concerns
- **manageable** – it should not be too large or too small for a donor to support, although the cost might be shared through several smaller grants.

Identify a project

Case study

Noparticulartown Skills Centre for Children and Young People

This local organisation provides relief and support to children and young people with disabilities and their families, by the provision of educational, recreational and leisure activities, and daytime respite care.

The club needs to generate another £5,000 a year to cover its costs. It also wants to refurbish the kitchen to make a small café for clients while their carers have an hour or so to go shopping, and this will cost £10,000. The club has £950 in the bank. What can it do?

- Put up the members' subscriptions and hire charges to cover the £5,000 a year deficit. However, many members and groups struggle to afford the current fee and might leave if it went any higher, so the club may end up making the problem worse.
- Have a one-off special appeal to members and users. This would solve the problem but is not sustainable.
- Apply to the local authority for a grant. Possible.
- Organise an annual major rock festival with a battle of the bands. Fine, but it's a bit ambitious and who is going to organise and fund it?
- Write to local trusts and companies to fund the deficit. Unfortunately, they wouldn't fund a deficit.

continued ...

Clearly there are problems with all the above strategies. Also, they don't really begin to tackle the kitchen project. So, the centre could try to divide its needs into more attractive projects and apply for funding for these individually.

- It could apply for funding to expand the after-school clubs to secondary school age. This would attract funds from various groups interested in the welfare of children. It could also be run on a fee-paying basis to bring in extra money. It could also try to interest the members in music through the existing musical facilities.
- It could recruit new members. For example, it could raise money for new instruments, recording equipment, etc. to get more musicians in, who would then pay fees.
- It could bring in adults (if allowed by its objects). For example, it could run a parenting course, sessions on drugs awareness for parents or health and fitness programmes. All these could be devised with the help of the young people and it could raise the money from a grant-making trust by showing how it is using a new and exciting approach to rebuilding family relationships. It would need to be careful, however, not to take the 'ownership' of the centre away from the children and young people.
- It could develop specific activities for children and young people with disabilities, perhaps centred on music therapy or a sports league for wheelchair users.
- It could raise money for other future income generators (for example, social or catering facilities, which it could also use to hire the premises out). Again, this would have to fall within the objects and if not it would have to set up a separate trading arm.

The advantage of breaking the work down into projects is that you can appeal to a wider range of funders. You are no longer restricted just to those concerned for young people. You can apply to people interested in music, health, parenting and family life, people with disabilities, etc. Having done this, setting up the café is a much easier proposition because:

1) the building is clearly being used for the benefit of a wide cross-section of the community
2) this brings in a number of potential new funders (in the above example, both the arts and sports councils)

3) you can look at the best way of getting that particular piece of work done (in this case, for example, you may be able to bring in people under a local training scheme for young unemployed adults).

By breaking the bigger picture up and dividing it into projects, you can focus on activities (for example, parenting courses, drugs awareness) rather than your own core needs (money for bills), widen the range of possible funders (you are no longer just about your current users) and force yourselves to be a bit more creative in your fundraising.

Full project funding – how to cost it

Costing a project

Imagine you are running workshops in drum and percussion (i.e. this is your project). You will have two basic categories of costs – direct and indirect.

The direct costs will include the equipment, publicity and tutors' fees – these are usually fairly easy to identify. The indirect costs (sometimes called support costs or hidden costs) can be harder to pinpoint. They generally include items such as staff time for those not involved on a day-to-day basis in the project (for example, a manager, admin worker or finance controller), depreciation, use and maintenance of the building (including rent, rates, heat and light), insurance, post, telephone, stationery and other office costs.

A difficult area is how to calculate the central or office costs. Obviously, you cannot work out in advance exactly how many telephone calls will be made or the stamps or office stationery that will be needed. The best way to come to a reasonable estimate is to try and work out how much of your organisation's time and facilities will be taken up by the project.

So if your project will be the fourth one in the organisation and it takes up the same amount of space as the others and requires the same amount of the manager's supervision time, then it would be reasonable to allocate a quarter of all your central costs to the project. However, if it is only taking up a tenth of the organisation's time and facilities, then allocate a tenth of these costs. Remember, you are not expected to predict things down to the last pound; rather, the funder simply wants to see a sensible way of calculating the full cost of doing this work.

This process may seem daunting, exacting and time consuming in the beginning. It may also seem a little approximate, particularly where you are allocating overheads to a project. It is worth trying to calculate these costs so that you include a reasonable estimate of the hidden costs as well as those you can more easily tie down.

In a climate where it is more and more difficult for groups to get funding for the less glamorous parts of their work, it is vital that applicants cost projects appropriately. They must include core costs. This is what full project funding is all about – trying to identify the real cost of the work you are doing.

If you are successful, funders may require detailed accounts of how the money was actually spent to compare this with your initial budget, which will have been a reasonable estimate. More and more funders expect to see these central costs included in a budget. They see it as a sign of good management and of a well planned piece of work, rather than the applicant trying to apply for 'double funding'.

To cost a project properly, you need to include all the direct and all the indirect costs that can reasonably be said to be necessary to the running of the project. This means you should allocate a proportion of your central (or core) costs to the project. The process of costing a project has several stages.

Describe the project

Be clear about what the project is. You should identify what the project will do for its users rather than how it will solve your funding problems. For example: 'We will develop our after-school club to include secondary school-age children. This will achieve the following: …'.

The direct costs

Write down a list of all the direct costs. For the after-school club these could include:

- staff costs
- extra tables and chairs (for homework)
- pens, paper and exercise books
- kitchen equipment
- drinks and biscuits
- advertising and publicity
- computers and software
- transport.

47

The indirect costs

Write down a list of all the relevant central costs. This is where you need to be more focused in your thinking because you must include all the hidden costs. At this point you are trying to establish how much the project actually costs to run.

The after-school club cannot run without a building; the building needs heat, light and insurance; the leaders of the club will need the use of a telephone and photocopier; they may need supervision, training and support, and so on.

Your list of indirect costs will include:

- rent and rates
- heat and light
- postage and telephone
- management and supervision of the project
- book-keeping
- insurance
- cost of training courses.

You should think of your work as a series of projects and build your full overhead costs into each of these. You should recognise that if the overhead costs have not been applied for, the project will not be fully funded and will fail.

Include the relevant central costs in each project budget. You can then use the attractiveness of the project to get the unattractive administrative costs paid for.

Costing the costs

Put a figure against all the areas of expenditure. This is pretty straightforward for the direct costs, although make sure you get more than one quote on each cost. The difficulty is how to cost the indirect expenditure. You cannot put a precise figure on this; all you can do is be reasonable. You should try and work out what proportion of the central costs the project needs.

Say the youth centre as a whole is currently used for 40 hours a week and you intend to run the after-school club for ten hours a week. This means it will be using the building 25% of the time. Say that it will occupy half the centre's rooms. Putting these two figures together you can then say that it takes up 12.5% of the centre's building costs. So allocate 12.5% of all the rent, rates, heat, light, postage, telephone, etc., to the after-school project.

If you have one youth centre manager who has responsibility for all the activities in the building, you will need to work out how much time this person will spend supervising the after-school project and allocate the salary and national insurance costs accordingly. So, for example, if the manager works a 35-hour week and will spend on average 3.5 hours per week on the after-school project, allocate 10% of the salary and national insurance to that.

You will also need to work out an allocation for the caretaker, cleaner, administrator or any other salary costs associated with the centre in relation to the project.

Is it reasonable?

Ask yourself: 'Does the total figure look reasonable?' Is it too high or too low? Does it look real value for money?

Many of the costs you will put down (such as premises) are effectively impossible to put a precise figure on, so the budget is flexible. The key thing is that you can justify how you have arrived at those figures if a funder questions you about them.

Finally

You now have to decide who will pay for what. Are you going to ask one funder for the whole amount of the project or are you going to ask various funders for different parts of it? Are you going to allocate some of your own money to the project (for example 10% of your local authority grant)? Remember:

- apply to a funder who is interested in your kind of work
- ask for an amount they can conveniently give
- stress the benefits of the project to your existing and potential beneficiaries and the community and show how it is real value for money
- more than one funder requires more than one set of monitoring and evaluation procedures – account for this in your budget.

Sample budget

Project name: Krash Bang Wallop – Drum and percussion workshops for clients of an organisation for young people with disabilities.

Course duration: two days a week for six weeks. Non-residential.

Number of participants: 10–12

Number of tutors: two   *continued...*

Costs:

1) *Equipment:*
   Hire/purchase of drums and percussion instruments £
   Video camera hire £
   Video cassettes £
   Editing equipment hire £
   Recording equipment hire £

2) *Staff:*
   Tutors (a) £
   Part-time project director (b) £

3) *Building use:*
   Heating £
   Electricity £
   Training room (c) £
   Publicity £
   Office expenses £
   Caretaking/cleaning £

4) *Overheads:*
   Insurance £
   Depreciation (d) £
   Miscellaneous £

Total costs £ ....

Notes

(a) Requires two people working ten hours per week for six weeks at £ ....
    per hour

(b) A part-time post for two months @ £ .... per month

(c) 25% of current facilities for 12 days, so allow 25% x 12 x £X room hire per
    day

(d) Equipment if bought is usually depreciated over three years so you would
    need to allow 33% of the purchase price of the equipment each year – this
    is so that you build into the budget the cost of replacing out-of-date or
    broken down equipment.

6 Preparing and writing a good fundraising application

Your fundraising application is the introduction of your organisation, which needs support, to those who can provide it, and you only get one chance of giving a first impression, so it needs to be good. It is the opportunity to sell your idea to someone who has the means to make it happen. The easier you make it for the funder to assess your application (by providing relevant information and evidence, including of meeting their criteria), the more they will be inclined to help you. This help may be a one-off cash donation, a grant spread over a number of years, the sponsorship of an event, gifts for a raffle, time and expertise from a member of staff or an item of equipment.

Your task is to make the funder interested in and engaged with your vision and ideas, aware of the good practice your organisation has in place, including stringent and transparent financial procedures, good governance and the ability to deliver the targets set for the project.

Before you begin your application

Writing successful applications is a skill. You might write the clearest, brightest, most engaging application, but if it misses an essential point or fails to meet the funder's criteria, you will not be successful.

Before you start, you need first to have prepared thoroughly. Most funders receive hundreds of requests each year; think carefully about how you can make your application stand out from the others. Look at any previous successful applications for a guide, and at failed applications for any feedback you have received.

There are many ways of asking for funding. You can ask face to face; you might make a presentation to a group of business people or a meeting of supporters; you might consider it best in certain circumstances to use the telephone. Wherever possible, make a personal contact, it's surprising how few people are asked personally for money when in some circumstances this would be the best way to gain their support.

The funding bodies outlined in this guide would most likely require an application letter or completion of an application form. This chapter will look at what to include and also how to improve your presentation.

Most of the effort of application writing goes into condensing a full account of the project and organisation and providing evidence of need, numbers of beneficiaries (including those who were not supported before), an exit strategy (how your project will continue when the funding ends), administrative and financial procedures including an audit trail, provisions for monitoring and evaluation and feedback from beneficiaries and others.

It is important not to provide reams of unnecessary paperwork but to stick to the criteria required and be concise and accurate. Funders have many applications to look through and cannot spend time reading and interpreting vast amounts of information.

It isn't possible to tell funders everything; generally they do not have the resources to consider all that you know about your organisation and the proposed project and many find that application letters are far too long. Put yourself in your reader's place and consider what it is you would need or want to know if you were responsible for public or charity money and wanted to fund a successful project.

A general rule would be one and a half sides of A4 maximum for a letter to a grantmaker and one side maximum to a company. Local authorities and central government departments may give you more space on their forms – generally speaking these officials will be more used to reading long project descriptions. This gives you the opportunity to provide more detail about the benefits of your project. You should still maintain a clear, positive and succinct style.

Funders' application forms, when they are used, should provide you with guidelines on how long your answers to their questions should be and what they need to know.

Your approach

Most of the larger trusts publish guidelines on what they will and will not fund. It is important to read these before applying to see if what you are proposing fits within their policies, meets their criteria for the programme to which you are applying and does not fall within their exclusions.

In your letter or application, select and concentrate on your main selling points, emphasising those which will be of most interest to the particular person or funder you are writing to. Don't ask funders to support your organisation. Instead, ask them to support the people you help, the work that you do and, preferably, a specific project.

Believe in what you are doing and be enthusiastic – positive messages are more inviting than negative ones. Try not to go in for the sympathy vote by focusing on the gloomy consequences of not getting the money. Paint an exciting picture of all the things that will happen when you do get the money. You need to enthuse people and make them want to be a part of your work.

Be aware of the traps that could prevent your application getting the attention it deserves; for example, asking for too little by not budgeting properly or writing what you think the funder wants rather than giving an honest, well thought through account of your project. A major grant-making trust states in its guidelines:

> A thoughtful and honest application always stands out in the crowd! Tell us clearly what the problem is, and how your project will do something about it. Give us relevant facts and figures, please don't use jargon, and don't be vague. You don't need to promise the moon, just tell us what you can realistically achieve.

> Your budget should show that you've done your homework and know what things cost.

> A thoughtful and honest application isn't a hurried and last minute dash to meet our deadlines with something dreamed up overnight. It is a serious and sincere attempt by your organisation to use its experience and skill to make a positive difference where it is needed.

You will need to make a number of key points that will catch the reader's attention, arouse interest in the work, and sell your proposal to her/him. Ask yourself:

- Why should anyone want to support us?
- What is so important about what we are doing?

53

In other words what is unique about your work – what makes it different, why is it necessary and what will it achieve? Importantly, why should this particular donor want to support it?

You should try your answers and application out on a friend who does not work in the same field and has little knowledge of your work. Your application letter should tell any reader everything they need to know about your appeal in a short time. Assume they will not read anything else you send. After reading the letter, if your friend cannot answer the following questions, then nor will your potential supporter be able to.

- What is your organisation about, what does it need and why does it need it?
- What good will the project do, why would he/she want to be associated with it, where will other funding come from and what will happen when his/her support has finished?

Funders need to feel they know the context you're working in and what you're trying to do and you need to reassure them by explaining your ethos, aims and activities in a way that is clear. An outsider's view can tell you whether you are assuming too much about your reader, whether you need more or less information to make your case and when you have got it about right.

Eight essential elements of an application

1) What your organisation believes in and wants to achieve
2) Why you are writing to this particular funder/donor
3) The need you wish to meet
4) The solution you offer
5) Why *your* organisation should do it
6) The amount you need
7) The future you have – your project's exit strategy and future plans
8) Your organisation's monitoring, evaluation, financial and administrative procedures

1) What your organisation believes in and wants to achieve

The funder wants to know what kind of organisation they are dealing with and it is helpful for them to know:

- what your ethos is – what drives your organisation
- how long you have been operating
- what your key activities are
- what you have done that has been especially worthwhile or innovative.

Show the funder that your organisation is professional, creative and one that they would want to be associated with.

2) Why you are writing to this particular funder or donor

It seems to be standard practice to tell the funder or donor how much you are requesting in the introductory paragraphs and you might want to stick with this standard form of approach. It may be, however, that you would prefer your funder to know what your organisation is about and who you benefit and also that you know something about their organisation before asking for money. An example of your opening sentence might then be:

> *Noparticulartown Skills Centre for Children & Young People is a registered charity set up to provide support, services, facilities and fun for children and young people with disabilities and respite care for their families. We are hoping to expand our activities by providing music therapy sessions in the form of drum and percussion workshops for our beneficiaries and we would hope these lively sessions would provide them with a sense of achievement as well as being fun.*

> *Your organisation is well known for supporting innovative and creative new projects in our area, with a particular focus on music therapy, and I am writing to ask if you would consider supporting us.*

3) The need you wish to meet

All voluntary organisations exist to meet a particular need – to make society better in some way. You need a brief and clear explanation of the need or problem that you exist to deal with and how your particular project will extend or add to this work. Your research should inform the funder about how widespread the need is and if it is local or has regional, national or international implications. If it is local, say what special features of the community make it special or interesting to support. Point to who will be helped by your work, which can often be a wider group than just the young people involved in the project. If you have user involvement you should emphasise this. Funders like to see young people being involved and responsible.

You should provide evidence, if you can, of the further need that will be met and how many more members of your user group you will benefit if your project goes ahead.

Emphasise any elements that are special or unique in the need you are trying to meet. Explain the problem, however complex, in a concise and compelling way and explain to the funder how important and urgent the need is and how you know this. Provide evidence if you can.

You may want to highlight what would happen if you were not doing anything about the problem. Do not be over-emotional or portray your beneficiaries as victims; this is an opportunity to give your reader assurance that something constructive can be done. However, do not undersell yourself or assume that 'everybody knows this is a problem'. If the funder thinks that it is not very pressing, they will find something else that is urgent and if they do not think that you understand the problem, they will assume you cannot solve it either.

You need to do the following.

- Describe the problem.
- Support this by evidence.
- Say why this is important – is the problem you are addressing worse than others? Or is the solution you are offering better than others?

4) The solution you offer

Once you have made clear the need and said how important it is to do something about it, you then need to show that you can offer a particular solution. For example: 'We will provide 14 trained, full-time, mentors to seven of the schools in our area that have had problems with truancy. We will speak to 500 young people in school years 8 and 9 (who, our research informs us, are the most likely to fall into truancy), and then place our mentors with groups of young people most at risk. Our mentors will provide structured programmes that will include debate groups; workshops for music and dance; sports activities; and informal advice sessions on employment and career opportunities.'

Be constructive

When making your case don't assume that the need you know about is obvious to the reader. If there is a need for a hall for young people in your area, say why it is needed, how you know this and in what way it will improve their lives. If you haven't properly identified the need you cannot offer a solution.

You need to point to the actual or expected results of your work and how these will be measured (often referred to as outcomes and monitoring and evaluation). This may be, for instance, how many young people will attend; how leaders will be attracted and trained from the local community; how resources will be shared with other groups; how an information pack will be distributed to local schools; and how charging for use of the hall will help with the sustainability of your organisation.

Be realistic

Make sure that what you want to do is workable, that it can be done in a reasonable time, by you, and that it gives *value for money* (a favourite phrase of funders). Don't promise what you can't deliver. If anything, err on the side of modesty and then you can broadcast the additional benefits that come from the project when the work is finished.

You should define clearly how you will overcome any problems that may come as a result of running the project (for example, for a school home-working club: safety, adult supervision, accountability or links with the school).

Support your case

Good arguments to support your case would be to look at other communities where a similar project has led to visible benefits for young people (for example, in young people's personal development, their integration into the community, enhanced opportunities for sport and art, access to courses and education or reduced vandalism and crime). You could point to a survey that shows how young people would use your facilities, or the results of an outreach project that reflects young people's use of time and shared resources. You might also want to refer to how the facility will be used to benefit the wider community.

In short, the donor should now be saying: 'I can see there is a real problem and the project would certainly make things better'.

5) Why *your* organisation should do it

You now need to establish your credibility. Why should your group run the project? Why should the funder trust you? What is different about the way that you do things? How effectively will you manage the project?

Sell your case

Think about your plus points. Do you use volunteers creatively? Do your trustees come from the local community? Do they participate in leadership training qualifications? Do they have a story to tell that would interest a funder? There must be something about your group or your work that is attractive and fulfilling to those who help. By training local leaders, for example, you have given the community a vital resource and encouraged people to discover commitment and talents that may otherwise have been left unused. This builds credibility for a group by showing commitment to all in the community, not just your own beneficiaries.

Provide evidence of your successes

Do you have examples of media coverage that give positive images of your organisation's work or have any of your young people achieved something as a result of your activities? Have you helped raise money for other causes in a committed and imaginative way? Has your group or an individual gained an award or recognition for a scheme or achievement?

A report in the local paper can help to support your case. Do you have a 'Local Girl/Boy Makes Good' story? Has your group produced a community leader? Do you have a famous former member who regularly supports events? Positive publicity can show the often life-changing results of working with young people and the importance of what you do; it can also show that you are here to stay, with a record of making things happen.

Are you successful in raising money from other sources? Do you have a mixture of supporters from a number of sectors? Do you have good working relationships with agencies, local businesses, schools, local authorities, etc. and what have these partnerships achieved? Financial stability will impress any funder and this is one of the keys to establishing trust with their money. The more secure your funding portfolio is, the more likely you are to be entrusted with other grants.

Strong links with other groups and organisations give a good indication of how integrated you are and further proof of how much added value your activities bring to the community – funding your group may bring knock-on benefits to other groups you work with.

Generally, can you show that your work is good value for money and more cost-effective than the alternatives? What makes your organisation's people the right people to be meeting this need? Is your approach an example of good practice that could be copied and applied elsewhere?

You should be able to come up with a number of good reasons why your group should be supported. The more you can do this, the more credibility you have. The more credibility you have, the more likely donors are to trust you with their money. Success can breed success, and funders will be attracted to a confident, enthusiastic approach. Your plus points will all help to sell your case, so make them clearly and confidently in your application.

6) The amount you need

Funders are keen to know about the project and the value and benefits of the work. But you also need to tell them very clearly what it will cost and how much you expect them to give. Some applications tail off when it comes to asking for money but there is no need for you to shy away from asking for what your project will cost; by now you should have made a good case for someone to support you and proved that you can be trusted with their money.

There are different ways to ask for what you want and you should think about the type of funder you are applying to. Where you are asking a funder for a small amount or where you think they would like to see some specific, immediate benefit from their donation, you can produce a shopping list. This can be very effective when raising money from companies: you can give a range of items, with costs starting at a level that all those you are writing to can afford and then suggest an item from the list that you think the supporter would like to pay for. By including more expensive items you can hopefully persuade them to give more. If you are looking for gifts in kind rather than cash this is the best way to give supporters an idea of what you want.

7) The future you have – your project's exit strategy and future plans

Make sure that you emphasise your long-term viability as this underlines your credibility and why funders should support you. If your future is not at all sure, funders will be reluctant to take risks and will think their money would be better used elsewhere.

Show how the project will be funded once the grant has been spent. If you are applying for money for a new facility, who will pay for its running costs once it is opened? How will you continue a project when the three-year grant has finished, for example?

8) Your organisation's monitoring, evaluation, financial and administrative procedures

For organisations that have been successful and received a grant, funders will want to know, sometimes during and always at the end of the project, how their money has been used and whether you have met the targets and reached the beneficiaries as promised in your application. You must have monitoring and evaluation procedures in place to be able to provide this evidence when it is required. This not only helps you with further projects, identifying need, etc., but will also predispose your funder to consider favourably any new application from you. These procedures do not have to be complex, they simply have to provide proof of how you have achieved your targets and spent the money.

As well as monitoring procedures, any funder will expect your organisation's financial and administrative procedures to follow good practice. All money in and out of the project must have a clear audit trail, showing which budget line it came from and how it was spent. The simplest of tasks, like keeping all receipts, can become problematic at the end of a grant if procedures haven't been followed. Also, your administrative requirements should be contained in your governing document (constitution, memorandum and articles of association, trust deed or rules) and should be followed as a matter of course in all your organisation's dealings.

How to ask for money

- You should state clearly how much the overall project will cost.
- Give the funder a clear idea of how much you would want them to contribute.
- Show how much other organisations have so far given, or committed, to the project.
- Show where the rest of the money is coming from (for example, 'The overall project will cost £30,000. We expect to raise £15,000 from our members and supporters, £5,000 from other fundraising events and £10,000 from grant-making charities. I am therefore writing to you and eight other major trusts to ask for a total of £10,000').

This will give the trust more confidence that you know what you are doing, and show that you are not solely reliant on one funder and can raise the necessary money.

The application

Only approach organisations, including companies, that you want to have associated with your organisation. Make sure that they are appropriate for your beneficiaries, your ethos and your long-term aims.

Remember to ask first if the funder has an application form to fill out, as there is no point spending time writing the perfect letter of application only to find out that you have to rewrite the whole thing on an application form. If you are unsure about the information required on the form, contact the funder for clarification. Sort out all the problem areas on the form before you ring and go through each in one phone call as this will save time for you and the funder.

The application letter

Now that you have done your research and pulled all your selling points together you need to put them into some kind of order. There are no golden rules for writing proposals, no perfect letters of application. What works for the club down the road will not necessarily work for you: try to inject some of your organisation's own personality into the proposal.

The following is a structure that many have found to work, and this can be a starting point for your own letter.

1) Project title
This can be really effective, especially if it is catchy and quickly describes what you want to do.

2) Introductory paragraph
This is the first part of the application to be read so it is important that it makes the funder want to read on. It should tell readers what the application is about and why it is likely to be relevant and interesting to them.

Try not to make your applications generic, they should be adapted to accommodate the aims and sympathies of the funder.

3) The introduction: what your organisation believes in and wants to achieve
Many applications say little or nothing about what the organisation is about; instead, they just state what the applicant wants. You should assume that readers know nothing about your organisation. What would they need to know to trust you with their money? You need to show you are good at what you do, reliable, well-used and well-liked – in three or four sentences.

4) The need: why something needs to be done now
The next stage in your application is to explain what the need is, how you know it exists and why it is important that something is done now. Remember, people are mainly interested in what your group does and how you benefit your beneficiaries or community. Don't ask people to support you; ask them to support your work and the people that you help.

Tips: plus points that make you better

Write down as many selling points for your group as you can. Below are some possible categories that may help you to see the strengths of your group.

People: What's different, good, or extraordinary about your volunteers, members, workers, etc.?

Financial stability: What's sound and reliable about your finances? What's successful about your fundraising?

Personal achievements: Has anyone achieved something notable through your activities? Have your members or volunteers gained experience, qualifications, employment, training, etc. through being part of the group? Do you have a local, regional or national profile?

Partnerships: Who have you linked up with? What has been achieved?

Mention the plus points that give you an edge such as:

Publicity: Have you had any coverage in the local press? Have you been successful at recruiting new members and leaders through outreach?

Perseverance: Do you have a good track record? How long has your group been running?

Performance: Has your group developed activities or projects that have been adopted and been successful elsewhere? Explain why your work is innovative, creative and used as a model by other groups.

Explain how you meet the following need(s):

- The needs we meet are particularly important because ...
- Our solution is new and groundbreaking because ...
- We are different/unique because ...
- Our other strengths are ...
- If we did not exist then ...

You need to show your organisation is unique. Be confident in your successes; list your five greatest successes in the past five years and then select one that's appropriate for your application letter.

And finally, to build your confidence further in preparation for the application letter, complete this tie-breaker in 20 words or fewer:

'We are the best there is in our work with young people because ...' Perhaps you could ask your users to help with this.

5) *Your proposals: what you intend to do about the problem*

You now need to show what you intend to do and how you intend to do it. Make sure you include your targets (outcomes) and how you will reach them. (If you are having problems with this part, maybe you could try predicting what the organisation will be like in two years' time and how things will have changed.)

6) *Why your organisation should do it*

You have so far said what your organisation believes in and wants to achieve, the need you want to meet and how you are going to meet that need. Now you need to show why you are the best people to take this on.

The funder will want to know that they can trust you to deliver what you say you can and that you have thought the project through to the end, including what you will do when funding stops. Your solution to the problem should be clear and practicable and your monitoring and evaluation procedures effective. Use your plus points to show your ability, professionalism and good track record to get the job done well. Quotes, especially from those benefiting from what you do or from those who have previously used your services are always helpful here.

7) *The budget: how much you need*

This is how much you intend to spend on the project and is an extremely important part of your application. You should have clear evidence of costs and these should clearly fit in with what you are paying for, such as staff hours. It should also relate to your outcomes; for example, seven staff will provide outdoor pursuit weekends for 14 children. Your budget will include the direct costs of the project and overheads. (See Chapter 4 *How much do we need?* and Chapter 5 *Fundraising for projects.*)

8) *Funding plan*

You need to show the funder where you intend to get the money from. It may be that you are asking this funder for the whole amount or you may be getting it from a variety of sources. Therefore, you need to say something like: 'The total cost of this project is £50,000. Our local authority has agreed to give us £5,000 and this will be matched by European money of £5,000. We aim to raise £10,000 from local supporters, £20,000 from the Big Lottery Fund and £10,000 from grant-making trusts.'

You also need to show how you intend to meet the longer-term costs (see Chapter 1 *Getting started in fundraising* for detailed information on this).

9) The rationale: why the funder might be interested and what their role is

There are many reasons why the donor may be interested:

- You are running a good project that is right at the heart of their stated aims and priorities.
- You have already received support from them and this further grant will allow you to build on that success.
- There is a personal contact (which it will pay to highlight).
- There is a particular benefit to the donor that you want to stress. (This is especially the case with companies, which will want to see a business or public relations return on their money.)

Sometimes, people sum up on a negative note: 'Wouldn't it be a tragedy if all this good work came to an end?' or, 'If we don't raise £30,000, the project will have to close.' Avoid this kind of negative persuasion. You've made a good, convincing case with positive reasons for supporting your work. There is no reason to assume you will not get the money, so be positive: your letter should leave the reader feeling optimistic and enthusiastic.

10) The signatory: who puts their name to the application

This person should be sufficiently senior

Whoever signs the application must be sufficiently senior. This should be someone with a good knowledge of the project. For example, the project leader, fundraiser, chair of the management committee, an appropriate director or an appeal patron. This shows you are treating the application seriously and gives it the necessary authority.

Be knowledgeable

Funders may well ask for more information. The person who signs the letter should be able to tell them what they need to know, including the overall financial position of the organisation. If the name on the letter cannot give this information it will seem as though the application has not been well organised and the project not well thought through. If you have a patron who signs the letters but does not know about the day-to-day running of the project, you should include the contact details of someone who will be able to answer more detailed questions.

Be available

Again, if funders want more information they don't want to have to leave a whole series of messages before they get the details they need to make a decision. Make sure your contact details are clear and that you have made provision for someone to take your messages and for them to be passed on quickly to you or for a voicemail facility to be in place.

Be open

Leave your potential supporters with plenty of opportunity to talk to you, find out more, or visit. Many will decline your invitations to come and look at the work or meet the young people, but an invitation shows confidence in your work.

Start making sense – a guide to writing simply

- Look at the layout critically. Would it entice you to read further? Look at line spacing, point size and font selection: are you put off by long sections of text? If you are, so will your reader. Always avoid jargon – although you might understand what you are talking about, outsiders generally will not. Remember to explain acronyms.
- Be direct and try not to repeat yourself – it adds to the flow of your application and keeps the length down.
- Use personal pronouns such as 'we', 'our', 'you' and 'your' rather than 'the organisation/association' or 'the users' etc.
- Use strong verbs and tenses, rather than weaker passive ones. 'Our young people work closely with local schools' reads better than 'Local schools have become involved with the activities organised by the young people in the club.'
- Weed out waffle. Say something sincerely, simply and succinctly.
- Read, re-read and rewrite.

A skeleton application letter

There is no such thing as a model application letter. Write your letter in your own style, in a way that is tailored to the funder and shows your work in its best light.

Here is an outline that we hope will be helpful when first drafting your application letter.

Dear .... [Wherever possible use the name of the correspondent. If you do not know it, make every effort to find out. It's important that you show

continued...

you have done some research in order to direct the letter to the appropriate person.]

I am writing on behalf of .... Our organisation was set up in .... by .... to provide .... Our major initiatives have included .... and recent projects have seen ....

I am writing to you about our .... project. Your organisation is well known/well known locally for supporting .... and we have seen the successes of groups similar to our own that you have funded in the past.

The need we are meeting is particularly important, having carried out research on .... and potential beneficiaries who state that ....

We know the project will be effective because [talk about your innovative approach/new ideas, etc.] ....

We consider we are the best people to do this work because ....

The project will cost in total £.......... and we intend to raise the money as follows: ....

We hope that you will want to be involved in this exciting new work for our beneficiaries and I am writing to you for £...................., which will provide ....

At the end of the grant we expect the project will be funded by .... /be self sustaining.

We would be more than happy for you to visit our organisation to see the work we do and to discuss this application, although I appreciate your time must be limited. If you require further information or you wish to discuss this application please contact me on ....

Yours sincerely

Ann Other

Chair ....

What do you send with the application letter?

If the funder has an application form this will provide instructions on what you should send to accompany it. If you are writing an application letter, you should send the following supporting materials:

- A set of your most recent accounts or a budget for the year if your organisation is new.
- A budget for the particular project you want support for, including estimated income and expenditure.
- An annual report (if you have one). If you have not done so before, think about your annual report as a fundraising tool; it is not only a statement of your financial activities, trustee body, etc., it can also say as much about your activities and success stories as you want it to.

You can also enclose anything else that will support the application (for example, you could provide one or two of the following: newsletters, press cuttings, videos, photos, drawings or letters of support). However, don't overwhelm the reader, pick an appropriate selection, and don't rely on these extra bits to get you the money – they will not compensate for a hopeless letter. Assume that funders will only read your application letter and the financial information (budget and accounts). They should be able to get the complete picture from these. If in doubt, ask yourself:

- Is this relevant to the application? Is it absolutely essential or a nice extra?
- Will it help the funder to make a decision in our favour?
- Does it present the right image? (Is the additional material so glossy that it implies you are a rich organisation? Can you get publicity material sponsored?)

Remember, everything is for a fundraising purpose. If the accompanying information does not help the application, do not include it.

What do you do with the application letter?

Think about your different supporters. You will have to take into account what each funder will be looking for and why. A company, for instance, will be looking at the commercial possibilities of linking up with you; i.e. what is good for its business. It may look for more tangible benefits in the short term than, say, a grant-making charity or local authority.

It may be best to send the application out in stages. Write to a few of your key supporters first (adapting the letter as necessary) and see if they will lead the appeal (that is, give you a grant that then encourages others to do the same).

When some of these have committed themselves to supporting you, then write to the rest saying that first, you have already raised £10,000 of the £20,000 needed and second, that X, Y and Z funders gave it to you.

Money tends to attract money. The more you raise, the easier it is to raise more. Highlight any money that has already been raised or pledged. Sending applications out in stages can improve your chances because you concentrate initially on those most likely to support you. Then you widen the net to include those who don't know you as well but will take their cue from other funders' confidence in you. However, this approach is more time consuming and needs more planning. It may not be the remedy for your project or for crisis funding when you are desperate to get money in as soon as possible.

What to do after the application letter has been sent

You should keep a simple record of what you have sent and where, including the supporting materials you have sent or the events you have invited funders to. You might want to include an sae with your application or send it recorded delivery to be sure it has been received. Apart from that, there is little you can do but wait for the outcome.

You can never be sure how funders' offices will respond to phone calls asking about the progress of your application. Some will discuss what stage your application has reached and when you might expect to hear a decision; others will not welcome any follow-up contact: they will not have the time or inclination to answer your enquiries, however general.

If you are unsuccessful, you may not realise for some time. You might not even get a rejection letter or telephone call, let alone an explanation of why you did not get a grant. It is, nevertheless, always worthwhile asking for feedback on your application so that you will know where you went wrong (with that particular funder) for next time. Some may refuse to provide this, others will be extremely helpful and some may tell you that your application was good but that they ran out of funds.

If you are successful

If you get a positive response, write to say thank you immediately and put these people on your mailing list for the future. Keep them informed of your progress.

Note any conditions on the grant that have to be met (such as sending a written report to the funder each year) and make sure you keep to them. It is important that if there is any variation in what you have been given the money for and what you are actually going to do, you should inform the funder and check this is acceptable. (This is particularly the case with grant-making charities.)

You will want to go back to those who have supported you for help in the future. Keep them interested in your progress and how the money has been spent to help young people. If individuals have benefited, personal accounts and progress reports can be an easy and friendly way of keeping funders interested and enthusiastic about what their money has helped to achieve.

Don't give up . . .

If you haven't heard regarding your application for some time, you might want to send those funders still considering your appeal a further letter to update them on progress (if you have anything further to add, such as a recent success story).

The letter can be quite short, saying: 'We understand you are still considering our funding application for our project "....................". However, you may be interested to know that we have so far raised £10,000 of the £20,000 we need. This has come from .... Please contact me if you need any further information about the project.'

Don't be afraid to go back to people who have previously turned you down, unless they have said they would never support your kind of work. There may be many reasons why you have not been awarded money: they may have funded something similar the previous week; they may have run out of money; they may have had a deluge of brilliant applications and yours was next on the list; they may have never heard of you before.

Remember that while it is your job to get money to continue your organisation's work, it is the funder's job to give funds to well thought out, creative, well budgeted, worthwhile and potentially successful projects whose organisation is sound managerially and financially and operates with good business practices.

Application checklist

- Does it have a personal address? Do what you can to find an individual's name. Check the spelling of the person's name and the funder you are writing to.

- Does the first paragraph catch the reader's attention?

- Are you clear about what you want and why you want it?

- Is your work likely to be interesting to the donor?

- Is it clear how much the donor is expected to give? Is this reasonable?

- Is the application well presented? Does it attract the eye with short paragraphs and no spelling mistakes?

- Does it back up what it says with good supporting evidence?

- Is it positive and enthusiastic?

- Does it take account of guidelines published by the donor? Does it make a connection with the supporter's interests?

- Is it written in clear, plain English and free of jargon?

- How long is the application? Remember it does not have to say everything, but it has to say enough.

- Crucially, is the application appropriate? A brilliant letter to the wrong people will not get support.

7 Raising support from the public

Until relatively recently, in terms of the history of charities, organisations raised money largely by asking those involved with the group, their relatives and friends and anyone else who would turn up, to support small fundraising activities such as a garage sale, coffee morning or car wash. Now the emphasis is more on spending dedicated time on an application or polishing up presentation skills to appeal to a major funder. However, the general public is a vital resource and while statistics change from year to year, it is generally accepted within the sector that it is the largest group donating to charities. While you are chasing the grant, don't forget also to appeal to the general public: figures suggest that around a third of the money available to charities comes from this source.

Fundraisers should keep in mind that while grants are now a major part of charities' income, getting the public to support your group can be more effective in terms of time and resources spent. If you need, say, £500 for a laptop, it might be more efficient to ask the local community rather than applying to a trust or company. The right appeal targeted to 200 people might be less time consuming and produce more immediate results. It also helps to make your case to other funders if you have a well-established track record of successful fundraising from the public.

Fundraising in this way can also bring good publicity to raise the profile of your group locally. However, you need to assess the scale of any proposed event or appeal, the help you can rely on and its expected return.

This chapter will give some pointers to planning, some money-making possibilities and some pitfalls to avoid.

Who might give

Every potential individual donor to an organisation has their individual motivations and preferred way of giving. The fundraiser must be clear about which individuals they want to approach for a particular type of gift and how to plan to attract the support of that group of people.

There are all sorts of reasons why people support and give to good causes, for example:

■ **They are already involved with and sympathetic to the cause.** Parents, helpers, organisers and patrons, for instance. These are usually the most dedicated fundraisers and donors. You should not have to convert them to your cause, they should already be aware of what you are doing and its importance.

■ **Young people themselves – your user group.** Young people are an enthusiastic and willing resource and can often show the older members in a fundraising team a different and more relevant approach. Over recent years young people have shown a particular concern with specific issues such as the environment, issues surrounding HIV and AIDS, homelessness and drug-related problems.

■ **They have previously been involved.** People who have been involved with the group in the past, for example, former members, volunteers, staff and trustees and people who have benefited from the club, are likely to want to support your initiatives. Occasional reunions, particularly if combined with an anniversary, can be a way of focusing their financial support. Past members will, hopefully, have some affection for the club and fond memories and they might be persuaded to support the present activities.

■ **They know someone involved with the work.** Sponsored events are a good source of fundraising and the network of extended family and friends connected with those taking part will want to sponsor the individual they know.

■ **They think the organisation is worth supporting because of the work it is doing.** This is an appeal to those who do not have any personal contact with your organisation but value the work that you do. Your activities may tie in with their interests in some way such as health promotion, education, job prospects, social skills or crime prevention.

■ **Individuals connected with established institutions.** Churches and other faith groups, schools and colleges, philanthropic groups of local business people and trade unionists might want to support your work because the interests of young people are also important to them.

■ **Employers.** Employers might be pleased to associate their name with your cause and through them you can often reach a large number of individual employees. This sort of contact can often bring gifts in kind and time as well as financial donations.

- **People in specific regions.** Often people will have an affinity to a particular village, town or city and be pleased to see that young people are involved in helping to improve their lives as well as helping to improve their community.
- **Where the organisation will attract press coverage and people will want to help.** The advertisement below will bring attention to the Scottish Spina Bifida Association's appeal because they have a famous patron who can use the media and 'spread the word'.

Case study

'What's your favourite 'F' Word?
Gordon is Fundraising!
The Gordon Ramsay Appeal.
Fundraising for the Scottish Spina Bifida Association

To aid us in our fundraising efforts, Gordon Ramsay, our Patron, has launched an appeal to help us reach our fundraising targets.

We are delighted to announce that Gordon Ramsay will be hosting a Gala Dinner on behalf of the Association on the 30th October at Stirling Castle. Only 250 tickets are available at £500 per head.

'The Scottish Spina Bifida Association provides family support services to over 3,000 people in Scotland affected by spina bifida and hydrocephalus. We require to raise over £500K every year to continue providing our services to all those affected by the disabilities in Scotland.

'We are asking you to join Gordon and make Fundraising your favourite F Word by organising a fundraising event at work, school or in the community. Everyone who takes part will receive a "F is for Fundraising" Certificate.'

There may be more than one reason why people connect with a cause. Some of the runners in the London Marathon, for example, will be involved because of any or all of the reasons previously listed.

Planning any fundraising should first take into account the support networks your group is immediately in touch with. You can then look at the wider audiences who may be attracted to the event and your cause.

Why people give

People support organisations for many different reasons. However, the more your fundraising message ties in with an individual's personal motivation, the more successful that approach will be.

The following are some of the reasons why people give to charity.

- **Being asked.** They have been impressed with your approach and what you are doing for young people in your area and want to give.

- **Concern.** This is a strong motivator for many donors. They may be worried about homelessness amongst young people, or want to improve the lives of young people by helping to channel their energies into specific projects. Making a donation provides them with an opportunity to do something positive for a cause they believe in.

- **Duty.** Another strong motivator, particularly for older donors. Many faiths promote the concept of charity, with some recommending that their members allocate a certain share of their income each year for this.

- **Personal experience.** People who have direct or family experience of, say, drug addiction, might be especially motivated to give to this type of cause; those with children at school may want to support their child's development; or someone may want to 'give back' to a youth theatre group they attended when they were younger.

- **Personal benefit.** Some people like the status or recognition that comes when their generosity is publicised, or like to be involved with the charity world.

- **Peer involvement.** When people know that their friends and colleagues have given or when these people are asking them to give and explaining the aims of their cause, it can be the motivation for them to contribute as well.

- **Tax benefits.** These are unlikely to be a prime motivator for giving, but can be an important factor in encouraging people to make certain types of donation and to give more generously.

It is important to understand why supporters and potential donors might want to give to your particular organisation. You can then tailor the message to make it more relevant and interesting to them.

You also need to be aware of why people don't give and whether the reasons need addressing by you. They may not be interested in your organisation and what it stands for or they may have given to something similar recently. Other demotivating factors might be that:

- your cause has had some bad publicity
- your cause appears to have high administration costs
- there is a concern the money is not getting to the intended beneficiaries
- you have not looked after your donors particularly well in the past.

Creating support

The clearer you can be about who your organisation's potential supporters are, the more successful you will be in reaching them. Start with your existing supporters: for example, a survey could help to find out what sort of people have supported your organisation in the past and why. If you have a database of your supporters, you could start your analysis there.

Those at the very heart of what you are doing – young people themselves, their families, friends and workers – are probably your most enthusiastic supporters. They are the people who understand what you want to achieve to make life better for the young people benefiting from your organisation.

Next in line will be previous members and organisations and agencies that your group has links with. These can include schools, sports clubs and arts venues that you use, as well as leaders in your community. These people do not know your group so well, but they have some affinity with it, as well as an interest in seeing it prosper.

You can also appeal to the wider community, such as companies you have business links with. (Is there a travel company you use regularly? Who do you bank with?) Is there a local event you could attend where you could provide refreshments at a stall run by young people involved with your group? They could provide information on what you do and make people aware of your aims and past successes.

Finally, you can organise events in the high street or shopping precinct, such as simple collection boxes or having a steel band, gospel singers, dancers or jugglers outside the entrance of your local supermarket: anything to attract the public's eye and put them in a generous mood. These will bring in people who may know nothing about your group but are attracted by the activity. If you are considering this type of fundraising you should consult the Charity Commission website as the Charities Act 2006 makes new provision for collections. You should also refer to the relevant Institute of Fundraising Codes of Practice.

If you think creatively about venues, activities and audiences you can increase your chances of success.

Even when you've raised core funding for your organisation, it makes sense to continue to raise money from the local community. It heightens your profile and nurtures local links, giving your project deeper community roots and a strong local identity.

Making contact

Here is a suggested five point plan to follow when starting to approach the public.

1) Identify your potential supporters: those people whose background and motivations make them likely to want to support your cause.

2) Create the right message to appeal to them, which:
   - starts from their understanding of the cause
   - builds on their motivation
   - takes account of their natural hesitations or reasons they might have for not giving.

3) Direct that message to those people in the right way. For example, if senior business people are your audience, they can be reached by a variety of means: through the business press, local rotary clubs, chambers of commerce and other associations of business people or personalised letters, or by asking business people who already support you to ask their colleagues and peers directly.

4) Make it easy for them to make their donation. Any materials that aim to get people to support you should include a clear means by which they can respond (whether by post, phone, fax, email or through a website) and clear contact details.

   To increase the likelihood of someone making a donation, if your organisation has the means, you could also consider the following options.

   - A dedicated telephone line for credit card donations and enquiries, with a named person on promotional literature and at the end of the line. This makes the facility more personal and shows a concern for customer care. You might also consider a freephone facility.

   - A CharityCard donation facility for Charities Aid Foundation (CAF) clients, which includes approximately 100,000 individual donors and about 2,000 companies. Around 4,000 charities now welcome the use of the CharityCard and are listed with their telephone numbers in a CAF directory and on the CAF website (www.cafonline.org).

- A secure website, so that donations can be made online.

- A freepost facility. However, almost all organisations now suggest that if a stamp is used this will save the charity money.

5) Support your fundraising with a good communications programme, as people are more likely to give to your organisation if they have heard about its work and the importance of the cause. Public relations is a key ingredient of successful fundraising, so if your organisation does not have a press officer, you will need to spend some time promoting the organisation and publicising its work.

Five things to remember when fundraising from individuals

1) State clearly how much money is needed for the project.

2) Express the need in human terms, giving images of the issue being tackled and examples of your successes. Avoid abstract statistics unless a particular point needs to be emphasised. The more people can understand and identify with a problem, the more they will feel they are helping real people and the more successful the appeal will be.

3) Ask for exactly what you want. Prospective donors will not necessarily know the size or nature of the donation expected of them. It is also useful to suggest a range of values, so the donor can choose their own level of giving. If relevant, a 'shopping list' might be used showing what different amounts can achieve – see Chapter 1 *Getting started in fundraising*.

4) Target the appeal carefully, making the message as personal and relevant to the donor as possible. When approaching existing supporters, refer to their previous generous support and what has been achieved with it, or if approaching local people, focus on the local benefits of your organisation's work. The more targeted the message, the more successful it will be.

5) Make your approach positive and forward thinking. Don't be tempted to think of your beneficiaries as victims, it can be patronising. Generally people want to support other people who, despite a disadvantage, are looking forward and building a positive future for themselves.

Building a supporter base

It is far easier to build on a base of existing supporters than to start from scratch. An existing donor is ten times more likely to support your organisation again than someone who has never given. However, if you have few or no current donors there are various methods you can use to acquire them.

Promotional or fundraising leaflets

Produce a leaflet giving details about your cause and illustrating your need for funds. This does not have to be expensive. Sometimes the simplest leaflet is most effective – for example, an A4 sheet, printed in two colours and folded to make a four-page leaflet with photographs of the organisation at work and a reply coupon so potential supporters can express interest or make a gift. You could ask your group to design it.

You might also give people options for how they would like to get involved: for example, by giving money, becoming a member or volunteering their time. Remember to include your website address, if you have one.

A membership or supporter scheme

Developing a scheme of this type can bring people closer to your organisation and keep them in touch with news and success stories. It can also provide a legitimate reason for communicating on a regular basis. See 'Membership schemes', page 85.

Supporter-get-supporter

Ask existing supporters to help by recruiting a friend, a colleague or a family member (see page 84).

Local newspaper, radio and TV coverage

A paper, radio or TV station might be interested in running a feature about a local charity. To make this opportunity as effective as possible, you should make sure that the contact details are for the best person possible to deal with the media.

Door-to-door collections or face-to-face fundraising

If your organisation is not well known, one way of addressing this is to approach people face to face. This can be particularly effective for a local cause. The term 'door-to-door collections' includes visits to pubs, factories and offices to collect money or to sell things, on the basis that part of the proceeds will go to a charity. If you are considering this type of fundraising, as previously mentioned, you should consult the Charity Commission website as the Charities Act 2006 makes new provision for this. You should also refer to the relevant Institute of Fundraising Codes of Practice.

Events

Potential supporters may be attracted to an event where they have the opportunity to visit an exclusive venue, hear a well-known speaker or participate in an entertaining evening. Once there they might well be receptive to hearing more about the cause that the event is to benefit. Once a donor has been recruited, the aim is to keep them involved so that they continue to give and, hopefully, develop their relationship with your organisation in other ways.

Major donors

Some of your donors may have the potential to do much more for you than others. They might identify themselves by making a significantly larger donation than the amount you asked for, or you might find out that they have greater potential through researching your supporter base. You might then decide to set up a fundraising programme specifically for these people.

Firstly you should make a decision about the point at which you will begin to treat people as major donors: this will be different for different organisations.

For a small charity a major donation from an individual might be £250 or even less; for a larger organisation with a developed strategy for encouraging big gifts, its major donor programme may only kick in with those giving several thousand pounds. To help you make this decision look at your current range of donations by value. You will probably find that there is a clear cut-off point above which donations become scarcer. Once you have identified these people, you need to decide whether they will get similar communications to your other donors but with higher levels of gift asked for, or a totally different type of letter concentrating on more ambitious ways in which they can help you. Either way, you should aim to make them feel more involved rather than simply sending a standard donor appeal.

You might organise special events and visits for them or get them involved in the fundraising itself – you will find the guidelines *Major Donor Fundraising* produced by the Institute of Fundraising a useful guide if you plan to concentrate on this group of your donor base. Visit the Institue's website at www.institute-of-fundraising.org.uk for information on this best practice guide.

Major donor programmes

If you feel that there are sufficient numbers of people who are or might become major donors, you could set up some sort of club to encourage them to increase their commitment to you. You could ask your existing key donors to advise you on who else you might approach, or ask them to approach their friends, colleagues and networks to ask for support. You need to make sure that this is going to be cost-effective for you, as these people are likely to take more of your time to look after, or steward, than your other supporters. Also, they may require particular types of benefits in return for their support, such as meetings with your chief executive or board members, crediting in your literature (such as your annual report) and even having some influence on the future of the organisation (you need to be particularly aware of such potential implications when considering this type of condition).

Encouraging giving

Individuals can support you in a wide variety of ways, for example with cash gifts or gifts in kind, or by buying raffle tickets, attending events or volunteering their time. The following sections look at the main methods by which you can encourage people to donate money.

One-off donations and appeals

Asking existing or prospective supporters for a one-off donation to support a cause is a key method of raising funds for many organisations. This can be done on a large scale by approaching hundreds of individuals through direct mail or, more directly, face to face with individuals or small groups of people, particularly when asking for a high value gift.

One-off donation appeals are often used to encourage new donors to support you. Once that first donation is made you might go back and ask for another or offer other methods by which you can be supported, for example, by making a committed gift. You will find that some people who have supported you with a single donation will be happy to become more committed. However be careful not to ask too soon or to alienate them with too many requests. You need to engage them with your work and show them results over a period before you make further requests.

Legacies

Legacies are an important source of charitable funds. Legacy fundraising can often seem a mysterious activity which generates large sums with apparently little effort from the fundraiser. In fact, some of the largest legacy-earning charities have carefully planned strategies for developing this income. Like other forms of fundraising, what you get out depends on what you put in. You should:

- decide whether you are the sort of charity that might expect to receive legacy income, bearing in mind that most legacies come from people who are aged 65 and over

- find out who has left you legacies in the past, if they supported you during their lifetime and why they gave.

You should consider whether to go for existing supporters, which is where you are most likely to find support, or whether to target the general public. You might also consider adding the name of your organisation to the Charities Aid Foundation (CAF) database, which has information helping people who would like to set up a legacy and a database of charities that might be supported. For full information see CAF's website www.cafonline.org.

One aim of having a supporter base is to build up a good understanding amongst your members of how they might help you. If some form of regular committed giving is a natural successor to occasional one-off gifts, then a legacy may be a step up from regular giving. In the process of communicating with donors, you will over time build relationships which might enable you to discuss legacies, which is a sensitive issue.

For further information on legacies see *The Complete Fundraising Handbook* published by the Directory of Social Change.

Committed giving

Committed or regular giving is one of the most valuable and consistent ways your donors can support you and will provide one of the best financial returns for any direct marketing activity. Getting people to give their first donation can be expensive, and may not cover costs through the immediate income produced, but it is often the first step in building up a base of supporters.

Follow-up mailings are what generate the real revenue – people who have already given respond much better to any appeal than those who have never given.

Getting your donors to commit to regular giving creates a continuing income stream, broadens your fundraising base and enhances your organisation's sustainability. Also you can apply income from regular givers to those parts of your work which are hardest to raise money for. To encourage people to make committed gifts you need to:

- stimulate their concern for the cause and interest in your work
- help them recognise the importance of long-term support – your work may take time to yield results and you depend on them continuing to give
- make it easy for them to give regularly: one way is to set up some form of membership or friends scheme, with pre-set levels of giving
- ensure that, where possible, donations are paid tax-effectively through the Gift Aid scheme (details given on page 90)
- reassure them regularly about the continuing value of their committed support.

This list will provide you with an agenda to develop your direct mail and donor acquisition programme, and then turn a new donor into a committed and enthusiastic long-term supporter.

Mechanisms for committed giving

There are three main ways in which committed giving can be developed.

- Through regular, usually monthly, payments which can be made tax efficient with Gift Aid.
- By means of a membership scheme. This will not always be tax-effective as there are restrictions on the level of benefit the member can receive. Some schemes are concerned primarily with generating income, others aim for high membership numbers to enhance the credibility and campaigning ability of the organisation.
- Through payroll giving, which is also a tax-effective way of giving.

The specific mechanisms available for the actual transmission of money are as follows.

- Using a banker's order or standing order, where the payments are sent from the donor's bank to you.
- Using direct debit, which reverses the control of the transaction. You, the charity, claim the payments from the bank when they fall due.
- Regular payments via a donor's credit card.
- Cash or cheque payments, though these are not so efficient to administer as you will usually need to remind donors when to send their payment.

Promotion of committed giving

Not every donor will want to enter into a long-term commitment with you, but you should give all of them the opportunity to do so. Your strategy will depend on your answers to the following questions:

- What are the interests and motivations of your supporters?
- How much income do you need to raise and how much are your donors prepared to give?
- How will you encourage your existing supporters to increase their commitment?
- Can you identify any other potential committed supporters?
- What opportunities do you have for reporting back to your committed givers, so as to maintain their enthusiasm and support?
- What else can you do to get them to feel more involved in the work of the organisation and the cause it is addressing?
- Are you able to administer and steward such a programme?

It is important not to take your committed givers for granted. Keep in regular touch and tell them what you are doing. Always recognise their commitment so they understand that you are contacting them because of their regular donation.

You can report back to your committed givers regularly through a newsletter, magazine or personalised letter from you or your chief executive or chair. Committed givers tend to want to see their donations going to the cause rather being used on expensive communications, so it's good to keep expenditure here to a minimum.

Some charities hold events where donors can meet staff or see the organisation in action. This not only provides a good opportunity to thank them, but also enables the most committed to become even more involved, get more information, meet other supporters and, importantly, the young people in your group.

The following are some of the promotional techniques you can use.

Approaching active givers

Analyse the response to your appeals. A number of your donors will have given more than once. These are your priority targets for committed giving. Contact them to point out the advantages of giving regularly and offer to send the appropriate forms. If there are only a few prospective targets, then contact them by telephone or try and arrange a meeting with them.

Promoting committed giving more widely to your donor base

One strategy is to undertake an annual appeal to promote regular giving and encourage payment by standing order or direct debit. Another strategy is to mention the value of committed giving in each mailing, pointing out that it helps the organisation plan for the future and allows people the opportunity to opt into giving in this way.

Regular upgrading of donation value

Once you have donors giving on a regular basis you might think about asking them to increase the value of their donation (but be careful not to ask them too soon, or for too much). It is administratively easier to do this if you have set up their donations via direct debit rather than a standing order, as the latter will require filling out a new form.

Using a sponsorship programme

Here the donor is linked to a specific project, community, family or person over a period. Such an approach can work well in fundraising terms, but has to be handled with care. Problems can arise where the donor really wants to help just one individual person (most projects generally provide support for the whole user group and the community), or where the donor builds up an expectation of a relationship with, for example, a sponsored child.

Recruiting large numbers of supporters with a low-value regular gift by direct debit

Some organisations such as the NSPCC use this very successfully. Once donors are giving monthly donations, there is the opportunity to go back to them and tell them what their donations have achieved and what could be done if they increase the value of their donation.

'Welcome mailings'

These are sent following an initial gift to an organisation from newly recruited donors. There is a two-fold purpose to these mailings: to welcome new donors and tell them more about the cause they have given to, and to ask them for more and regular support, often suggesting a regular monthly gift through their bank.

'Member-get-member' or 'supporter-get-supporter'

This is simply an invitation to an existing member or supporter to nominate or recruit another. This method relies on the personal enthusiasm of existing members and their ability to persuade their friends and colleagues, but the technique generally works well.

Membership schemes

Many voluntary organisations have membership schemes. Some are aimed primarily at people who are interested in getting more involved – helping the organisation to campaign, attending cultural events, volunteering their time – but also giving money. Membership schemes of this type may have their annual subscription levels set deliberately low to encourage as many people as possible to join, therefore increasing the organisation's influence and campaigning ability.

Some membership schemes have a fundraising purpose – the primary aim being to generate income for the organisation.

Benefits of membership

1) Membership offers a convenient peg upon which to hang the request for committed and long-term support.

2) Membership can enhance your campaigning ability. Organisations like Amnesty International and Friends of the Earth invite people to become members to harness their support for the cause.

3) Membership can open up the organisation to democratic control through annual meetings, giving the members some feeling that they control the direction of the organisation.

4) Your membership list is also a good place to look for donations. These people have demonstrated their commitment to the cause and so qualify as perfect prospects for obtaining further financial commitment.

5) Membership can easily be structured to invite different levels of contribution (to reflect people's commitment, ability to pay, etc.).

Why people become members

There are a number of reasons why people will sign up as members of your organisation.

■ **Personal benefit:** the member joins principally because of the benefits they believe they will gain. Examples of this are the RSPB and the National Trust, which give members discounted entry into their reserves or properties.

■ **Support:** the member joins to express support for the work of the charity. In this case membership is organised to encourage members to subscribe at affordable rates as a way of making their contributions on a continuing basis.

■ **Campaigning:** members are signing up to show their support for particular policies or causes.

- **Influence:** members join many local organisations simply to be able to influence their affairs. This will be done through regular meetings and AGMs.
- **Clubs:** the member joins a club – such as the 'Friends of the Anytown Young People's Theatre Group' – to signal their support for the work and also to receive benefits from membership. Subscriptions may be higher in such cases and there may be expectations of involvement in activities and events.

Membership and regular giving

The value of membership subscription income depends on the following factors.

- **The number of members:** the more you have, the better. Once you have established a scheme, your aim should be to find ways of recruiting new members economically.
- **The annual subscription level:** this will depend on your objectives, whether it is to make money or, alternatively, to involve as many people as possible. Some organisations give members a choice of subscription levels.
- **The cost of running the scheme:** this includes the cost of member acquisition, collecting membership fees and communication costs (such as sending newsletters and annual reports). You need to analyse costs very carefully to establish the real net value of the scheme.
- **The value of any additional income** that is generated from further appeals to members.

It is most common to ask people to give on a monthly, quarterly or yearly basis. You might even suggest a certain level of donation and ask the donor to select the frequency. The value of encouraging regular giving is something that can be tested quite easily in a mailing. Usually requests for monthly or quarterly giving will be no less effective than an annual payment, and will produce much higher average annual donations.

Categories of membership

One of the key issues in this area is the way in which membership and committed giving are priced and styled. Membership fees have to take into account the possibility of attracting large numbers of people who are prepared to be identified with your organisation. They also need to allow concessions to people on low income and encourage higher levels of support from wealthy supporters, benefactors and corporate members.

Many organisations have several categories of membership with different levels of annual subscription. Other categories of membership can be created such as a sponsor or a patron. One organisation has three categories – 'Friends', 'Good

Friends' and 'Best of Friends'; another has 'Gold', 'Platinum' and 'Silver' membership. The fundraiser's challenge is to lift members from one category to the next.

Life membership is an opportunity to get a single large payment in one go, as well as enabling a member to be seen as an important benefactor of the organisation. But life means life, unless you state otherwise, and you are committed to servicing the membership for the duration without any expectation of an annual income. Therefore the price needs to reflect this.

Administration

The administration of a membership scheme demands a high degree of organisation, especially if you wish to maximise the benefits of your fundraising efforts. There are several issues to consider.

How do you get members to renew their subscriptions? The best system is where the member has to do nothing – the membership continues until cancelled, and the subscription is paid automatically through the donor's bank account by direct debit (or via their credit card).

If there is a fixed-term commitment and this comes to an end, you will want to ensure that as many people renew as possible. The usual way to do this is by sending reminder letters, either a few months before the expiry, giving them time to renew, or to coincide with the expiry, to remind them that renewal is due.

The telephone is also a valuable tool for renewal. You will need to decide at what point in the renewal cycle you use the phone – before the renewal date, at renewal or afterwards. It is also a good medium for asking a donor to increase the value of their donation and reminding those who have just not got round to renewing to do so, and you can also gather useful information about why members may not be renewing.

Membership renewal can be done on one fixed date each year (for example with annual membership running from 1 January to 31 December). Those that join through the year will pay pro rata.

An alternative is that each member's membership expires exactly 12 months after the annual subscription was paid. This requires more efficient organisation, as you will be dealing with renewals on a rolling basis throughout the year.

If you have a large membership you will need a reliable computer database to help you handle renewals. A key issue is the ability of the system to identify renewal points so that you can mail not only on the point of renewal but also before and after to stimulate the highest possible renewal rate.

Raising the subscription rate: Changing the annual subscription rate can be a very laborious process, because members have to be informed of the change and any standing orders you are administering will need to be cancelled and replaced with new ones for the appropriate amount. As a result, some organisations review their subscriptions quite infrequently (perhaps once every three or four years) and take a conservative view of the need to increase rates. This means that membership fees can often lag behind inflation.

One way around this problem is to ask for subscriptions to be paid by direct debit. You will still need to inform your members in advance of any rise in the subscription, giving them a chance to cancel if they do not want to pay the higher amount, and you have to agree to reimburse any sums debited from a bank account in the event of a dispute.

Making membership payments tax efficient: Under Gift Aid, any payment can be made tax effectively provided the donor is a UK taxpayer and has declared (by ticking a box or filling out a form) that they wish the charity to reclaim the tax paid on all their donations.

If you want to make membership payments tax efficient you will need to check with Her Majesty's Revenue & Customs (HMRC) to make sure it accepts that the membership benefits you offer are within the current limits. If your primary aim is to generate funds, it makes sense for you to make your scheme tax-effective and encourage as many members as possible to pay in this way. In addition, if the member is a higher rate taxpayer, they will benefit from higher rate relief.

VAT liability on membership subscriptions: When more than an annual report and a right to vote at the AGM are offered to a member in return for their subscription, HMRC will treat the subscription payment as being partly a payment for a service, and some or all of it may be taxable (for those organisations registered for VAT, or where the taxable subscription income takes them over the VAT registration threshold). Many organisations are keen to offer benefits to encourage people to subscribe. If you are unsure about the tax implications, you should consult HMRC before finalising your membership scheme. More information can be found in *A Practical Guide to VAT* by Kate Sayer and Alastair Hardman, published by DSC in association with Sayer Vincent.

Maintaining donor records: Your committed givers and members will be giving money to you regularly and possibly supporting you in a number of other ways. You need to keep track of their support to identify people who might give you extra help when you need it, or to invite to special events such as receptions, or simply to personalise your appeals to them. All this information needs to be on one record, not only in order to develop a full picture of each donor's support, but also to avoid any duplication of mailings. If you are not yet ready to invest in one of the big tailor-made databases, the 'How to' guide *Building a Fundraising Database Using your PC* by Peter Flory, published by DSC, will provide you with a step-by-step introduction to setting up a simple database using Microsoft Office.

In collecting any data about your supporters you must of course ensure that you comply with the requirements of the Data Protection Act. For more information on this visit: www.ico.gov.uk.

Payroll giving

Giving at work has been around for some time in Britain. Originally it involved large numbers of factory workers giving a few pence per week and signing an authorisation to have the amount deducted from their wages each pay day.

Luke FitzHerbert, former co-director of the Directory of Social Change, led a project in the mid 1980s to launch payroll giving in Britain. In 1987, the government created a new scheme for tax-deductible payroll giving as part of its policy of encouraging charitable giving. This was seen as an opportunity for charities to mobilise support from the millions of people in employment and gave what had been a very marginal form of giving a completely new lease of life. In the past the scheme has not delivered anything like what was expected of it and still does not generate as much revenue for charity as it could.

Payroll giving is, though, continuing to grow and raised almost £109 million for UK charities between April 2007 and March 2008, an increase of 22.5% from the previous year. In the same period almost £109 million was received and distributed by the Payroll Giving Agencies to UK charities from employees donating from their pre-tax pay. More than 717,000 employees donated through payroll giving between April 2007 and March 2008, an increase of 11.5% from the previous year. It is now an established way of giving and provides charities with a mechanism for regular committed income.

Most recently the Institute of Fundraising has been working with HMRC to promote this tax efficient opportunity for giving. As part of this scheme grants and matching funds have been offered to employers who wish to initiate payroll giving for their staff, as well as the award programme the Payroll Giving Quality Mark. More information on this can be found at www.payrollgivingcentre. org.uk.

Tax-effective giving

Gift Aid

Under the Gift Aid scheme, UK charities can claim back the basic rate tax that an individual has already paid.

Gift Aid is a way for charities or community amateur sports clubs (CASCs) to increase the value of monetary gifts from UK taxpayers by claiming back the basic rate tax paid by the donor. It can increase the value of donations by a quarter at no extra cost to the donor.

The following is an extract from the HMRC website:

> *Gift Aid is an easy way to help your charity or CASC maximise the value of its donations, as you can reclaim tax from HMRC on its 'gross' equivalent – its value before tax was deducted at the basic rate. This is 20 per cent from 6 April 2008. You can work out the amount of tax you can reclaim by dividing the amount donated by four. This means that for every £1 donated, you can claim an extra 25 pence.*
>
> *In addition, HMRC will automatically pay your charity or CASC a further three pence for every pound donated. This 'transitional relief' – to adjust to the fall in basic rate tax (from 22 per cent to 20 per cent) – is available on Gift Aid donations made from 6 April 2008 until 5 April 2011. This means that for every £1 donated, your charity or CASC can receive 28 pence, so the total value of the donation is £1.28.*
>
> **Donations that qualify**
> *Gift Aid can only be claimed on gifts of money from individuals, sole traders or partnerships, in any of the following forms:*
>
> - *cash*
> - *cheque*
> - *direct debit*
> - *credit or debit card*
> - *postal order*
> - *standing order or telegraphic transfer.*
>
> *Gifts made by cheque only count as received once the cheque has cleared. Your charity or CASC can accept gifts of money made in sterling or any foreign currency.*

Payments that don't qualify for Gift Aid

These include:

- *donations of money from a company*

- *donations in the form of a loan waiver or debt conversion – for example, an individual may lend money to your charity or CASC and then, at a later date, agree that it does not have to be paid back – this is not a gift of money, it is the waiver of a loan*

- *gifts made on behalf of other people, for example a membership subscription paid on behalf of somebody else – this is a gift of membership from the payer to the member, not a gift made to the charity or CASC*

- *gifts that come with a condition about repayment*

- *gifts with enforceable conditions about how your charity or CASC should use the money – for example on condition that it buys goods or services from the donor*

- *payments received in return for goods or services – these are not gifts – for example payment for admission to a concert, payment for a raffle ticket or an entrance fee for an adventure challenge event*

- *a 'minimum donation' where there is no choice about payment – this is simply a fee for goods or services, it is not a gift*

- *gifts made using 'charity vouchers' or 'charity cheques' provided by another charity.*

Gift Aid declarations

Before your charity or community amateur sports club (CASC) can claim tax back on a donation made by an individual, you need to obtain a Gift Aid declaration from that donor.

A Gift Aid declaration can be made in writing, electronically or verbally, and must contain certain information about the donor. You also need to show that you have advised the donor that they will need to pay sufficient UK tax at least equal to the amount that your charity or CASC will reclaim on their donation(s).

You must keep these records in support of your Gift Aid repayment claims. Each donation included in a claim must be supported by a Gift Aid declaration.

A Gift Aid declaration can be made either in writing or orally and may cover donations made since 5 April 2003 and all future donations. The donor needs to understand that they are giving you authority to reclaim tax from HMRC on the gift.

Any payment made to a charity by a taxpayer is eligible for tax relief as long as:

- *the donor fills out a Gift Aid declaration which is then kept by the charity*
- *the charity maintains an 'audit trail' linking the payment to the donor – the charity needs to record each donation separately and be able to prove to HM Revenue & Customs how much each donor has given.*

Not all charities take advantage of Gift Aid, in particular the UK's smallest non-profit organisations (those with a voluntary income of less than £100,000). Therefore it appears that there is still work to be done in terms of promoting the benefits of Gift Aid to this group.

You can get further advice on implementing a Gift Aid programme by visiting HMRC's website – www.hmrc.gov.uk/charities (see also www.tax-effective-giving.org.uk, which is a part of the Institute of Fundraising website). Here you will also be able to find exactly what information is required to be included in a Gift Aid declaration, and a model form.

The Gift Aid declaration can state that it covers all donations from the date of the current gift onwards (and going back up to six years prior to the date of the declaration), so one declaration can cover all future claims, although the donor can cancel this at any time.

The level of benefits the donor can receive are limited to 25% for a donation or subscription up to £100, £25 between £101 and £1,000, 2.5% above £1,000, with an overall maximum of £250. So, in theory, you can add 25% (on 2008–09 tax rates) to the income from, for example, a sponsored run if:

- *all your sponsors are taxpayers*
- *they all complete or have completed a Gift Aid declaration*
- *you can prove that they have made the payment.*

Once you have proper record keeping in place, the system is now so simple that you can reclaim tax on almost any donation, whatever the size, as long as the donor is a taxpayer.

You should be aware that there is now a time limit for making claims for tax on donations made by Gift Aid. Any charity which is a company for tax purposes must make any claim within six years from the end of the accounting period to which the claim relates; while a charity which is a trust for tax purposes must make any claim within five years of 31 January in the year following the end of the tax year to which the claim relates.

CAF accounts

Another method of giving tax effectively is where the donor uses the services of the Charities Aid Foundation (CAF). Here they pay a sum to CAF as a charitable donation and tax is reclaimed on this. The total amount, made up of the value of the donation and the tax reclaimed less an administrative charge to CAF and a compulsory donation to the National Council for Voluntary Organisations (NCVO) (which set up the scheme), is kept in an account for the donor. The donor can then make charitable donations from the account, either using vouchers which they give to the charity as they would a cheque, by quoting their CharityCard number, or by asking CAF to make regular direct payments to a charity from their account.

Gifts of shares to charity

Since April 2000, individuals (and companies) have also been able to get tax relief on gifts of certain shares and securities to charity when calculating their income for tax purposes. The tax relief applies where the whole of the beneficial interest in any qualifying shares or securities is disposed of to charity either by way of a gift or by way of a sale at an undervalue.

The following categories of shares and securities can be donated using this relief:

- shares and securities listed or dealt in on the UK Stock Exchange, including the Alternative Investment Market (AIM)
- shares and securities listed or dealt in on recognised foreign stock exchanges
- units in an authorised unit trust (AUT)
- shares in a UK open-ended investment company (OEIC)
- holdings in certain foreign collective investment schemes – broadly, schemes established outside the UK equivalent to unit trusts and OEICs.

NB

Definitions of AIM, AUT and OEIC are given at the end of this chapter.

To check whether the shares or securities qualify for the scheme, contact HMRC for advice.

Where an individual makes use of this relief, they are able to deduct the 'relevant amount' from their total income for tax purposes. The relevant amount is either the full market value of the shares (where the transfer is a gift), or the difference between the market value and the actual cash received (where transfer is a sale at an undervalue). This figure is then adjusted by adding to it any incidental costs of disposing of the shares – for example brokers' fees.

Tax relief can be claimed at the donor's top rate of tax via their self-assessment tax return, and for capital gains tax (CGT) transfer is deemed to have taken place at cost (so no CGT is payable) unless the shares are sold at an undervalue, where the sale price is taken as being the transfer price.

Since April 2002, the same tax relief has been available for donors who give land and buildings to charity.

Looking after your supporters or stewardship

Your donors and supporters are a key part of your fundraising future. They have demonstrated their commitment to you through giving, and you should try to retain this commitment and strengthen their ties to your organisation. This is often referred to as donor or supporter care, stewardship or customer relationship marketing. This section concentrates on two aspects of developing your supporter relationships – thanking them and increasing their involvement.

Thanking your donors

Being thanked makes donors feel good about their giving, and tells them that their donation has been received and is being put to good use. Thanking your donors gives you the opportunity to find out the depth of their interest, and perhaps some of the reasons why they support you. It can also enable you to tell them more about your work and your future plans, and all this will hopefully help you to get further support from them.

Your best prospects for a donation are those people who have already given to you, so when and how you thank them can be crucial. There are several ways of saying thank you.

By post

Some charities reply to all donations, while others reply only to certain types or levels. It can be expensive to thank people for every donation whether large or small, especially if there are a lot of them, but there are important advantages in thanking donors at some point, even if you do not do it every time. If you are concerned about saving administrative costs, you might ask donors to tell you if they do not want an acknowledgement from you every time they give.

When you do say thank you, try to do it immediately, say within three days of receipt of the donation. Try and make the letter as personal as you can, recognising how long the person has been supporting you and their level of giving. It might be useful to develop a set of generic letters which you can then adapt as necessary. Some organisations get their chair or director to sign the letter. This is not necessary except for very large donations. Your smaller and regular donors may be more interested in getting to know you (the fundraiser) or a donation administrator, whom they will be able to contact if they have a query or want further information.

By telephone

If you want to respond quickly and personally, particularly for larger donations, the telephone is ideal. As soon as you receive an exceptional gift, ring the donor and thank them personally.

By email

If you know a supporter's email address (and this is something you should be collecting along with their postal address and telephone number), this can be an immediate way of saying thank you and also has the advantage of being very cost-effective.

Face to face

Personally visiting important donors can be a time consuming business. However, it can also be extremely worthwhile. The visit should be made by an appropriate person. Depending on the level of donor, this might be the fundraiser, a member of the management or fundraising committee or a trained volunteer. Be careful not to impinge too much on the donor's time – they might not appreciate taking time from their schedule to meet with you and a visit might be counter-productive, so make sure that it is welcomed.

Donors may be wary about the object of such visits until they have actually received one. A simple chat to tell the donor more about your work and to thank them for their gift will sometimes naturally lead on to discussing other ways they can help without your having to introduce the subject yourself or ask directly. There might also be something you were unaware of that your group could do for them.

Through an event

If a face-to-face visit is not appropriate, another way of meeting and thanking supporters is by setting up an event, such as a reception or open day. A senior person from the organisation might attend and give a short talk; then staff, committee members or other volunteers can be on hand to talk to those who have been invited to the event. This requires careful planning and briefing of your staff, committees and volunteers to ensure that everyone is spoken to.

You might hold the event at your centre – people are often interested in seeing how an organisation works and meeting the people who work there. Or you could organise a site visit to see a project at work and enable the donors to meet some of the beneficiaries and the local community.

By public acknowledgement

You can also thank people through a public announcement – such as an advertisement in a newspaper or a mention in your newsletter, magazine or annual report. Think carefully about your annual report. Not only can you credit your donors, but this also sends signals to others that you need donations and will publicly acknowledge any support you receive. Indicating the level of gifts creates a certain peer group pressure for others to give at similar levels. Perhaps more importantly it gives credibility – 'If those people have given, then they must have faith in the organisation'.

As an organisation grows, the number of donors may get too large to list everyone, but the major donors should still appear. Taking paid advertising to thank donors might be expensive but can be worthwhile if there are other messages to communicate (for example that the cause has widespread or prestigious support). Remember to get the donor's permission before you do this and also check how they wish to be credited, as some will not want to see their names publicly in print.

Challenges for the fundraiser

- To get the donor to give again.
- To persuade the donor to give regularly and frequently, ultimately on a committed basis.
- To encourage the donor to increase their level of giving.
- To get the donor to give in several different ways.
- Possibly, to encourage the donor to leave a legacy.

Fundraisers should never allow fundraising to become divorced from the advocacy work. It is important to ensure that there are a number of ways for people to support an organisation: giving money, volunteering, fundraising and campaigning. Some people will only be able to do one of these. However, many may want to do more – and by becoming more involved, this will strengthen their concern and commitment to you.

Recruiting volunteers from your donors

It is sometimes assumed that volunteers and donors are two separate categories of supporters which should not be mixed. Many charities feel that they should not ask their donors to volunteer, although they may want to. It might be a question of not feeling confident, or of waiting to be asked. Even if they do not wish to volunteer, their support may be all the stronger when they are made aware that their time would be valued.

Working with young people gives a ready and responsive group of volunteer fundraisers. Young people are often the most enthusiastic about raising money on behalf of others. They can also be energetic in taking part in imaginative fundraising events for their own group.

Other fundraising ideas

Local fundraising

It can be worth approaching local bodies that may be able to help your fundraising by raising money on your behalf. Some will welcome presentations from you. Local groups include: chambers of commerce; community foundations; faith communities, for example churches, synagogues, mosques, temples and gurdwaras; inner wheel clubs; lions clubs; local businesses; local colleges/schools; local police and fire brigades; masonic lodges; rotary clubs; local round tables; and student committees.

Distinctive, attractive appeals work best, as do requests for small amounts of money.

Fundraising events

Before organising your event you need to be sure of why you are asking people for money. It will help to decide the type of event and the way it will be run if you have considered why people will want to give. As mentioned above, people give for a number of reasons which can be simplified to four:

- they like the *organisation*
- they like the *people*

- they like the *cause*
- they like the *event.*

Make sure you know who the event is aimed at and that it will be attractive to them. Once you have decided on your event you then need to answer some key questions. A small team of people can help to think through these points and share both the organising and administrative load.

- Why are you doing this? Is the event attractive in itself, or is it the cause?
- What are the risks to you in organising this event? (How easily could it go wrong? How much money do you stand to lose?)
- Who are you raising the money for, yourselves or for an outside cause?
- Who will organise the event?
- Who will come to the event?
- What is the local competition likely to be, especially around certain times of year?
- Where will it be held?
- Is it safe?
- Have you considered whether your insurance provisions are adequate?
- Do you need permission? Have you checked for any statutory regulations that may apply?
- How much money do you hope to raise?

This last question becomes increasingly important the higher your initial outlay. It will be no good to you or your group if you organise the best 'Battle of the Bands' ever if you cannot guarantee a paying audience. The young people from your group may learn much in the process about teamwork, creativity, organisation and marketing, but if your organisation is seriously out of pocket, you will have difficulty recouping the loss.

Remember too, that all outside events are at the mercy of the weather and you should make contingency plans.

There are basically two kinds of fundraising event:
- ticket events where money is raised through ticket sales
- participation events where money is raised through sponsorship of those taking part.

It may be best for you to start event fundraising in a small way if you are new to this. People sometimes start with a great idea for a grand scheme but are over-ambitious. You should do what you know your group can achieve and build from your success. Organising a car boot sale may not have the appeal of a music festival in the park, but for a first 'event' will be easier to run and have fewer risks attached.

Sponsored events – a guide

Asking someone to sponsor someone for an event is the most common way that groups and individuals raise money from the public. It is easy to see the advantages:

- easy and quick to organise
- easy to contact supporters
- reaches a potentially large number of donors through personal contact
- includes participants who are members of the group and helps the group's identity
- they're fun
- can have little initial outlay
- almost unlimited number of activities that can be sponsored
- can raise large sums
- can be used to focus on areas of interest: for example, a fast for famine relief, gardening for people in sheltered housing to improve their and the community's environment, or a bed race for the local children's hospital.

With imagination and enthusiastic volunteers, you can take a sponsored event and do something different with it. If you can give the activity a new twist you build new enthusiasm for the event itself.

Publicity can also be increased if the event is even slightly off the wall. You could for example, hold a fancy dress football match, shave a youth leader's head (pay to watch) or do face painting (by students on staff). Not only does this maintain the momentum of long-term fundraising, it also keeps the young people's interest from flagging. This is an important factor when young people are doing the hard work of raising money and where interest and enthusiasm can soon be lost. Youth workers have to be imaginative and have different, creative ideas for events to keep interest high.

Publicity

Attractive publicity materials can give any event an added boost and place it firmly within a youth context. Comic Relief, which organises the Red Nose extravaganza, is among the leaders in the field.

Red Nose Day is a UK-wide fundraising event organised by Comic Relief every two years which culminates in a night of extraordinary comedy and moving documentary films. It's the biggest TV fundraising event in the UK calendar. On Red Nose Day everyone in England, Scotland, Wales and Northern Ireland is encouraged to cast inhibitions aside, put on a red nose and do something a little bit silly to raise money – celebrities included. It is an event that unites the entire nation in trying to make a difference to the lives of thousands of individuals facing terrible injustice or living in abject poverty.

You might want to visit Comic Relief's website for ideas on events: www.comicrelief.com.

Sponsorship incentives for participants

Usually, people look at the incentives to give money from the donor's point of view, but you should also consider how to encourage those participating in the event when asking for sponsorship. This is particularly important for younger children, who may be easily discouraged if they only have two or three names filled in on their forms. It won't matter to them if these people have given a generous £10 each; to young children it will be the number of names on the form rather than the size of the gift that gives them encouragement. You might want to mark in some small way the person with the most creative sponsorship form, or who found a sponsor from furthest away; you might consider making the sponsorship a team effort, where older participants can help the younger ones.

Celebrating the success of the group after any event and showing how the amount raised will be used will keep motivation and enthusiasm high for those who have been involved.

Organising a fundraising event is probably not the time to raise money for core costs such as the rent or salaries. There may be exceptions to this rule, but generally you will be more successful if you are raising money for equipment or a specific activity or trip that directly benefits your user group.

You might try something like the following:

Dear Sponsor

We'rethebest Youth Drama Club is raising money to buy material and accessories to make costumes for our next production 'West Side Story'.

We also need to purchase new stage lights as our existing ones were second hand (ten years ago) and are clumsy and not very effective.

With the money raised we aim to buy:

Material for costumes	£200
Accessories	£75
1 stage lights kit	£970 (including VAT and delivery)

Total amount to be raised: £1,245

The costumes will of course be made by our skilful and willing volunteers and following this musical will be kept and altered for future stage events.

The stage lights kit is both compact and economical. There are two dimmer bars which control four lights each. The control desk supplied provides four channels that are dimmed individually. There is also a master dimmer, black-out switch, sound-to-light synchronisation and two tripods. We consider that this represents good value for money as well as being easy to assemble and store and will be a real asset to our productions.

You have generously donated to previous fundraising events and we hope you will encourage our young thespians with a kind donation this year.

The dates of the production are 16th to 21st November and we hope to see you there even if you are not able to give this time.

Very best wishes

Ann Other

Chair

We'rethebest Youth Drama Group

Helping people to give

The public are no different from other donors when it comes to wanting to be told how to give and even how much. Many will not have much idea when handed a sponsorship form of how much they should sign up to.

Give donors the option of sponsoring a total amount as well as the number of units. It is always a good idea to give a total amount, rather than sting the sponsor after your group's efforts. If the sponsor has pledged 50p a length of the pool, a claim for £25 after 50 lengths by your new Olympic hope might be more than they anticipated and you might even have trouble collecting your hard-earned money. You should also think about the type of unit – 10p a kilometre, for instance, will generate more income than 10p a mile.

As mentioned above, you might want to offer a small incentive for the participants but these should only be token. Certificates or badges to be presented may well be enough.

Do the right thing – do you need a licence?

The regulatory hurdles you will have to clear will depend upon the event you are running. It is also worth doing a risk assessment on your event. The Health and Safety Executive (Infoline: 0845 345 0055; website: www.hse.gov.uk) can give guidelines.

Depending on the event you are running you may have to consider the following:

- Bye-laws – check with the local authority's leisure and recreation department, or other authorities such as rivers, waterways, footpath, coastal and heritage.
- Car boot sales – contact the licensing office of the local authority for guidance.
- First aid, fire and police regulations – contact the appropriate body.
- Food hygiene and safety – contact environmental services at the local authority for guidance.
- Health and safety – check all aspects of your activity with the local authority and the local health and safety office.
- Premises licence – this provides for the sale of alcohol by retail, provision of regulated entertainment or provision of late night refreshment. Contact your local authority for guidance.
- Lotteries – see information from the Charity Commission's website given below. The Gambling Commission also has information on regulation.
- Public liability and other insurance – check with your insurer.

- Safety certificates – where you are organising fairground rides, motorised tours, balloon rides or the like you need to apply for appropriate licensing. The leisure and recreation department, environmental services or the licensing office of your local authority can give guidance.
- Street closures – you need to apply for a street closure order from the local authority.
- Sunday trading – contact the local authority to find out the current regulation.

Please also note the following guidelines taken from the Charity Commission's website:

Telephone fundraising and broadcast appeals
Where the telephone is used to raise funds it is the trustees' duty to ensure that the public are clear which charity the funds are for, what percentage of the donation will be spent on the objects of the charity and also to ensure that all funds raised are transferred directly to the charity. (See also [the paragraph on page 106 on professional fundraisers and commercial participators] which affect telephone fundraising and broadcast appeals.)

The Institute of Fundraising has produced a code of practice for telephone fundraising – visit the website at: www.institute-of-fundraising.org.uk.

Chain letters
Chain letters are not illegal but their use is generally discouraged by us [the Commission] and the Institute of Fundraising because they can be difficult to control. Once started they are difficult to stop and can give rise, when the appeal target has been met, to claims that the charity is misleading the public.

Statutory provisions controlling fundraising
The Charities Act 2006 is a major piece of legislation affecting charities and the following paragraphs are taken from *A Guide to the Main Provisions which Affect Charities* at the Commission's website – www.charity-commission.gov.uk.

You should be aware that at the time of writing not all of the provisions had been put into place and you should check with the Commission for the current requirements. The Office of the Third Sector has published an implementation plan outlining when each part of the Act will come into force. This can be found at: www.cabinetoffice.gov.uk.

Fundraising solicitation statements

Currently professional fundraisers and commercial participators fundraising for charities must have a written agreement with the charity, and must make a statement telling potential donors that they are getting paid when they ask for money. This is so that potential donors can make an informed choice about giving.

The Act makes two main changes to these 'solicitation statements':

- *They will have to include the amount the professional fundraiser or commercial participator will be paid for fundraising for the appeal, or if the specific amount isn't known, to give a reasonably accurate estimate of what they'll receive.*

- *Slightly different statements will also have to be made by employees, officers and trustees of charities who act as collectors. This doesn't apply to volunteers.*

Public charitable collections

The Act provides for a new system for licensing charitable collections in public. It applies to all such collections, including face-to-face fundraising, involving requests for direct debits.

There is a new role for the Commission in checking whether charities and other organisations are fit and proper to carry out public collections and we will be responsible for issuing 'public collections certificates', valid for up to five years.

We need to develop the right regulations and guidance so that we can take on this new role. We also need the necessary resources to set up the new systems and this will take time to set up. We don't envisage taking on this function for a few years yet.

Collections in public places

Previous legislation referred to 'street' collections. The Act extends this to collections in 'public places' which includes some privately owned land, such as railway station ticket halls and supermarket forecourts. Once a charity has a public collections certificate it will be able to apply to a local authority for a permit to hold collections at certain times in certain places in that local authority area. Local authorities will ensure that there are not too many collections taking place at the same time, in the same place.

Door-to-door collections

Previous legislation referred to 'house-to-house' collections. The Act refers instead to 'door-to-door' collections, to make clear that this includes business premises. A charity with a public collections certificate will be able to conduct door-to-door collections without permission from a local authority, but it must inform the local authority that the collection is taking place.

Local, short-term collections

Some collections will be exempt from licensing and will not require either a certificate or permit, but organisers will have to notify the local authority that the collection is taking place; so small-scale activities like carol singing should not be disproportionately affected.

Lotteries

There are two main types of lotteries of interest to charities, both regulated by the Lotteries and Amusements Act 1976 as amended by the National Lottery etc Act 1993:

- small lotteries
- society lotteries.

Small lotteries

Small lotteries do not need to be registered but they have to be incidental to an exempt entertainment. Exempt entertainments are defined by the 1976 Act and include fêtes, bazaars and dinner dances. Certain conditions have to be met which include no cash prizes, the sale and issue of tickets and announcement of the results must be carried out during the entertainment and on the premises where it is held and no more than £250 can be spent on buying prizes. Trustees are advised to seek professional advice if they are in any doubt.

Society lotteries

Where a charity is promoting the sale of lottery tickets which will exceed £20,000 in value (or if taken together with sales from previous lotteries in the same year will exceed £250,000) it will be necessary to register with the Gambling Commission. Charities conducting lotteries below these thresholds are required to register with the local authority.

There are detailed statutory regulations about the conduct of lotteries covering accounts, age restrictions, the maximum price of tickets and the amounts which may be paid out in prizes and deducted for expenses. Trustees are advised to consult the appropriate local authority or the Gambling Commission for further advice.

Competitions and gaming
Competitions such as bingo and the use of gaming (slot) machines are mainly regulated by the Gaming Act 1968 [repealed by the Gambling Act 2005] and trustees are advised to consult the Gambling Commission.

Professional fundraisers and commercial participators
Where trustees decide to raise funds by employing a professional fundraiser or by entering into a promotion with a commercial participator they need to be aware of the provisions of Part II of the Charities Act 1992 (as amended by the Charites Act 2006) and The Charitable Institutions (fundraising) Regulations 1994 (SI 1994/3024).

These extracts were taken from CC20 – *Charities and fundraising* and *A Guide to the Main Provisions which Affect Charities.* You should refer to the Charity Commission's website for further advice.

Celebrities
Working with someone who is well known can help to raise the profile of your event or your organisation. There are a number of advantages to attracting a 'name' to your cause:

- increased media coverage, locally and nationally
- more people may come to an event
- other funders may attend a celebrity event
- a morale boost for those participating and organising the event
- this person can act as a positive role model for young people
- you may be able to obtain discounted rates or items from suppliers
- this person may have contacts and links with other groups and 'names'.

If you do not already have a celebrity connected with your fundraising, look at whether you have a patron, notable trustees or any famous names who once had a connection with your organisation. Celebrities will rally to your cause if they:

- like and trust the group and agree with what you are trying to do
- have some connection with you
- like the event.

Ten tips on working with the famous

1) Think about your audience.

2) Choose someone your audience knows and likes and **who you are pleased to have associated with your group** – you should be very selective in this.

3) Choose someone who is sympathetic to your cause, ideally someone with first-hand knowledge and who has a connection with your organisation.

4) Contact any celebrity well in advance of any event.

5) Be very clear about what you want their involvement to be.

6) Offer to pay expenses (mileage, materials, meals, accommodation, etc.) and budget accordingly.

7) Brief them well, and advise them about any press coverage.

8) Make sure those who will be meeting and those introducing them know what to do.

9) Don't overrun, unless they initiate it.

10) Say thanks and keep them in touch with what you are doing.

For further information on working with famous people refer to *Patrons, Presidents and Personalities* by Eileen Hammond, published by DSC.

As with everything else in fundraising, you need a mixture of the tried and trusted with the new and eye catching.

In general, fundraising from the public is one of the most exciting ways of raising money. It can be a lot of fun. Remember though to start small, start early, be realistic and make sure you have contingency plans for when things go wrong.

Checklist – how to organise an event

Lancashire Community Futures (a community council) has produced a checklist to cover planning, preparation and running a village event. You can adapt the following to your own activity, but remember this cannot cover all eventualities and you should use this as the start for your planning, rather than the last word.

If you are thinking of holding an event, a logical approach to the planning process will always produce a better organised, safer and more enjoyable event. This list has been designed to be a step-by-step guide and checklist, taking an organising committee through all the stages necessary in planning a wide range of community events.

The list follows the logical order of event planning, starting with:

1) Feasibility – the following points should be considered to ascertain the feasibility of your event before planning starts.
   - What type of event are you planning?
   - Why are you holding it?
   - When will you hold it? Will it clash with other events?
   - Where will you stage it (safely)?

2) Once you are satisfied that the event is feasible, the next stage is to plan it.

3) After deciding that your idea is sound and getting committee approval the final task is to appoint an overall event coordinator – who has overall control – and an organising committee.

Organising a community event

Planning

Agree the date of the event, and set realistic timetables for preparation. Consider the main areas of planning. The outline plan for your event should cover at least the following areas.

Safety	Assigned	Finalised
Insurance	☐	☐
Risk assessment	☐	☐
Health and safety	☐	☐
Safe site	☐	☐
Occupier's Liability Act	☐	☐
Health & Safety at Work Act	☐	☐

Budget		
Draft budget and contingency	☐	☐
Break-even point	☐	☐
Sponsorship/grant aid	☐	☐
Costs/sales	☐	☐
Trade/concessionaires	☐	☐
Reinstatement deposit	☐	☐

Publicity		
Sponsors' requirements	☐	☐
Trade adverts	☐	☐
Advertising costs	☐	☐
Publicity material costs	☐	☐

Programme	Assigned	Finalised
Time/date – other local events	☐	☐
National events	☐	☐
Holidays	☐	☐
Legal considerations –		
Food hygiene	☐	☐
Planning permission	☐	☐
Licences – alcoholic drinks	☐	☐
Music/dance	☐	☐
Personalities/guests	☐	☐

continued...

Site

Mains services

Car parking

Access to/from

Marquee hire

Reinstatement

Staffing

Numbers required

Paid

Volunteers

Preparation

Having planned the event and agreed the timetable for preparation, you must assign tasks to members or sub-groups, and arrange dates for their completion. For larger events, sub-committees for each area of preparation, e.g. safety or publicity, should be set up. The event committee must meet regularly to make sure everything is going to plan – or to iron out any problems. Members of the organising committee should take responsibility for individual areas. Completion dates should be set.

Safety	**Assigned**	**Completed**
Signs	☐	☐
Barrier hire	☐	☐
First aid personnel	☐	☐
PA systems/radio	☐	☐
Public liability	☐	☐

Budget		
Costs – services	☐	☐
Staff	☐	☐
Site	☐	☐
Equipment	☐	☐
Supplies	☐	☐
Income – sponsorship	☐	☐
Admission charge	☐	☐
Trade stands	☐	☐

continued...

Advertising on site/programme ☐ ☐
Tickets/programme sales ☐ ☐
Insurance ☐ ☐

Publicity

Radio/TV ☐ ☐
Programmes ☐ ☐
Press release ☐ ☐
Sponsors' requirements ☐ ☐
Handbills ☐ ☐
Posters ☐ ☐
Photographer ☐ ☐

Programme	**Assigned**	**Completed**
Start/finish times	☐	☐
Food hygiene	☐	☐
Planning permission	☐	☐
Insurance – high-risk activities	☐	☐
Specific items	☐	☐
Third party claims	☐	☐
Consequential loss	☐	☐
Cancelled event	☐	☐
Damage to site	☐	☐
Weather insurance	☐	☐
Catering/bars	☐	☐

Site

Signposting ☐ ☐
Site plan ☐ ☐
Electricity/water ☐ ☐
Toilets – disabled access ☐ ☐
First aid post ☐ ☐
Lost children area ☐ ☐
Seating – fire/safety regulations ☐ ☐
Car park – disabled/vehicle recovery ☐ ☐

continued...

Staffing

Recruitment – parking, tickets,
officials, catering, security

☐ ☐

Uniforms/bibs

☐ ☐

Expenses/meal tickets

☐ ☐

Troubleshooters

☐ ☐

On the day

Arrive early – earlier than you think you'll need. Ensure individual members
know their delegated tasks. Check all tasks have been completed. Run
through the event and the volunteer jobs. The event coordinator should not be
tied to one job, but should be free to assist and troubleshoot where necessary.

Safety	**Assigned**	**Checked**
PA/radios and coded messages	☐	☐
Marshals – bibs	☐	☐
Barriers – secured	☐	☐
Signs – Keep Out, Exit, etc.	☐	☐
First aid post – signposted	☐	☐
Experienced personnel	☐	☐
Firefighting equipment	☐	☐
Police	☐	☐
Electrician	☐	☐

Money

Float	☐	☐
Prize money/cheques	☐	☐
Secure cash boxes	☐	☐
Tickets – start no.	☐	☐
End no.	☐	☐

Publicity

To the event signs	☐	☐
Programmes on sale	☐	☐
Radio/TV on the day	☐	☐
Banners/flags	☐	☐
Reporters/photographers	☐	☐

continued ...

Site	Assigned	Checked
Car park – security disclaimer	☐	☐
Toilets – clean, check regularly, well positioned, accessible	☐	☐
Lost children area – staffed, signposted	☐	☐
Seating – set out, checked, anchored	☐	☐
Electrical supply/generator	☐	☐
Water/drainage	☐	☐
Catering outlets – clean and priced	☐	☐
Bars – plastic glasses: clean and priced	☐	☐

Staffing	Assigned	Checked
Easily identified	☐	☐
Briefed/specific duties	☐	☐
Given meal tickets/expenses	☐	☐

After the event

Thank your team but try to maintain momentum to ensure that all post-event jobs are completed. Discuss problems and how the event could be improved next year. Start planning now!

	Assigned	Checked
Return site to original condition	☐	☐
Extra litter collection	☐	☐
Thank you letters	☐	☐
Debriefing	☐	☐
Press release/photographs	☐	☐
Bank money – prepare accounts	☐	☐

Remember – this list cannot cover all eventualities. Space has been left for you to fill in the individual requirements specific to your event.

Produced by: Lancashire Community Futures, 15 Victoria Road, Fulwood, Preston PR2 8PS Tel: 01772 717461

A sponsored event checklist

Make sure you plan and set objectives well ahead.

1) Choose the right activity for your target audience and cause.
2) Set a date and find a suitable venue.
3) Get any permissions you need, such as permission to use a public place.
4) Produce sponsorship forms.
5) Involve other organisations, as they can be a good source of participants.
6) Organise local publicity and get media sponsorship.
7) Get local business sponsorship to cover costs and pay for any prizes being offered.
8) Prepare for the day: ensure you have all the stewards, equipment and information that you need for the event.
9) Prepare simple monitoring and feedback forms for evaluation at the end of the event and decide how you will distribute and collect them.
10) Thank everyone.
11) Chase up all uncollected pledges.
12) Make Gift Aid claims.
13) Log all details on your database.
14) Evaluate the results against your objectives.

A number of websites have ideas for events and activities, and tips on how to run them, including Save the Children. Send for, or download, its free guide at: www.savethechildren.org.uk/en/docs/fundraising_guide.

Tips: A few suggestions for you to think about

Auction of promises – tell everyone you know and sell services from the sublime to the ridiculous.

Battle of the bands – enjoy yourself and get money for it.

Dress down day – or dress up day.

Face painting – by young people on youth leaders/students on staff.

Football tournament – in fancy dress.

Grow your own – plant seeds and watch them grow, sell them at a parents' evening.

Set up a page on Facebook – invite your friends and family to join your Facebook group and create a link to raise money for your cause.

Smarties – buy all your friends a tube of Smarties, ask them to fill it with £1 or 20p coins and give it back to you.

Sponsored silence – see how long you can last without talking – it's harder than you think.

Glossary

AIM is the London Stock Exchange's international market for smaller growing companies. On AIM you will find a wide range of businesses, ranging from young, venture capital-backed start-ups to well-established, mature organisations looking to expand.

AUT A unit trust scheme authorised by the Financial Services Authority (FSA). A UK unit trust must be authorised before it can be offered to the general public in the UK.

OEIC stands for an open-ended investment company, which works in a very similar way to a unit trust except that an OEIC is legally constituted as a limited company (plc). OEICs have been operating outside the UK for some time but only since 1997 has it been possible to operate an OEIC in the UK. OEICs are not trusts and do not therefore have a trustee. However they have a depositary, which holds the securities and has similar duties to a unit trust trustee.

8 Raising money from grant-making charities

Grant-making charities give to a great many causes and often their purposes are wide in order for them to be as flexible as possible. Many will have 'general charitable purposes' as their stated objects and will only be specific about their targeted groups in their grant programmes or in their criteria for grantgiving. Many will be interested in supporting the work of youth organisations even if they have no legally stated preference for this area of work.

This chapter provides a listing of charities interested in supporting young people, often with significant grants. The list is not definitive, as there are too many to detail in this guide.

We hope to show you how you can strengthen your approach and make the most of the wide variety of resources that are available. It should be read along with Chapter 6 *Preparing and writing a good fundraising application*.

About grant-making charities

Grant-making charities are set up to give money away in grants for charitable purposes. As with all charities, they are founded for a variety of reasons and with different legal frameworks. Their social and political perspectives vary, as do their approaches to grantmaking; their income usually comes from investments or their own fundraising. There are various key factors that influence how each one operates, and you need to develop an understanding of these in order to increase your chances of success.

Grant-making charities are extremely diverse in their purposes, vision, aims, activities, assets, structure and procedures. One of the largest grant-making charities is the Wellcome Trust, which gives over £300 million each year but mainly to medical and scientific research, and so is not relevant to the majority of fundraisers.

Comic Relief is set up to tackle poverty and social injustice in the UK and Africa, and in some of the poorest countries in other parts of the world. Grantgiving is in the region of over £50 million with around £20 million being awarded in the UK; young people are a specific category in the charity's programme of giving and although new categories were due to be announced early 2009, it is likely that this will continue.

The Garfield Weston Foundation has a wide range of purposes and youth is an area that is funded. In 2007 the charity gave £1.9 million in 189 grants to youth organisations and projects including Worldwide Volunteering for Young People, YouthNet UK, clubs for young people, music groups, holiday schemes, motivational activities and sports programmes.

At the other end of the scale are much smaller (usually local) bodies that may have as little as a few hundred pounds a year to distribute but are worth approaching if you operate within their area of benefit.

There are funders that operate internationally, nationally, regionally or only locally; some will only give to organisations, others only to individuals, many will only support registered charities and, surprisingly, some national charities also make purely local grants. Many have a particular interest in supporting projects close to where they are based.

Some also have defined areas of the country where they give their local support (on the basis that it is more effective to concentrate their resources on a particular area, and that it is difficult to assess applications from all parts of the country). For example, the Wates Foundation supports projects in south London. Such grantmakers usually also want to focus on need, so any local project should try to make a convincing case that local needs are particularly pressing; comparative local data can be useful and you should contact your local authority for your ward profile, which provides useful demographic information.

If you live in an area where funders are sparse, you could try making a case to a national charity based not just on need, but on the lack of available local funding to meet that need.

Part of the skill in tailoring an application lies in identifying an area of work that a grantmaker will support and highlighting that aspect in your proposal. Most grant-making organisations say they receive many more applications than they can support but that often the standard is not good enough for them to consider awarding a grant. Generic letters are often sent by groups without being tailored to each grantmaker's particular interests and priorities – these are generally rejected. You need to make sure that each application you send is relevant to the particular charity from which you are requesting funds and that you ask for the amount needed, backed up with evidence.

Many grant-making charities see their role as being to support innovation – new ideas, new ways of approaching or tackling a problem, new needs and new organisations. They will be careful not to fund anything that could be interpreted as being a statutory responsibility even if cuts have been made and there is a need there.

Grantmakers will also be reluctant to fund your core costs over a long period. Some organisations owe their existence to grantmakers that were prepared to shoulder whatever risk there may have been during the early stages of an organisation, but this is not the norm. In order to obtain funding beyond the initial start-up period (usually a maximum of three years), organisations are required to repackage their work into new projects, even if they are still addressing the same long-term need. Whilst this involves extra work for an organisation, it requires a review of its future aims and target areas and this can often result in an innovative project and a realistic and current overview of the whole organisation.

Successful fundraising from grantmakers requires identifying suitable funders, finding out as much as you can about them, finding an aspect of your work that they will want to support, trying to get them interested in your work (even before you approach them for a grant) and persuading them that your project is workable and value for money.

How are grant-making charities run?

The running of a grant-making charity will depend on the provisions set out in its governing document, whether that is a will, trust deed, constitution or memorandum and articles of association. It is basically the set of rules by which the organisation is run and will set out its objects, provisions for its administration and management, membership (if any), trustee body and future appointments, amendments and dissolution provisions (in the event that the charity needs to be wound up). The following information will help you to understand how most grant-making charities carry out their work.

The donor or founder

The charity may have been set up by the will of a benefactor, a donation from a philanthropist or by funds raised by local people or given by a local businessperson. Often the name of the charity will indicate this. Many are established with a capital sum provided by a founder during his or her lifetime or in their will. This could be cash, shares in a company or even land. The founder could be a successful businessperson – such as Paul Hamlyn or John Moores, who both set up foundations – and some are set up with donations from the public such as the Diana, Princess of Wales Memorial Fund, which was founded in her memory.

Some have no permanent funds, but rely on continuing fundraising to provide them with money for distribution; the two largest of these are the BBC's Children in Need and Comic Relief, both of which raise money through major television appeals.

Companies may set up a charity as a vehicle for their own charitable giving; that is, instead of donating money to an established charity, or having a 'charity of the year', they establish their own through which they give grants to other charitable organisations. Depending on the way it is set up, such a charity can be truly independent of company influence, while others are obliged to follow grant-making policies that are in the interest of the company (in which case you should probably approach them in the way that you would approach a company – see Chapter 10 *Winning company support*).

How a charity is founded can have a significant impact on its grantmaking and although the declared area of interest may simply be recorded as 'general charitable purposes', the founder's wishes will guide the trustees in their giving. The founder and his or her family may often play a leading role in the charity's affairs as trustees, supporting concerns and projects which particularly interest them. Like other charities, all charitable grant-making organisations in England and Wales must be registered with the Charity Commission and file their annual accounts according to the requirements of the statement of recommended practice (SORP) and other financial regulations. Over time, the founder's influence can diminish as outside trustees are appointed, which has happened, for example, with the Joseph Rowntree and Nuffield Foundations.

Examples of major charities established by successful business people

- Esmée Fairbairn Foundation (Ian Fairbairn, M & G Group, unit trusts)
- The Gatsby Charitable Trust (David Sainsbury, J Sainsbury, supermarkets)
- The Paul Hamlyn Foundation (Paul Hamlyn, publishing)

- The Mackintosh Foundation (Cameron Mackintosh, musical theatre)
- The Tudor Trust (Sir Godfrey Mitchell, Wimpey, construction)
- The Wates Foundation (the Wates family, builders)
- The Garfield Weston Foundation (Garfield Weston, Associated British Foods)
- The Westminster Foundation (Duke of Westminster, landowner)
- The Wolfson Foundation (Sir Isaac Wolfson, retailing)

Trustees

The trustees are the people who are ultimately responsible for the administration and management of the charity and they make the grant decisions. They can have different titles, including managing trustees, committees of management and boards of directors, and they should meet on a regular basis, depending on what their governing document provides for. In the case of grant-making charities the meetings will include considering applications, recommendations from their staff (if any) and awarding grants.

Staff

The majority of the larger and medium-sized charities have paid staff; they are not trustees and will rarely make the final decision over whether a project should be funded. However, they will receive correspondence, visit applicants or request more information and then make recommendations to the trustees about whether a grant should be awarded. The trustees will, in almost all cases, have the final say on what is and is not supported.

Policies

Most funders will have some sort of grant-making policies. Some will set up specific and changing programmes, others will have stated preferences for the types of organisation they want to fund. The policies will say:

- what kinds of activity they will support: for example, sports clubs, youth organisations, environmental charities, projects for minority groups, animal charities
- where they support them: for example, throughout the UK, only in Merseyside, or within five miles of a city centre
- what kinds of grant they like to give (capital or revenue)
- what they will definitely not support.

Charities with such policies rarely give grants outside their stated policy and if you don't fit the criteria, don't apply unless you have a project that you feel they would be specifically interested in.

Written applications

Most grantmakers receive written applications on a form that they have provided or by letter. On the basis of these applications they decide who they will give a grant to, for how much and for how long. Some, however, do not consider any applications at all – they go out and find the projects they want to support. When a grantmaker states that it does not respond to unsolicited applications or that it only supports projects known to the trustees, it's probably best not to apply as you will be wasting their time and your own. If you have a personal contact with one of the trustees or you're confident that the trustees would not want to miss out on the opportunity to fund your new and innovative project, then you could telephone and make enquiries or write with a brief description asking if they would be interested.

Some dos and don'ts when applying for grants

Do

- Plan a strategy
- Plan ahead
- Select a good project
- Believe in what you are doing
- Select a target
- Write an application tailored to the needs of the funder you are approaching
- Use personal contact where you can
- Prepare a realistic and accurate budget for the project
- Be concise
- Be specific
- Establish your credibility
- Keep records of everything you do
- Send reports to keep the grantmaker informed
- Try to develop a partnership or long-term relationship
- Say thank you

continued...

Don't

■ Send a duplicated mailshot

■ Ask for unrealistic amounts, whether under or over budgeted

■ Assume funders will immediately understand the need you are addressing

■ Make general appeals for running costs

■ Use jargon

■ Convey any sense that your beneficiaries are victims

■ Beg

What kind of funding do grant-making charities give?

Cash

Most grantmakers simply make cash donations and these vary in size depending on their annual income. In the listing of grantmakers at the end of this chapter, examples of grants given to youth organisations range from £100,000 to the Outward Bound Trust to £1,500 for a girls' brigade. Small local trusts may give as little as £50 or less.

Short-term/pump priming

Most grants are given for one to three years, as the trustees want to keep themselves free to respond to new requests. Many have a maximum grant limit. They also want to feel that, unless you are proposing to eradicate a problem totally, the work will continue after their support has ended. A few grantmakers may venture beyond this and invest significantly in an organisation over a longer period, but this is not the norm. Neither do they see their role as paying for core services for a long period, they prefer to kick start new and exciting projects and look for sustainability. Your application should include a feasible exit strategy showing that your young people will be provided for when the grant has finished.

Once you have come to the end of your grant, the grantmaker will rarely give more money for the same thing. However, you can go back for funding for a different project. Therefore, unless you are new or very small, do not ask them to support your organisation as a whole, ask them to support a particular piece of work or meet a specific need. (See Chapter 5 *Fundraising for projects*.)

Revenue and capital

Grants can be awarded both for revenue (such as salaries, rent and rates) and for capital (such as building and equipment costs), although not all grantmakers will give for both and you should check this before making an application. If you are applying for revenue costs, try to show how the project will be sustainable once the grant money runs out. If it is for a capital project, show how well the facility will be used, how the running costs will be met and if it will provide a new source of revenue for you.

Innovation/difference

One of the most important parts of any application is where you show what is new about your proposed project. What makes it stand out from the rest? Is it a brand new project? Are you moving into a new area? Do you have a new approach to a problem? Are you reaching a new group (for example, homeless young people at risk, or those truanting from school)? Are you using new ways to solve old problems (for example, using sport or the arts to empower young people with few skills, or using peer group education to teach about health)? Are you giving young, disadvantaged people new skills (for example, encouraging local people from deprived communities to take part in youth leader training)? Do your activities break down barriers in communities in new ways (for example, organising music events to bring divided communities together)?

This approach will help to keep your own organisation flexible and looking forward to meet current and potential need in different ways. This is important for organisations for young people where the style of the approach as well as their changing needs should be regularly reassessed.

Non-statutory funding

Grant-making charities will not fund what they consider to be the responsibility of the state (i.e. that central or local government should be funding). Just because the state is cutting back on its commitments, it does not mean that grantmakers will or can step in.

The Charity Commission has published a leaflet called *Grant Givers and Funding of Public Services* which explains the position of the Commission on charities providing services on behalf of public authorities. A copy of this can be downloaded from the Commission's website – www.charity-commission.gov.uk – and should be read in conjunction with leaflet CC37 *Charities and Public Service Delivery*. The following is taken from the Commission's website.

Organisations are advised to ask themselves the following questions:

- *Are you relieving a statutory duty?*
- *Is it an effective use of charity funds?*
- *Is it in the interests of the charity's beneficiaries?*
- *What value will it add, or what enhancement will it provide?*

Statutory duties can be hard to identify and grantmakers should decide what they will and will not fund and set a policy. They should separate legal from moral questions and take advice from the Commission if necessary.

When considering applications for grants they should determine that it's within the applicant charity's purposes and whether the grant should be ring-fenced.

In general trustees should consider whether there is a statutory duty to provide the service in question, whether statutory funding is available, if this is a proper and effective use of charity funds and an effective way of helping beneficiaries and what added value the grant will make.

The Commission's advice to charities is:

- *We are neutral – it's a decision for the trustees.*
- *You should be paid the full cost of delivering services for government – know your full costs.*
- *Defend your independence.*
- *Think about the value you can add.*
- *An effective, working Compact is needed.*

To summarise, in order to have the best chance of success, make sure that your application matches the following.

- **The grantmaker's policies and priorities.** There is no point sending an application to a funder which has no interest in the work that you do.
- **Its scale of grantmaking.** There is no point approaching a small charity for a large grant, or a major one for a small item of expenditure.
- **Its ethos and approach.** You will have the greatest success with those that share your outlook and values.

Which grant-making charities give money to work with young people?

There is a large number of grantmakers that might give to your youth organisation. They may respond to your application if your activities are educational, have social welfare objectives, or just because you work with children and young people and they want to support that. It might also be that you are within a geographical area of interest to them.

Even if a grantmaker doesn't have a stated priority to give to young people's activities, your work may still be eligible. For example where it gives support to education, you may be eligible if you work with, say, those who have been excluded from school or for an innovative approach to vocational training. Similarly, where a grantmaker is concerned with drug abuse, your young people's project to set up a dedicated helpline may fit well with its interests.

Local grant-making charities

Generally, it pays to find local charities to apply to first, as these will have geographical limitations on the number of organisations that they can help. A great deal of local giving is done on a friendship basis where trustees give to projects they know and like. You should make a real effort to get to know local trustees personally and send them regular information on your current activities and recent successes. It is beyond the scope of this book to list all local grant-making charities, although a few larger ones have been included as examples of the great work that these trusts carry out – they are the Francis C Scott Charitable Trust, which gives in Cumbria and north Lancashire, the Jack Petchey Foundation, which gives in London and Essex, and John Lyon's Charity, also giving in London. You can find out about local trusts by:

Word of mouth
Ask your own trustees (management committee/board of directors), leaders, volunteers, staff, parents or neighbouring groups. Where someone has been successful with a local grantmaker, build on their experience.

Your local or regional association headquarters
If you have one of these it may have details of grantmakers in the area.

Your local council for voluntary service (CVS)
Your local CVS is a good source of information on which organisations give in the area and to whom. Details can be found at www.navca.org.uk.

Local directories of trusts
These are produced locally by CVSs and nationally by the Directory of Social Change. DSC publishes a range of grant directories on trust giving for fundraisers, including its own *Guides to the Major Trusts Volumes 1 and 2* which include the results of independent research and analysis of what the trusts actually give to in practice. DSC also produces *Guides to Local Trusts* and the

Directory of Grant Making Trusts (DGMT). All of DSC's information on trusts and foundations can also be accessed via the www.trustfunding.org.uk subscription website.

The local press

Some grantmakers advertise their application procedures and closing dates through local papers or community networks, and donations to local organisations may be covered in news stories.

Community foundations

Community foundations work in a specific geographical area to provide grants for local charitable activity. They have been active in the UK since the 1980s, although the idea originated in America in 1914. They raise money from industry and other grant-giving bodies to distribute in the local area.

Community foundations operate in two main ways:

- by building an endowment of capital given by charities, companies and individuals in their area, and from legacies. The income from this is then used to make grants
- by working with other donors to help them distribute their money more effectively. Donors can direct their funds to a favoured cause or within a specified geographical area. Themed funds can address a particular issue, such as crime prevention, and projects can be supported with donations from several sources.

Community foundations are promoted, supported and trained by the Community Foundation Network (CFN) which 'aims to promote the concept of community foundations in the UK, stimulate and support their growth and best practice, and give support to individual community foundations and their networking with others. CFN's objective is to ensure a network of thriving community foundations throughout the UK, each one able to strengthen their local community through strategic grantmaking and excellent service provision to donors'.

A growing network of approximately 60 foundations is now established across the country. According to the Network's website about 90% of the UK population has access to a community foundation. They also play a central role in distributing part of the Children's Fund. (See Chapter 12 *Raising money from government* for further details.)

Details of your nearest community foundation can be obtained from the Community Foundation Network 020 7713 9326; www.community foundations.org.uk or through your local council for voluntary service.

Children and young people will be a natural area of interest to community foundations and some will make them a priority. You should let them know what you are doing and find out how they can support you.

National grant-making charities

Where there is no local charity that works in your area you will have to look further afield and approach national charities. These organisations usually have more money but are the most heavily applied to. Circular letters to them almost always fail; carefully targeted applications have a much greater chance of success.

Ten large grantgivers to young people's work

The following have stated an interest in supporting work with children and young people. Their priorities differ greatly within this field. All have entries included in the listing at the end of this chapter. Some have specified a grant amount for children and young people or young people (alone) – see the following table – with others we have estimated a figure. For those trusts that have specified their grant total for children and young people, some will include their support of individuals as well as organisations.

Grantmaker	Grant total	Grants to children & young people or young people	Year
BBC Children in Need	£33 million	£33 million	2006/07
Jack Petchey Foundation	£12.4 million	£12.4 million	2007
Comic Relief	£71.3 million	£5.7 million	2006/07
Henry Smith Charity	£26.2 million	£4.7 million	2007
John Lyon's Charity	£4.1 million	£4.1 million	2006/07
Rank Foundation	£4.9 million	£3.2 million	2007
KPMG Foundation	£3 million	£3 million	2006/07
Tudor Trust	£20.7 million	£2.7 million	2007/08
Garfield Weston Foundation	£51.7 million	£1.9 million	2007/08
Dulverton Trust	£2.9 million	£1.1 million	2007/08

Who to apply to and how to do it

Almost all grant-making charities receive far more applications for projects than they can fund. This does not mean that you should not apply but rather that you will have to put time and effort into making a good application to an appropriate organisation and you should be selective in this.

Most of the larger charities publish guidelines as to what they will and will not fund. It is important to read these before applying to see if what you are proposing fits within their policies and does not fall within their exclusions.

The crucial question in deciding whether to make an application is: 'What do we and the grant-making charity have in common?' What you want to do must meet with what the grantmaker is seeking to fund. This may be in terms of geography, where you operate in the same area, or there may be a particular target group (for example, young people – those with disabilities or who are disadvantaged) who you want to involve in your activities and who the grantmaker wants to help.

The activities may be an area where the grantmaker has a long-standing interest, such as increasing the leadership skills of young people, if so, you need to engage them with what your vision is and how you hope to achieve your aims.

Presenting your case

For grantmakers without application forms, you need to present your case clearly in an application letter and we would suggest it should be no longer than two sides of A4. In many cases it is all the funder has to go on to make a decision and so you need to include all relevant information including: who you are; what you are going to do; how you are going to do it; who is going to do it; what difference it will make; how much it will cost; and how it will be financed when the grant ends.

Documents such as annual reports, a recent set of audited or independently examined accounts and details of other funding that has been raised or pledged should be attached, but this is supporting material – don't rely on it. The case you make in your application letter should be compelling to the reader. Pass the letter to someone who doesn't know your organisation – if they still don't know what you do and intend to do by the end of the letter, you need to re-draft.

The eight essential elements of an application (given in Chapter 6 *Preparing and writing a good fundraising application*) are all highly relevant to grantmakers. However, before you start drafting your letter or form, you should consider the following suggestions.

Find out what charities your organisation has already applied to and whether it was successful

For those applications that failed, look at why and how you can improve a second application. Those that have supported you are likely to support you again, especially if you have done a good job and reported back to them your achievements. They will be unlikely to fund you for the same project but would probably be pleased to consider a new one.

Devise one or a series of projects for which you need money

Unless you are very new or very small, it is unlikely that a grant-making charity will support your entire organisation; they will want to support a particular piece of work that fits in with their specific interests, hence the emphasis on projects. Also, make sure you can show how your project fits into the charity's grant-making policies.

Work out what is new about this work

Does it give new opportunities to young people? Does it try to solve a longstanding problem in a new and exciting way? Is it developing a new service in that town or village? If there is nothing new about the project, your chances of raising significant grants are less favourable.

Decide how the project can be funded in the long term

Grantmakers generally only give grants for up to three years. It could be argued that if they were to make very long-term grants they would be tying the hands of future trustees and would not be able to adapt to change. However, they do like to see long-term benefits and you will need to persuade them that you can pay for the work once their funding has run out. A well thought out exit strategy will show the grantmaker that you have considered the sustainability of your project and how your beneficiaries will be provided for when funding for the project has come to an end.

Maximise the impact of your personal contacts

Ask around your organisation, your beneficiaries, members, volunteers, supporters, management committee (trustees) and staff. Does anyone know any charity trustee or administrator of a grant-making charity personally? If so, get them to make contact and see how the land lies. Personal applications are always the best.

Look through the guide books, this one and others

There are various trust directories to look at and the local CVS will have details of them. DSC publishes an extensive range.

Get hold of the grantmakers' guidelines

This is crucial to a good application. Read them carefully and address the points they raise in your application. For example, if the guidelines ask how the project will be evaluated, you need to give a clear idea of what procedures you have in place to record: how many have used the project, if your targeted groups have been reached, what their feedback said, what they feel the benefits have been and how this information will inform future decisions and activities.

Where the grantmaker has paid administrators, you can ring them to discuss your application

You could ask: would it be eligible, do you have to be a registered charity, when would it be considered, do you need to fill out an application form? Most of the larger grantmakers are prepared to have a preliminary chat over the phone. However, if you get the impression that they don't want to talk, ask whether they would prefer you to write an initial letter, or how it would be best to make an initial approach.

Write to the charities you have identified as having a common interest with you

The letter should not be more than two sides of A4. In this letter you should state clearly:

- who you are
- what you do
- why the project is important
- what you need
- what it will achieve
- where you will get the money from
- how it will be monitored and evaluated
- how it is sustainable.

You should also send a budget for the particular project, a set of accounts for the organisation as a whole, an annual report and maybe one or two other documents to support your application, such as a recent newspaper cutting.

Monitoring and evaluation

Monitoring and evaluation are important tools, not only to collate information for the report to your funder at the end of a grant but as a way of keeping track of the progress of your project and informing your decisions on future activities. Some grantmakers ask for nothing from an organisation following a grant being given, however, most do. Some will ask for a narrative report and some will ask for detailed analysis of the project, together with targets met, budget lines and the difference the grant has made.

A handful, unfortunately, may have monitoring requirements that look similar to those of the European Social Fund and require monitoring and evaluation requirements totally disproportionate to the amount awarded. However, the grantmaker is a charity itself, responsible for the best use of its charitable assets and required to demonstrate its public benefit, an audit trail for its expenditure and transparency and accountability in its work. Applicants should take this into account and include the administration costs of monitoring and evaluation in the project's budget.

These suggestions will help you with the basic elements to include in your application.

You should now consider what will make your application stand out from all the others and here are some ideas to help you with that:

Build contacts

You will probably be able to identify 10 or 15 key charities from which you have a good chance of getting support, maybe now or maybe in the future. If you can, send some information before you actually write to them for money. This could be your annual report, some press coverage or a newsletter. The main purposes are: (1) to show yourselves in a positive light; (2) to try and get your name known before you write for money; and (3) to show that you are committed to a longer-term relationship with them.

Many grantmakers complain that the only time they hear from people is when they want money and that they actually like to hear about an organisation's activities and new initiatives from time to time. Some of the major charities may themselves seek out projects to support and if they already know about you, you will feature more prominently on their grant-making radar.

Supporting material should be professional but not expensive and glossy. Most grant-making charities are run by busy people with little time to wade through long project descriptions and brochures. A letter saying: 'In May last year you supported us with ...., and we are now pleased to say that ....' is all you need. Remember, this is not an appeal letter; you are not asking for money at this stage. Be brief, enthusiastic and informative. Send the funder this kind of information once or twice a year. If you don't know people personally, this is the next best thing.

If the project is new or unknown to the potential grant-making charity

Ask well-known sponsors or supporters, or local community leaders to say how well-run the organisation is and how much the project is needed. This helps create a bridge between you and the grantmaker.

Offer to visit the potential funder to explain your work

Or better still try to get them to come and see you. Put them on your VIP list for events you may be running. They probably won't have the time to attend but if they do, hopefully your application will look familiar when it arrives for consideration. Take time to show them round, introduce the kind of people they want to meet and generally get them enthusiastic about what you are doing.

When you do get a grant, remember this is the beginning of the relationship, not the end

Keep them informed of how things are going (they will probably ask for monitoring information anyway). Always try to be positive and enthusiastic. If you get one grant and spend it well, you have a good chance of getting another grant for something different later on; funders often base decisions on the effectiveness of a previous grant.

Tips for applying to a grant-making charity

One national grant-making foundation gives the following guidance to those applying for grants:

In making your application it is important to realise that yours is one of many competing for limited resources. It is helpful to us if your application is:

- clear, concise and to the point – say what you do or propose to do, how much it will cost and how it will impact on your clients

- transparent, open, direct. Do not try to hide what you want funds for in the guise of something else

- realistic – don't just pick a figure out of the air and work your project/programme around it.

Starting with the need, justify the need and outline a tangible response to meeting the need that makes sense.

We have found that projects are very strong in telling us about their aims and objectives, but weak in telling us what they do and how it impacts on young people and children.

Grant-making charities supporting organisations working with young people

The following list includes large grant-making charities that have made young people a priority in their grant distribution. Most give throughout the UK, with the exception of the Francis C Scott Charitable Trust, John Lyon's Charity and the Jack Petchey Foundation.

BBC Children in Need

CC no. 802052

Contact
David Ramsden, Chief Executive,
PO Box 1000, London W12 7WJ
Tel: 020 8576 7788; Fax: 020 8576 8887;
email: pudsey@bbc.co.uk;
website: www.bbc.co.uk/pudsey

Trustees
Stevie Spring, Chair; Tim Davie; Neena
Mahal; Beverley Tew; Sir Terry Wogan;
Lesley Douglas; Yogesh Chauhan; Alan
Broughton; Susan Elizabeth; Peter
McBride; Nicholas Eldred.

Areas of work: Welfare of disadvantaged
children

Total grants: £33 million (2006/07)

Youth grants: £33 million

Beneficial area: UK.

General

The charity, registered in 1989,
distributes the proceeds of the BBC's
annual Children in Need appeal (first
televised in 1980). Around 2,000 grants
in total may be made in a year, with
amounts ranging from a few hundred
pounds to a normal maximum of about
£100,000 (although larger grants are
made).

Grants are made for specific projects
which directly help children and young
people (aged 18 and under). About half
of all applications result in a grant
(though no doubt the success rate is
higher for smaller applications and the
amount given even in successful cases
may often be less than the full amount
requested).

In 2006/07 it had a total income of
£36.5 million. From this, 88% came from
donations, Gift Aid and legacies.

The trustees approve all grant awards on
the basis of the assessment of
applications by third party assessors and
the recommendations of eight regional
advisory committees. Grants are awarded
to properly constituted not-for-profit
organisations working with
disadvantaged children in the United
Kingdom (and The Isle of Man and
Channel Islands). Grants are for periods
of one, two or three years. Where a grant
is awarded for a period of greater than
one year each annual instalment is only
released after the receipt of a satisfactory
report on the prior year's expenditure.

During the year the charity received
3,579 applications for grant aid with a
total amount requested of
£166.5 million. Awards were made to
1,350 organisations to the value of
£33 million. Awards varied in value from
£200 to £180,500. An additional
£1.75 million was given over two years to
the Frank Buttle Trust to make smaller
emergency welfare grants to individual
children; the Renfield Centre Children's
Fund in Scotland received £344,500.

Grants were broken down by area of
disadvantage as follows:

Type	Amount
Poverty/deprivation	£14,000,000
Illness, distress, abuse or neglect	£10,000,000
Disability	£6,700,000
Behavioural difficulties	£2,300,000

The charity is committed to ensuring
that grants are distributed across the
United Kingdom – a breakdown of how
funds were allocated is shown below.

Area	Amount
London and South East England	£6,400,000
UK-wide	£4,900,000
Midlands and East England	£4,000,000
Scotland	£3,800,000
North West England	£3,000,000
North East England	£3,000,000
South and West England	£2,900,000
Wales	£2,500,000
Northern Ireland	£2,500,000

Grantmaking in 2006/07

Grants to charities and organisations during the year fell into the bands detailed below:

- £1–£1,000 (41 grants)
- £1,001–£5,000 (343 grants)
- £5,001–£10,000 (263 grants)
- £10,001–£25,000 (309 grants)
- £25,001–£100,000 (356 grants)
- Over £100,000 (38 grants).

Within the 2006/07 accounts an overview of grants awarded contained the top ten grants awarded by amount, ten medium-sized grants and ten smaller-sized grants. The examples of beneficiaries taken from each category are:

Top ten grants – Frank Buttle Trust (£1.75 million); Renfield Centre Children's Fund (£344,500); Carers' Association in South Tyneside (£180,400); African Youth League (£160,600); Asylum Aid (£145,300); Carers' Federation Ltd (£145,000); Mencap Eden (£139,200); InterAct (£138,100); Adoption UK (£137,000); and the Nia Project (£134,100).

Median grants – Median grants were for around £11,000. Beneficiaries included: Shape, Cornerstone Community Care, Hollybush Centre Ltd, St Joan of Arc School – Glasgow, Lambeth Play Association, Mencap & Gateway Sheffield, Women's Aid Aberconwy, Manor Street Clifton Community Group, West Alness Residents' Association and Criw Niwbwrch Cyf.

Smaller grants – The examples given ranged from £200 to £600, and included those to: Woodside Parish Church Starter Pack Group, Glencolin Residents' Association, Fauldhouse Pre-school Playgroup, Girlguides Rainbows 119th Joanmount Methodists, Football Club Loughside, Football Club Upper Ardoyne Juniors, Extreme Youth, Boys Brigade 93rd Belfast Company, Stepping Stones North Edinburgh and South Holland User Group.

Information available

Information was provided by the charity.

Exclusions

The appeal does not consider applications from private individuals or the friends or families of individual children. In addition, grants will not be given for:

- trips and projects abroad
- medical treatment or medical research
- unspecified expenditure
- deficit funding or repayment of loans
- retrospective funding
- projects which are unable to start within 12 months
- distribution to another/other organisation(s)
- general appeals and endowment funds
- the relief of statutory responsibilities
- projects for pregnancy testing or advice, information or counselling on pregnancy choices
- the promotion of religion
- additional projects for organisations that already hold a BBC Children in Need grant where funding is not coming to an end.

Applications

Straightforward and excellent application forms and guidelines are available from the website or from the following national BBC Children in Need offices:

England (and general helpline): PO Box 1000, London W12 7WJ. Telephone number: 020 8576 7788.

Northern Ireland: Broadcasting House, Ormeau Avenue, Belfast BT2 8HQ. Telephone number: 028 9033 8221.

Scotland: BBC Scotland, G10, 40 Pacific Drive, Glasgow, G51 1DA. Telephone number: 0141 422 6111.

Wales: Broadcasting House Llandaff, Cardiff CF5 2YQ. Telephone number: 029 2032 2383.

There are four closing dates for applications – 15 January, 15 April, 15 July and 15 October. Applicants should allow up to three months after each closing date for notification of a decision.

Application forms must be completed online – visit the website for more information (www.bbc.co.uk/pudsey).

Note: Incomplete or late application forms will not be assessed.

Percy Bilton Charity

CC no. 1094720

Contact
James R Lee, Secretary, Bilton House, 7 Culmington Road, London W13 9NB Tel: 020 8579 2829; Fax: 020 8567 3650; website: www.percybiltoncharity.org.uk

Trustees
Miles A Bilton, Chair; James R Lee; Stefan J Paciorek; Kim Lansdown.

Areas of work: Disabled, disadvantaged young people, older people
Total grants: £447,500 to organisations (2007/08)
Youth grants: £204,500
Beneficial area: UK.

General

The following information is taken from the charity's website.

Background

The Percy Bilton Charity was founded on 9 July 1962 by the late Percy Bilton for exclusively charitable purposes. Percy Bilton was an entrepreneur who in the 1920s and 1930s built up a group of successful property companies which in the 1970s was listed on the London Stock Exchange. He endowed the charity with a substantial parcel of shares in Percy Bilton Ltd, which later became Bilton plc.

Although the companies were legally separate, the charity shared in the success of Bilton plc, for many years receiving a steadily increasing dividend income. The investments in both Bilton plc and in the unquoted company were sold in 1998 and the total proceeds are now invested in a diversified investment portfolio.

During his lifetime, Percy Bilton took a keen personal interest in the activities of the charity, retaining his involvement until his death in 1982. The directors of the charity, who are its trustees, have continued the charity's activities in accordance with the charitable objects set out by the founder.

Summary

Main grants are normally for building projects or for items of capital expenditure (though not for office equipment or furniture). They range from about £2,000 up to a usual maximum of £5,000 and are made to organisations working with:

- disadvantaged/underprivileged young people (under 25)
- people with disabilities (physical or learning disabilities or mental health problems)
- older people (aged over 60)

There is also a small grants programme that provides funding of up to £500 for small charities working with people who are disabled, older people and young people for furniture and equipment.

Guidelines for applicants

The charity provides the following information.

Types of grant

We have two programmes for organisations:

(1) Large grants – one-off payments for capital expenditure of £2,000 and over, i.e. furniture and equipment; building/ refurbishment projects. Please note that we do not fund running costs.

(2) Small grants – donations of up to £500 towards furnishings and equipment for small projects. This programme is more suitable for smaller organisations.

Amount of grant

The amount offered will usually depend on the number of applications received in relation to the funds available for distribution. You may therefore not receive the full amount requested.

Major appeals

In the case of major appeals and minibuses please apply after 75% of the funding has been secured, as offers are conditional upon the balance being raised and the project being completed within one year. We also require grants to be taken up within 12 months of the offer and it is essential to ascertain that your project is likely to be completed within this timescale before applying.

Who the charity will fund

The charity will consider capital funding for the following projects and schemes:

■ *Disadvantaged/underprivileged young people (under 25)*

Supported housing schemes and educational and training projects to encourage disadvantaged young people who may be homeless and/or unemployed away from crime, substance/alcohol misuse and homelessness.

Facilities for recreational activities and outdoor pursuits specifically for young people who are educationally or socially underprivileged or disadvantaged.

■ *People with disabilities (physical or learning disabilities or mental health problems)*

Residential care, respite care, occupational and recreational establishments for children, young people and adults with physical or learning disabilities or enduring mental health problems.

■ *Older people (aged over 60)*

Day centres, nursing and residential homes, sheltered accommodation and respite care for the frail or sufferers from dementia or age related disorders.

Projects to encourage older people to maintain their independence.

Grants in 2007/08

In 2007/08 the charity had assets of £17.6 million and an income of £723,500. Grants were made totalling £600,500, of which £447,500 was given to organisations, £112,000 was donated to individuals and £41,000 was given in food parcels to older people.

Grants to organisations were catagorised as follows:

Large grants

Disability	£146,000
Young people with a disability	£114,000
Older people	£71,000
Disadvantaged young people	£66,500

Small grants

Disability/older people	£26,500
Disadvantaged young people	£24,000

Beneficiaries receiving larger grants included:

Disadvantaged/at risk young people

Friends of Longridge – Marlow (£6,000), for the purchase of the freehold of Longridge Boating Centre in order to secure the site which is used for water sports training and activities for youth groups; A690 Youth Initiative – Sunderland (£5,200), for the provision of a mobile cage structure to provide a safe environment for street-based sports activities for young people who are not interested in engaging with traditional centre-based youth provision; Caldecott Foundation – Kent (£4,000), towards the construction of 'Willow Trees', a six-bedded residential home for children with severe behavioural problems who receive care, therapy and education at the foundation; Avon Tyrrell UK – Hampshire (£3,000), towards the construction of a six-berth log cabin to provide upgraded accommodation at its outdoor residential centre for young people of all backgrounds and abilities; and EC Roberts Centre – Portsmouth (£1,800), towards the purchase of an interactive tactile panel for use by children attending the Centre which offers support and assistance to families facing homelessness and relationship breakdown.

Children and young people with disabilities

Children's Hospice South West – North Somerset (£17,000), for the purchase of a wheelchair accessible multi-people vehicle to transport families to and from the hospice and on day trips; Haven House Foundation – Essex (£5,000), to purchase washable flooring to replace unhygienic carpeting at the children's hospice; Children's Adventure Farm Trust, Cheshire (£4,000), for the installation of a 'spider's web' climbing frame for the adventure playground at the activity centre which is accessible to children with a wide range of physical, learning and sensory disabilities; Blaen Wern Farm Charitable Trust – Wales (£3,000), for external building works at the residential centre for children with disabilities and their families/carers. Works include providing a tarmac surface to the car park, erecting fencing and installing a new cattle grid; and Norman Laud Association – West Midlands (£1,800), for the purchase of a plasma flat screen television for the

lounge at the respite care home for children with disabilities.

Disability – general

4SIGHT – West Sussex (£5,000), for the installation and equipping of a training kitchen as part of the refurbishment of the Bradbury Resource Centre for people with a visual impairment; Thames Hospicecare – Windsor (£4,500), for the purchase of furnishings and equipment for the refurbished outpatient clinic at Thames Valley Hospice; Carlisle Mencap (£4,000), towards the refurbishment of California House, a residential and respite home for people with a learning disability; Sanctuary Care – Worcestershire (£3,500), for the purchase of a wheelchair accessible minibus for Shaftesbury Place residential home for adults with physical disabilities; Northampton Mencap (£3,000), for the construction of a purpose-built headquarters and social centre for adults with a learning disability; Phoenix Group Homes – Essex (£2,700), for the installation of a new fitted kitchen at the residential and day project at 6 Oxford Road for adults with alcohol misuse and mental health problems; and United Response – Sheffield (£1,800), for the purchase of IT equipment for use by 43 residents of its supported housing in Sheffield who have learning disabilities and a range of communication needs.

Older people

Northwood Day Centre – Stoke-on-Trent (£6,500), for the purchase of a Parker bath with spa and booster pump to be used by district nurses for their patients as well as older people in the local community who have difficulty using a bath at home owing to health issues and poor mobility; Age Concern St Helen's (£5,300), to purchase computer equipment for IT classes for older people with special needs to be held at venues in the community such as sheltered housing complexes; Voluntary Action Rutland (£4,000), for the construction of an extension to the Rutland Volunteer Centre to provide a resource centre facility for older/disabled people; Extra Care Charitable Trust – Telford (£3,600), to purchase exercise equipment as part of the health programme for its sheltered housing scheme for older people in Telford; The Hand Partnership – Norfolk (£2,400), for the purchase of three electric scooters for loan to older people with mobility problems; and Furzedown Project – London (£2,000), for the purchase of a wheelchair accessible minibus for the day centre which provides activities for older people, many of whom are housebound or disabled.

Information available

Full accounts were available from the Charity Commission. The charity has a clear and consise website.

Exclusions

The charity will not consider the following (the list is not exhaustive):

- running expenses for the organisation or individual projects
- salaries, training costs or office equipment/furniture
- consumables (e.g. stationery, food and drink)
- publication costs (e.g. printing/ distributing promotional information leaflets
- projects for general community use even if facilities for disabled people are included
- projects that have been completed
- items that have already been purchased
- provision of disabled facilities in schemes mainly for able-bodied people
- general funding/circular appeals
- playschemes/summer schemes
- holidays or expeditions for individuals or groups

- trips, activities or events
- community centres or village halls for wider community use
- community sports/play area facilities
- pre-schools or playgroups (other than predominantly for disabled children)
- refurbishment or repair of places of worship/church halls
- research projects
- mainstream pre-schools, schools, colleges and universities (other than special schools)
- welfare funds or other grant-making bodies for further distribution
- hospital/medical equipment
- works to premises not used primarily by the eligible groups.

Applications

If in doubt regarding the suitability of an appeal, contact the charity either in writing, giving a brief outline, or by telephone. If you have already received a grant, please allow at least one year from the date of payment before reapplying. However you can reapply after 12 months.

Large grants (£2,000 and over)

Please apply on your organisation's headed notepaper giving or attaching the following information.

1–6 must be provided in all cases and 7 as applicable to your appeal:

1. A brief history of your charity, its objectives and work

2. Description of the project and what you intend to achieve

3. A copy of your most recent annual report and audited accounts

4. Details of funds already raised and other sources that you have approached

5. Proposals to monitor and evaluate the project

6. Any other relevant information that will help to explain your application

7. The following additional information that applies to your appeal

Building/refurbishment appeals

- A statement of all costs involved. Please itemise major items and professional fees

- Confirmation that the project has ongoing revenue funding

- Confirmation that all planning and other consents and building regulations approvals have been obtained

- Details of ownership of the premises and if leased, the length of the unexpired term

- Timetable of construction/refurbishment and anticipated date of completion

Equipment appeals

- An itemised list of all equipment with estimate of costs. Please obtain at least two competitive estimates except where this is not practicable e.g. specialised equipment

Contribution towards purchase of minibuses

Please note that minibuses can only be considered if used to transport older and disabled people with mobility problems.

Please give details of provision made for insurance, tax and maintenance, etc. We require confirmation that your organisation can meet future running costs.

Small grants (up to £500)

Please apply on your organisation's headed notepaper with the following information:

1. Brief details about your organisation and its work

2. A copy of your most recent annual accounts

3. Outline of the project and its principal aims

4. Breakdown of the cost of item/s required

5. If your organisation is not a registered charity, please supply a reference from a registered charity with which you work or from the voluntary service council

The Church Urban Fund

CC no. 297483

Contact
Lucy Palfreyman, Director of Finance and Resources, Church House, Great Smith Street, London SW1P 3AZ Tel: 020 7898 1647; Fax: 020 7898 1601; email: enquiries@cuf.org.uk; website: www.cuf.org.uk

Trustees
Peter Doyle, Chair; Ven. Richard Atkinson; Rt Revd Peter Broadbent; Patrick Coldstream; Michael Eastwood; Ven Paul Hackwood; Yvonne Hutchinson; Andrew Hunter Johnston; Revd Dennis Poole; Derek Twine; Betty Thayer; Revd David Walker.

Areas of work: Welfare and Christian outreach in deprived communities in England.

Total grants: £2.6 million (2007)

Youth grants: £642,000

Beneficial area: The most deprived areas of England.

General

The Church Urban Fund was set up in 1988 in response to the Church of England's Faith in the City report which drew attention to the increasing levels of poverty in urban areas and to the widening gap between rich and poor. The report suggested that the church should 'set up a fund to help churches work more closely with their local communities to help people tackle poor housing, poor education, unemployment and poverty'. An initial capital sum was raised from what was presented at the time as a one-off appeal, and income from this provides about half of the fund's present income. Most of the rest comes from continued donations and legacies.

The trust was set up to support faith-based groups working in the poorest communities in England. Grants are allocated through the Church of England diocesan areas delivering essential support to the places of greatest local need. The poorest areas are targeted using a measure known as the multiple indices of deprivation. The trust offers support to groups working in both urban and rural areas, the priority being the most deprived and marginalised communities. In carrying out these objectives, consideration is given to initiatives or projects that involve ecumenical cooperation with other Christian bodies or cooperation with people of other faiths. The vision of the trust is to bring about lasting and positive change in the lives of people most on the margins of society.

The trust supports projects that:

- tackle major problems in the local area, such as poverty, unemployment, disaffected young people, lack of community facilities, loneliness and isolation, inadequate housing and homelessness
- equip communities to address local needs and issues and encourage people to take control of their lives
- empower the church to taken an active role in wider community development, particularly through inter-faith and ecumenical developments
- are innovative, will make a practical impact and can develop partnerships with other agencies.

The trust encourages the dioceses of the Church of England to become more involved in the process of grantmaking. The aim here is to streamline and speed up the grantmaking process, use local knowledge and experience and be more responsive to the needs and aspirations of local community groups and churches. Dioceses are at different stages of engagement with this.

Each diocese will have established and developed a set of key strategies, objectives and priorities for tackling poverty and disadvantage in their area. Each will also have been advised of an indicative sum that could be awarded to work within the diocese.

In 2007 the trust had assets of £3.4 million and an income of over £2.7 million. There were 210 grants made totalling over £2.6 million. Grants specifically to organisations working with children and young people totalled £642,000, although such groups may also be included under 'social welfare' and 'community-based activities', meaning that the total amount benefiting young people may be much higher.

The trust currently offers two grant programmes described as follows:

Church urban fund grant – the main programme

This offers grants of up to £30,000 over a three year period. This maximum sum is reserved for those projects with the highest priority and in general awards are between £15,000 and £25,000. The minimum level that can be granted is £5,000 for capital and £5,000 per annum for revenue. Revenue grants are normally spread over three years. Projects can be awarded less than the minimum award level if they request such an amount.

The trust particularly assists churches in deprived areas in their outreach to their local community and aims to support the mission of the church. The following criteria are applied by the trust when awarding grants:

- the project needs to be based in the local community and to have local community involvement in identifying needs, initiating responses and running the project
- the project must be open to all regardless of faith, ethnic origin, disability, gender or sexual orientation
- projects do not have to be Anglican but there needs to be a strong link between the project and a faith group. The project needs to be endorsed by the Diocesan Bishop and be a demonstrable response to the strategy or priorities or set by the diocese
- the project must have charitable purposes
- the project must be able to raise part of the required money from other sources
- the project needs to be directly tackling the effects of profound poverty and should be working in the 10% most deprived areas in England. The trust uses the most up-to-date and appropriate government issued indices of multiple deprivation (IMD) as a guide and measure to determine the local areas (super output areas – SOAs) to be prioritised.

Exceptions

The following is an explanation of exceptions to the criteria given by the trust, applicants are advised also to refer to the grants policy and procedure manual available from the trust's website:

The area IMD score is made up of seven component domains, these being: barriers to housing, crime, education and skills, employment, health deprivation and disability, income and, finally, living environment. As with the SOA score, each domain is also scored 1 to 32,482 (the total number of SOAs). If the project is not within one of the priority SOAs, but is directly addressing one of the above

domains that has a score of 1 to 3,248, an application can be submitted for consideration.

- *If the organisation or project is serving a target group that is deemed to be intrinsically disadvantaged and not covered by the geographic IMD scores or domains, for example, homeless people, people with drug and alcohol problems, refugees and asylum seekers, prostitutes/people working in the sex industry.*

Priorities

Priority will be given to:

- projects based within areas where there are the greatest levels of deprivation in England
- projects identified by dioceses as being key to the reduction of deprivation in their area
- projects which, by their nature, are limited in the funds they can access and therefore are in particular need of trust support
- projects where the trust's support will make the greatest impact.

Mustard seed programme

This is a rolling programme where there are no deadline dates and requests of up to £5,000 will be considered. The programme aims to provide grants to enable churches and faith-based organisations to engage in social action through supporting them to initiate, develop and formulate ideas and opportunities in preparation for undertaking larger pieces of work. [From 2008 the budget for this programme is £300,000 each year.]

The trust provides the following information on the mustard seed programme:

- grants can be given for specific activities but not for ongoing revenue expenditure, deficit funding, or retrospective spending

- the grant requested should represent the major part of the funding required
- grants are made for one year only with the expectation that the money will be spent within 12 months from the date of the award
- applications for a further mustard seed grant in the following year from the same organisation will not normally be considered
- among other things, grants are provided to increase the capacity of community groups, for the preparation of plans and presentations, to undertake social audits and community consultation exercises and to provide support to management committees and project leaders.

Grants in 2007

Grants awarded were categorised in the following areas:

	No.	Amount
Community-based activities	49	£963,000
Youth and children's work	40	£642,000
Social welfare	27	£409,000
Opening up churches and other buildings	16	£239,000
Mustard seed grants	52	£150,000
Homelessness and housing	10	£140,000
National development work	4	£50,000
Flood disaster relief grants	4	£24,500
Employment and training	1	£22,500

Information available

Full accounts were available at the Charity Commission.

Exclusions

Grants are not made for:

- projects outside England
- individuals
- projects not directly tackling profound poverty or specific issues caused by poverty
- direct support for other grant-giving bodies

- publications, research and campaigning activities
- revenue and capital funding for regional and national voluntary/community organisations and public and private sector organisations
- replacement of statutory funding
- projects without faith links
- work that has already been funded by CUF for six years
- activities open only to church members, and evangelistic activity not part of a response to poverty
- clergy stipends including church army posts
- internal reordering of churches for worship, church maintenance and repairs
- work that does not increase the capacity of the organisation e.g. Disability Discrimination Act (DDA) compliance, unless as part of a wider scheme
- organisations with significant reserves
- ongoing costs of credit unions
- general appeals
- 100% of funding.

The trust will not make retrospective grants or help pay off deficits or loans.

Applications

The trust has produced a detailed and helpful grants policy and procedure manual and applicants are advised to read this before making an application. The manual is available from the trust's website.

Church Urban Fund grant – the main programme

To help ensure that projects are rooted in their communities, the fund has developed a two-stage application process in which proposals are considered by the local diocese before being forwarded to the national office. The first step is to contact the CUF link officer in your diocese. A list of all link officers can be found on the trust's website or obtained by email to resources@cuf.org.uk. Applicants should clearly state the location of their project. As an integral element of the process all applicants must liaise and work closely with the link officer in the development of their ideas and bid. All applications must be submitted to the respective link officer in the first instance (any applications sent directly to the trust will be forwarded to the diocese for consideration and validation).

The officer will help you to determine whether your project meets the fund's criteria. They will also guide you through the process of securing a recommendation from the diocesan bishop, who prioritises all requests against the overall urban strategy for the diocese and forwards them to the fund.

When the application reaches the trust's offices, a member of the grants unit will contact the project to arrange an assessment visit. The application and the recommendation of the grants officer who has visited the project are then carefully considered by the grants committee, whose award decisions are ratified by the trustees.

The fund always receives more applications than it has resources to support. Therefore, even if a project fits the criteria, it may not be possible to make a grant.

The trust's funding committee meets four times a year, in the first week of March, June, September and December. Deadlines for applications vary between dioceses as each has its own assessment process prior to submission to the trust.

Mustard seed grant

The trust welcomes applications from churches and faith-based groups that 'want to turn their ideas into action'. There is a simple application form to fill in, available from the trust's website. Alternatively, a form of application, tailored to the individual project, can be used. For the latter, the following checklist should be used and contact made with a member of the development and regeneration team at the trust.

Applications must provide the following information:

- details of the organisation or church (name, charity number, address, telephone, email, contact name)
- a description of the project with brief details of the cost, management and timing
- some background information and colour to put the application in context, e.g. it would be helpful to have a brief description of the organisation, its size and history, present make-up, aspirations and the needs of the area and the people that you will be working with
- the funding programme and progress to date
- the position of your finances. Please include the organisation's latest audited or examined accounts.

Applications can be supported with videos, websites, CD-ROMs or any other creative ways of presenting the message.

The trust will undertake the assessment of applications. It will want to talk to those setting up the project, this may be face-to-face or by telephone. The aim of these conversations is to assist in effectively describing the project and to help ensure that the issues involved have been thought through. It is expected that work supported under this programme will grow into more substantive and established activities.

The Clothworkers' Foundation and other trusts

CC no. 274100

Contact
Ruby Dlay, Grants Manager,
Clothworkers' Hall, Dunster Court,
Mincing Lane, London EC3R 7AH
Tel: 020 7623 7041; Fax: 020 7397 0107;
email: foundation@clothworkers.co.uk;
website: www.clothworkers.co.uk

Trustees
G C Robin Booth; David D Bousfield;
Paul H Boweman; Neil W D Foster;
Melville E V Haggard; Michael G T
Harris; Oliver C Howard; John C
Hutchins; Michael W Jarvis; Richard
Jonas; Antony H Jones; Richard Jones;
Peter J Langley; Alastair P Leslie; Henry J
A McDougall; Christopher G McLean
May; Michael J H Malyon; John M W
Papworth; Alan A M Mays-Smith;
Timothy E Morgan; Peter J S Rawson;
Timothy J L Roberton; Richard
Saunders; C W David Sutcliffe; Robert D
Wade; Paul C R Wates; Anthony H West;
Timothy Bousfield; Michael Howell;
John Jones; Sir Jonathan Portal; John
Wake.

Areas of work: General charitable
purposes, in particular, medicine and
health, children and young people,
textiles, relief in need and welfare,
education and sciences and the church.

Total grants: £6.5 million (2007)

Youth grants: £973,500

Beneficial area: Worldwide. In practice
mainly UK.

General

The Clothworkers' Company is an
ancient City of London livery company,
founded in 1528 and the 12th of the
'Great Twelve' companies. One of the
functions of livery companies was to
support their members in times of need.
As they grew wealthier, they were also
able to benefit outsiders. The
Clothworkers' Company acquired a
number of trusts, established by
individual benefactors for specific
charitable ends. These totalled over 100
by the 20th century. In addition, the
company has always made payments to
good causes from its own funds.

The Clothworkers' Foundation was set
up in 1977 by the company as the
independent arm for the whole of its
charitable work. The governors, the
trustees of the foundation, comprise
members of the Court of the
Clothworkers' Company.

The foundation's early income came
from a leasehold interest in a City of
London property, 1 Angel Court.
Subsequent funding from the company,
together with the sale of the long
leasehold interest in Angel Court in 1994,
represents the assets of the foundation
which are substantially invested in stocks
and shares. Income from these
investments, together with unrestricted
donations from the company, is given
away each year to a wide range of
charities. During its first 30 years, the
foundation has made grants totalling
around £65 million.

The objects of the foundation are for
general charitable purposes and the
foundation seeks to improve quality of
life, particularly for people and
communities that face disadvantage.

Livery Fund

This fund has been established to collect
voluntary donations from members of
the Clothworkers' Company, together
with any matching donations made by
the company itself and is administered by
the livery charity committee. The
committee will determine each year one
or more UK registered charities to receive
grants made by the fund. All income is
distributed annually.

In early 2006 the foundation undertook an in-depth review of its grant-making policy. 'The review considered the external environment, the approach taken by other foundations and our own existing policy. Like all grantmakers we have seen a growing demand on our funds and are subject to increasing public scrutiny, new accounting requirements and Charity Commission recommended practice. These factors have led to a refocusing of our grant-making policy.' Overseas, arts and heritage projects are now excluded from the foundation's grantgiving. The new policy was implemented from early 2007.

Grant programmes

The foundation has two programmes that are open to unsolicited applications: the main grants programme and the small grants programme.

The following information is taken from the foundation's website.

Main grants programme is open to UK registered charities:

- *with an annual turnover of under £10 million*
- *applying for a grant of over £1,000 for capital costs*

Small grants programme is open to UK registered charities:

- *with an annual turnover under £250,000*
- *applying for a grant of between £500 and £10,000 for capital costs*

Applications to the Main Grants Programme and Small Grants Programme must fall under one of the following areas:

Encouragement of young people

Preference will be given to organisations working with economically disadvantaged young people in deprived areas.

Social inclusion

Support for organisations which seek to tackle such problems as substance misuse, homelessness, offending and family breakdown.

Older people

Priority will be given to projects focusing on those in need or at risk of social exclusion.

Disability

Support for organisations tackling the needs of physically and/or mentally disabled people, but not work purely to meet the requirements of the Disability Discrimination Act.

Visual impairment

Support for organisations addressing the needs of blind or visually impaired people.

Textiles

UK academic institutions involved in textiles, technical textiles and colour science. Heritage projects involving textile collections, particularly those of national importance.

Grant-making policy

The foundation's priorities as outlined on its website for funding are as follows.

Capital costs include:

- *building purchase and renovation*
- *equipment (including IT hardware)*
- *vehicles*
- *training costs and professional fees relating to capital projects being funded by us.*

We do not fund revenue costs including:

- *running costs for your charity/project*
- *events*
- *training costs (unless they are included as part of a larger capital appeal).*

Ineligible costs include: salaries, expenses, administration, hire of space/premises, marketing and publicity, utility bills.

For charities which, by their nature, have no capital requirements, we will consider funding one-off projects such as production of publications (not regular newsletters, etc.) or setting up a new website.

Grantmaking in 2007

In 2007 the foundation and associated trusts had assets of £112.1 million and an income of £8.7 million. The Clothworkers' Foundation alone had assets of £88.7 million and an income of £8 million.

There were 172 grants made during the year by the foundation and associated trusts, to an impressive range of charities and organisations working across the UK, totalling £6.5 million. Grants specifically to youth organisations totalled £973,500, although as with other trusts, organisations working with young people may have been supported under other heading such social inclusion.

Encouragement of young people – 60 grants totalling £973,500

Beneficiaries included: New Philanthropy Capital (£50,000), for a research project on young offenders to provide advice to funders; Longridge Scout Boating Centre (£40,000), to purchase their site; Leeds Theatre Trust (£30,000), for the creation of a permanent, designated arts space for at risk young people; Rural Media Company (£25,000), towards IT, communications and finance systems and to purchase a vehicle to enable delivery of creative media activities to young people in Herefordshire; Ark (£20,000), for the refurbishment of accommodation for care leavers and vulnerable young people in Milton Keynes; Youth at Risk UK (£15,000), towards a learning programme for 20 young people at risk of offending, based in Leicestershire; Ripon YMCA (£10,000), towards the refurbishment of a hostel for single young people in north Yorkshire; Wrexham Play Association (£8,000), for a playbus for outreach work with children and young people from disadvantaged communities; Free Time Children's Club (£3,000), to purchase resources for an after-school club for children in South Lanarkshire; and Splendid Things (£2,000), to purchase equipment for a young people's film club in Liverpool.

Information available

Accounts were available at the Charity Commission. Good website with detailed annual report.

Exclusions

The foundation does not make grants to:

- non UK-registered charities
- organisations with an annual turnover of over £10 million (charities working in textiles with an annual turnover of over £10 million, wishing to make an application, are requested to contact the foundation)
- non-capital costs i.e. running costs, salary costs
- organisations that have received a grant from the foundation in the last five years
- heritage projects (other than textiles)
- environment projects
- arts and education projects are unlikely to be funded unless they are predominantly focused on disadvantaged young people, or older or disabled people
- projects that do not fit in with one of our programme areas
- individuals
- general or marketing appeals
- educational establishments
- grantmakers
- overseas work/projects
- medical research or equipment
- political, industrial, or commercial appeals
- relief of state aid or reduction of support from public funds
- events

■ appeals from any organisation where the money will be used for religious purposes, or projects which promote a particular religion.

Assistance to individuals for educational purposes is limited and is made through the associated Clothworkers' Charity for Education.

Applications

There are separate application forms for the main and small grants programmes available either by contacting the correspondent or from the foundation's website, which also gives full details of the application process and criteria for funding. Both programmes require the following information:

■ full project brief (about two–three sides of A4)

■ full project budget

■ latest accounts for the organisation as submitted to the Charity Commission

■ copy of the correspondence confirming Northern Ireland charitable status if registered in NI.

The foundation does not accept draft applications or applications by email; please post your finished application. Applications are accepted at any time, there are no deadlines. Decisions normally take six weeks for the small grants programme and six months for the main grants programme.

Any applicants who have specific queries after reading the foundation's guidelines should contact the grants manager on 020 7623 7041. The foundation does not, however, provide advice on matters which are covered on the website.

If your application is not successful, it is suggested you wait six months before reapplying.

Comic Relief

CC no. 326568

Contact
Gilly Green, Head of UK Grants, 5th Floor, 89 Albert Embankment, London SE1 7TP
Tel: 020 7820 5555;
Minicom: 020 7820 5579;
email: info@comicrelief.com;
website: www.comicrelief.com

Trustees
Peter Benett-Jones, Chair; Richard Curtis; Jana Bennett; William Cayton; Emma Freud; Matthew Freud; Mike Harris; Lenny Henry; Colin Howes; James Hytner; Claudia Lloyd; Alec McGiven; Laurence Newman; K Rowling; Michael Souter; Albert Tucker; Nalini Varma; Duncan Bannatyne.

Areas of work: Social welfare.
Total grants: £71.3 million (2006/07)
Youth grants: £5.7 million
Beneficial area: UK and overseas.

General

Since 1985 Comic Relief has raised around £500 million to tackle poverty and social injustice in the UK, Africa and, more recently, in some of the poorest countries in other parts of the world. This entry is concerned with the UK grants.

Comic Relief operates three grants funds for work within the UK: Red Nose Day programmes (between 2005 and 2008 six areas were funded – young people, older people, mental heath, refugees and asylum seekers, domestic violence and disadvantaged communities); Sport Relief; and The Robbie Williams' Give It Sum Fund.

The charity principally receives its income through the generosity of the public via its Red Nose Day fundraising event. This is held every two years in partnership with the BBC, and the extent of the grantmaking depends entirely on the success of the preceding event.

In 2002, Comic Relief started a second initiative, Sport Relief. Half of its income goes to the International Children and Young People's programme, the other half to projects in the UK that are using sport to increase social cohesion and inclusion.

The charity also administers Robbie Williams' Give It Sum Fund for community-based projects in his home area of North Staffordshire.

For the period 2005–2008 the charity concentrated its funding on six programme areas:

- young people – focusing on those with mental health or alcohol problems and those exploited through prostitution, trafficking and on the internet
- older people – focusing on promoting advocacy and campaigning, and tackling isolation and loneliness
- mental health – focusing on advocacy and campaigning and user-led mental health groups
- refugees and asylum seekers – focusing on supporting vulnerable women, building community links
- domestic violence – focusing on young people affected by this
- disadvantaged communities.

In 2006/07 grants across all programmes totalled £71.3 million. Grants for the benefit of young people in the UK totalled around £5.7 million.

New areas are to be announced early in 2009 – please check Comic Relief's website for current information. It is likely that the strong focus on young people will continue.

Information available

Grant programme and guidelines; how to apply; trustee report and accounts available on the charity's website.

Exclusions

There are certain types of work and organisations that Comic Relief does not fund. If your proposal falls into one of these categories, please do not apply:

- animal welfare
- general appeals, sponsorship or marketing appeals
- mainstream educational activity, schools and colleges
- general youth work
- individuals or organisations that distribute funds to individuals
- promotion of religion
- trips abroad
- replacement of statutory funding
- activities primarily the responsibility of central or local government or health authorities
- medical research or equipment, hospitals or medical centres
- minibuses
- work that has already taken place
- capital grants for compliance with the Disability Discrimination Act.

Applications

At the time of writing Comic Relief was carrying out a review of its UK grants programmes. See www.comicrelief.com/apply_for_a_grant for up-to-date information.

The Ernest Cook Trust

CC no. 313497

Contact
Mrs Ros Leigh, Grants administrator, Fairford Park, Fairford, Gloucestershire GL7 4JH

Tel: 01285 712492; Fax: 01285 713417; email: grants@ernestcooktrust.org.uk; website: www.ernestcooktrust.org.uk

Trustees
Anthony Bosanquet, Chair; Harry Henderson; Andrew Christie-Miller; Patrick Maclure; Miles C Tuely; Victoria Edwards.

Areas of work: Educational grants focusing on educating children and young people about the environment and rural conservation; arts, crafts and architecture; and literary and numeracy.

Total grants: £1.5 million (2007/08)

Youth grants: £1 million

Beneficial area: UK.

General

Ernest Edward Cook was a grandson and joint heir to the fortune of Thomas Cook, the famous travel agent. He presided over the banking and foreign exchange business of the firm, and was probably responsible for the successful development of the traveller's cheque. When the travel agency was sold in 1928, Ernest Cook devoted the remainder of his life to the preservation of English country houses, the estates to which they belonged, the paintings and furniture which they contained and also to the wellbeing of the communities of those estates.

Before his death, Mr Cook had made arrangements for the continuing care of his estates by either The Ernest Cook Trust or The National Trust, of which he was for a long time by far the greatest benefactor. He left his extensive collection of paintings to the National Art Collections Fund, for the benefit of provincial galleries.

The Ernest Cook Trust was established in 1952 and its purposes are to maintain the estates given to it by Ernest Cook and to give grants to support educational and research projects. Many of the schemes it

supports relate to the countryside and environmental and architectural conservation, and all are educational in emphasis.

The trust's grants policy is influenced by Ernest Cook's two great passions, namely art and country estates. Grants, which must always be for clearly educational purposes, aim principally to focus upon the needs of children and young people. To that end the trustees are keen to support applications from the UK which educate young people about the environment and the countryside. Projects which introduce pupils to the wide spectrum of the arts are also encouraged.

All applications are expected to link in with either the national curriculum or recognised qualifications and particular weight is given to projects that improve levels of literacy and numeracy.

'It is appreciated that sometimes a contribution will be required towards the salary of an education officer, but the trust always expects to be a part funder and does not usually commit funds for more than one year; successful applicants are normally asked to wait two years before applying for further help.'

A few research grants are awarded if the work links in to the trust's purposes.

Grants range from £100 to £4,000 in the small grants category, of which modest amounts for educational resources for small groups form a large part. At the two main meetings grants are mostly in the range of between £5,000 – £15,000, with only a few larger awards for projects closely connected with the trust's educational interests. One award of £50,000 is made annually; application for this is by invitation only.

In 2006/07 the trust had assets of £82.8 million and an income of £3.4 million. In 2007/08 the trust made grants totalling over £1. 5 million, categorised as follows:

Arts, crafts and architecture – 184 grants totalling £848,000

Beneficiaries included: Edward Barnsley Trust (£25,000), to cover the cost of an apprentice; Chetham's School of Music (£21,000), towards an early years music project; English National Ballet (£12,700), for the spring education programme; Artsway (£10,600), towards a project to encourage artists to work in schools; Foundation for Young Musicians (£10,000), towards bursaries for young musicians; Liverpool Cathedral (£9,000), to cover the cost of instrument tuition for members of Girl's Voices; Scottish Ensemble (£7,500), to help with the school-based element of the Lifelong Learning Programme; Withywood Community School (£6,800), towards the cost of ten music lessons for 60 pupils; Children's Music Workshops (£5,000), to help with the Bess of Hardwick project for schools; and Langham Arts Trust (£4,000), towards the cost of Proms Praise for Schools. Small grants of £3,000 or less included those to: Canterbury Festival, Scottish Schools Orchestra Trust, Victoria Baths Trust, Same Sky, Lifeforce, Bishopsland Educational Trust and Donagh Weefolk Playgroup.

Environment – 139 grants totalling £512,500

Beneficiaries included: Oxford University Botanic Garden (£25,000), towards the Oxfordshire 2010 Challenge for schools; Year of Food and Farming (£20,000), towards educational work in the North East and South West; Good Gardeners' Association (£10,000), towards the cost of an education officer; Royal Entomological Society (£9,600), to cover the cost of the school and farm wildlife programme; Rockingham Forest Trust (£8,000), towards the People in the Forest project; Groundwork London

(£7,500), towards the cost of an education officer for the Eco Schools project; Yorkshire Agricultural Society (£7,000), towards the cost of the information boards, education adviser and information packs; Arable Group Ltd (£6,000), for bursaries for students taking part in the TAG Asset programme; and Scottish Seabird Centre (£5,000), towards educational resources for the website. Small grants of £3,000 or less included those to: Marine Connection, Gordon Infant School, Footprint Trust Ltd, University of London, Conservation Volunteers Northern Ireland and a range of primary schools across the UK towards educational projects.

Literacy and numeracy – 42 grants totalling £109,000

Beneficiaries included: National Library of Wales (£10,000), towards the cost of 2,000 education packs; Volunteer Reading Help (£8,400), to recruit, train and support ten volunteer reading helpers; and Independent Photography (£3,800), towards an art/literacy project. Small grants included those to: Bethnal Green Bengali Women's Group, Arab Cultural Community, Rowandale Integrated Primary School, Manor High School, Barbican Centre, Get Hooked on Fishing and Ramsden Hall School.

Other – 39 grants totalling £88,500

Beneficiaries included: Engineering Education Scheme in Wales (£10,500), towards bursaries for the scheme; RNLI (£7,000), towards the salary of a learning officer; Farmor's School Bursaries (£5,100), 17 awards of £300 were made to pupils at Farmor's School on the ECT's Fairford Estate. The awards were for the purchase of resources for the pupils' continuing education; Down's Syndrome Association (£2,000), towards web-based resources for teachers; Wavertree Trust (£1,200), towards an interactive whiteboard for NVQ courses; and

Chimneytots Pre-School (£500), towards the cost of a wobble board.

Information available

Accounts were available from the Charity Commission. Information is also available via the trust's website.

Exclusions

Applicants must represent either registered charities or not-for-profit organisations. Grants are normally awarded on an annual basis and will not be awarded retrospectively.

Grants are not made to:

- individuals
- agricultural colleges
- education work which is part of social support, therapy or medical treatment
- building and restoration work
- sports and recreational activities
- work overseas.

Support for wildlife trusts and for farming and wildlife advisory groups is largely restricted to those based in counties in which the trust owns land (Gloucestershire, Buckinghamshire, Leicestershire, Dorset and Oxfordshire).

Applications

There is no application form. Applicants are asked to send a covering letter addressed to the grants administrator as well as describing their educational project clearly on no more than two additional sheets of A4, specifying how any grant will be spent. A simple budget for that project should be included, noting any other funding applications. The latest annual report and accounts for the organisation should also be provided. Please do not send further supporting material or email applications.

Successful applicants will be asked to complete an Agreement which includes the ability to pay the grant by the BACS.

The Agreement also requires the applicant to submit a report on the funded project; failure to do so will ensure the rejection of any further application and may result in a request to repay the award.

The full board of trustees meets twice a year, in April and October, to consider grants in excess of £4,000; applications for these meetings should be submitted by 31 January and 31 August respectively. Meetings to consider grants of £4,000 or less are normally held in February, May, July, September and December. Notification about the date of payment of grants is given when the offer is made.

If necessary, please contact the Grants Office to discuss a potential application: staff will be pleased to assist you.

The Dulverton Trust

CC no. 206426

Contact
Col Christopher Bates, Director, 5 St James's Place, London SW1A 1NP Tel: 020 7629 9121; Fax: 020 7495 6201; email: trust@dulverton.org; website: www.dulverton.org

Trustees
Christopher Wills, Chair; Sir John Kemp-Welch; Tara Douglas-Home; Lord Dulverton; Lord Gowrie; Dr Catherine Wills; Richard Fitzalan Howard; Sir Malcolm Rifkind; Dame Mary Richardson.

Areas of work: Young people and education, welfare, general.

Total grants: £2.9 million (2007/08)

Youth grants: £1.1 million

Beneficial area: Unrestricted. Mainly UK in practice. An interest in the Cotswolds. Limited support to parts of Africa. Few grants for work in London or Northern Ireland.

General

Background

This is one of the trusts deriving from the tobacco-generated fortune of the Wills family. It has an endowment worth £79.6 million and a body of trustees which combines family members with others who have achieved distinction in public life.

The Dulverton Trust is unusual in saying that an application outside its guidelines may be accepted if it is supported by an individual trustee – most trusts say that their trustees decide their grant-making intentions and policies first, and then stick to them.

There is a clear, reported family connection with the Cotswold area (though no longer apparently with Bristol, where many of the Wills factories were located). Sir John Kemp-Welch is a former Chairman of the London Stock Exchange; Sir Malcolm Rifkind is a former foreign secretary; and Lord Gowrie is best known for his interests in the arts (although the trust excludes the arts entirely from its grantmaking).

General

During 2007/08 the trust received 1,137 appeals for funding, 263 of which received a grant, making the success rate just over one in four. Though there are wide areas of 'exclusion' these can be funded if an application is recommended by a trustee. Grants paid during the year totalled £2.9 million.

Apart from a few special programmes, the trust makes one-off grants and will not normally consider further applications until at least two years has passed. Grants given are not necessarily for the amount requested (but note that the trust, unusually, has been known to give more rather than less than the requested amount, when it has investigated the project concerned).

Grants in 2007/08

Grants during the year were distributed amongst the categories above as follows:

	%	Amount
Youth and education	36.8%	£1,100,000
General welfare	18%	£727,700
Africa	11.8%	£345,600
Miscellaneous	8.5%	£250,200
Minor appeals	8.5%	£250,000
Preservation	6.8%	£200,000
Conservation	3.9%	£113,000
Peace and security*	3.5%	£104,100
Religion	1.3%	£37,000
Local appeals (Cotswolds)	0.9%	£25,000

does not include a capital grant for the Ditchley Foundation of £250,000

The following analysis of the trust's youth and education category during the year is provided by the trust in its excellent annual report (with grant figures added where necessary):

Youth and education

Youth and education continues to be the largest single category supported by the trust, accounting this year for 36.8% of the grants by value; the largest number of perennial grants also falls within this category. This reflects the priority placed by trustees on assisting the development of young people, particularly those suffering from disadvantage. The largest grant again went to provide Dulverton and Michael Wills Scholarships to allow a number of very able eastern European students to study at Oxford University. Although £150,000 had been allocated, the university was able to award scholarships to the value of only £110,000 because several offers were not taken up; only one Michael Wills Scholarship was awarded. Detailed discussions were held with the university in January 2008, and more robust selection and liaison procedures are in place for future years. There are two scholarship schemes for International Baccalaureate students, for two eastern European and two British students at Atlantic College, and for two African students at the

Pestalozzi International Village. Following a review in February 2008, trustees agreed that the forward grant for Atlantic College would be extended for another four years starting in 2009, but for two African students.

Many of the projects supported help disadvantaged young people in different ways, including those run by the Cadet Vocational Qualification Organisation [£30,000], Victory Outreach UK [£30,000], Skill Force Development [£25,000], Challenger Trust [£25,000], UK Youth [£25,000], Focus Charity [£20,400], Kidscape [£20,000], Rainer [£20,000], Wings South West [£20,000], School-Home Support Service UK [£19,200] and Weston Spirit [£17,000].

The trustees continue to believe that introducing young people to challenging experiences in the 'great outdoors' is important, hence the support for Brathay Hall Trust [£30,000], Federation of London Youth Clubs (for the Hindleap Warren Outdoor Education Centre) [£30,000], British Schools Exploring Society [£25,000], Outward Bound Trust [£15,000] and Raleigh International [£15,000]. Support for sail training was provided through Fairbridge (for Spirit of Fairbridge) [£32,000], Trinity Sailing Trust [£25,000] and Ocean Youth Trust South [£19,500].

The importance placed on the introduction of inner city primary school children to the countryside was underlined by the grants to the Countryside Foundation for Education [£25,000], Country Trust [£11,000] and Farms for City Children [£5,000]. The trustees place emphasis on the encouragement of young people to consider a career in science and engineering, hence the grants to the Royal Academy of Engineering [£25,000], Industrial Trust (which was added to the Perennial Grant list in 2007) [£15,000], the Worshipful Company of Engineers [£15,000] and the Arkwright Scholarship Trust [£14,400].

Information available

Full annual report and accounts were available from the Charity Commission. The trust also has a clear and concise website.

Exclusions

The trust will not usually give grants for:

- individuals (only to registered charities)
- museums, galleries, libraries, exhibition centres and heritage attractions
- individual churches, cathedrals and other historic buildings (except for limited support under the preservation category)
- individual schools, colleges, universities or other educational establishments
- hospices, hospitals, nursing or residential care homes
- expeditions or research projects
- activities outside the stated geographical scope.

The trust is rarely able to support charities whose main beneficiaries live within Greater London or Northern Ireland.

It will not normally support the following areas of activity:

- health and medicine, including drug and alcohol addiction, therapy and counselling
- support for people with disabilities
- the arts, including theatre, music and drama
- sport, including sports centres and individual playing field projects
- animal welfare or projects concerning the protection of single species
- expeditions and research projects
- individuals volunteering overseas
- conferences, cultural festivals, exhibitions and events

- salaries for specific posts
- major building projects, including the purchase of property or land
- endowments
- work that has already taken place (retrospective funding)
- appeals which seek to replace statutory funding.

Applications

The following information is taken from the trust's guidelines, which are downloadable from the website.

How to apply

Please read the guidelines carefully, making sure that none of the exclusions apply to your charity or project. If you believe that your appeal falls within the funding policy of the trust, you are welcome to apply as follows:

1) *Send your application by post to the director. We reserve the right not to respond to appeals by email from unfamiliar sources.*

2) *There is no set application form, but please restrict your application to two pages.*

3) *Make sure you include your organisation's full contact details, together with an email address. Also please confirm your charitable status, giving the registered charity number.*

4) *Include a brief description of the background, aims and objectives of the charity; details of the specific purpose for which funding is sought together with the funding target; and the balance of funding outstanding at the time of the application.*

5) *Finally, please enclose a copy of your most recent annual report and accounts if they are not available on the Charity Commission's website.*

If you wish to make initial enquiries, establish eligibility, discuss timescales or need to seek further guidance about an application, please telephone the trust's

office and ask to speak to one of the directors.

When to apply

Our trustees meet four times a year to consider major appeals: in February, May, July and October. Minor appeals are considered four times a year at variable times between the main agenda meetings. There are no deadlines or closing dates.

The selection procedure can take between three to six months so it is advisable to apply in plenty of time, especially if funding is required by a certain date.

Assessment process

Each application is considered on its merits and all will receive a reply as soon as possible, although research and consultation may delay a response from time to time.

We will usually acknowledge receipt of your application by email, so please remember to include a current email address. If you do not have one, we will send you an acknowledgement by post.

All rejected applications will receive notification and an outline explanation for the rejection will usually be given.

Applications that are listed for consideration for a major grant will normally receive a visit from one of the trust's directors who will subsequently report to the trustees.

Following the trustees' meeting, successful applicants will be notified of their award in writing. The trustees' decisions are final.

The Freemasons' Grand Charity

CC no. 281942

Contact
Ms Laura Chapman, Chief Executive,
60 Great Queen Street, London
WC2B 5AZ
Tel: 020 7395 9261; Fax: 020 7395 9295;
email: info@the-grand-charity.org;
website: www.grandcharity.org

Trustees
The council, consisting of the president,
deputy president, vice president, and 30
council members, listed in the annual
reports.

Areas of work: Social welfare, medical
research, hospices and overseas
emergency aid.

Total grants: £3.2 million (2006/07)

Youth grants: £346,500

Beneficial area: England, Wales and
overseas.

General

This trust is the central charity of all
freemasons in England and Wales. It
provides grants for four purposes:

- the relief of 'poor and distressed
  freemasons' and their dependants
- the support of other masonic
  charities
- emergency relief work worldwide
- the support of non-masonic charities
  in England and Wales.

Under its current guidelines for support
to non-masonic charities, the trust makes
grants in the following areas:

- medical research
- youth opportunities
- vulnerable people, including older
  people and children, disabled people
  and those with healthcare needs
- hospices
- emergency grants.

In 2005/06 the trust had assets of
£66.7 million and an income of
£18.2 million. Grants to non-masonic
charities were made totalling
£3.2 million, including £346,500 to youth
organisations.

Grant programmes

Major grants

Grants of between £5,000 and £50,000
are made only for a designated purpose
and generally to larger charities. Funding
may be granted for up to three years in
certain circumstances where there is
evidence of an ongoing need for
charitable grant funding.

- The average grant size is likely to be
  between £10,000 and £25,000.
- A very few major grants of over
  £50,000 may be approved each year.
- The purpose might be to fund a salary
  or to deliver a specific project.
- Grants may be made for capital
  projects provided the application is for
  an identifiable element of the project.

Minor grants

Core funding grants of between £500 and
£5,000 are given to smaller charities
whose annual income does not exceed
about £1 million.

Grantmaking in 2007

There were 11 grants of £10,000 or more
made during the year under the heading
of 'youth opportunities'. The
beneficiaries were: Skill Force (£50,000),
to fund the expansion of the Skill Force
educational support programme into the
Manchester area; The Marine Society and
Sea Cadets (£47,000), as a contribution
towards a new training ship for sea
cadets; Pheonix Futures (£30,000), to
fund a skills and employability
programme for young people in
residential drug rehabilitation services;
Voice for the Child in Care (£40,000), to
fund a pilot project to improve access to
independent advocacy services for

children in care; Centrepoint (£30,000), to fund the roll-out of a partnering project with four local youth homelessness charities; Childhood First (£25,000), to fund a support package for young people leaving care; Happy Days Children's Charity (£24,500), to fund day trips for disadvantaged children with special needs; Depaul Trust (£25,000), to fund a community centre and hostel for homeless young people in Birmingham; Brathay Hall Trust (£20,000), to fund bursaries to enable disadvantaged young people to attend courses at Brathay Hall; Fairbridge Cymru (£20,000), to fund the salary of a development tutor for disaffected young people in Cardiff; and Cruse Bereavement Care (£20,000), to fund a website and telephone support service for bereaved young people.

Information available

Accounts were available at the Charity Commission. The trust also has a clear website.

Exclusions

Local charities (i.e. serving an individual city or region) should apply to the provincial grand lodge of the region in which they operate (these are listed in telephone directories, usually under 'freemasons' or 'masons').

Those not eligible for a grant are:

- individuals (other than for the relief of 'poor and distressed freemasons and their poor and distressed dependants')
- charities that serve an individual region or city, for example, a regional hospital, local church, day centre or primary school
- organisations not registered with the Charity Commission, except some exempt charities
- activities that are primarily the responsibility of central or local government or some other responsible body

- organisations or projects outside of England and Wales
- charities that are deemed to hold funds in excess of their requirements.

Grants are not normally given to:

- activities that are primarily the responsibility of central or local government
- animal welfare
- arts
- capital building costs
- environment
- organisations with political objectives.

Applications

Application forms are available from the trust's office or from the website. This form must be completed in full, accompanied by a copy of the latest annual report and full audited accounts; these must be less than 18 months old.

Hospice grant applications are made on a separate form, available from either the appropriate provincial grand lodge or the trust's office.

Applications may be submitted at any time throughout the year.

Applications are not accepted for 'emergency grants' which are made as 'the need arises' and at the trustees' discretion.

GCap Charities

CC no. 1091657b

Contact
Simon Knapp, Controller of Finanace and Operations, 30 Leicester Square, London WC2H 7LA
Tel: 020 7054 8389;
email: gcap.charities@gcapmedia.com;
website: www.capitalfm.com

Trustees

Martin George, Chair; Nigel Atkinson; David Briggs; Moira Swinbank; Paul Soames; Peter Williams.

Areas of work: Children, young people and disadvantaged adults.

Total grants: £1.2 million (2006/07)

Youth grants: £1 million

Beneficial area: London (Capital Radio), Cardiff (Red Dragon FM), Oxfordshire (Fox FM), Hampshire (Power and Ocean FM), Sussex (Southern FM), Kent (Invicta FM), Birmingham (BRMB) and Newcastle and Manchester (Century FM).

General

The following is taken from GCap Charities' trustees' report and financial statements, year ended 31 March 2006.

As a result of the merger [between Capital Radio plc and GWR plc to form GCap Media plc] *a review was undertaken in the year of the extended group's network, in particular analysing the existing charitable activity within ex-GWR stations. A decision was made to expand the fundraising and operational activities of GCap Charities [formerly Capital Charities] by incorporating the charitable activities of ex-GWR station activities within the group. In order to facilitate this, the Charity Commission was consulted and on its advice the objects of Capital Charities Ltd were expanded and its name changed to GCap Charities Ltd. This took effect from April 2006 with the merger of the additional charities taking place from this date once any conditions had been complied with.*

[The group now includes] *the following additional regional branches: Bristol (GWR Bristol), Cambridge (Q103 FM), Reading (2-Ten FM), Norwich (Radio Broadland), Gloucester (Severn Sound), Swindon (GWR Swindon), Ipswich (Suffolk Group Radio), Crawley (Mercury FM) and Bournemouth (2CR FM). The*

group also includes a restricted fund for Classic FM Music Makers. Fundraising operates nationally for this brand due to the national transmission of Classic FM.

Fundraising and operations continued within the following stations in GCap Media plc's FM network: London (Capital Radio), Cardiff (Red Dragon FM), Oxfordshire (Fox FM), Hampshire (Power and Ocean FM), Sussex (Southern FM), Kent (Invicta FM), Birmingham (BRMB) and Newcastle and Manchester (Century FM). Operations in Nottingham were discontinued during the period due to the sale of the station following the merger between Capital Radio plc and GWR plc to form GCap Media plc.

It is to within these confines that the rest of the following information refers.

On a general note, while GCap Charities may effectively be a collective of local funders, the size and scope of funds available in the potential beneficial area is greater than the actual giving of many UK-wide funders. Furthermore, the charity is committed to awarding grants in the locality that the money is raised so that once reasonable management and administration expenses have been met it is able to confirm to donors that money raised locally is spent locally.

For marketing purposes the Help a London Child (HALC) brand name has been retained, along with 'Help a Local Child in . . . ' in each of the company's broadcast areas.

Unfortunately, specific information regarding fundraising and grantmaking by GCap Charities is London centric. However, we believe this to be applicable throughout the company's network of stations.

Guidelines

The following information is also taken from the trustees' report.

GCap Charities is committed to making a real difference to the lives of vulnerable children and young people living in the areas in which we operate by the award of grants to organisations supporting children and young people up to and including 18 years old who:

- *experience poverty and disadvantage*
- *have/are experiencing abuse, neglect, homelessness, violence or crime*
- *have an illness or disability*

In accordance with the objectives of the charity the grant-giving strategy has been to focus on awarding small amounts to a large number of small grassroots children's projects all over the relevant radio station's transmission areas. The charity invites applications for grants through its standard application form which is regularly reviewed and updated by the grants panel to ensure applications comply with the funding criteria as stated above.

The trustees have in each area of operations delegated to a panel of experts from the voluntary sector the task of assessing application forms and making recommendations on what grants the charity should make. They are guided in their recommendations by a list of conditions as to what the charity will fund to ensure that the money is used in the best interests of the intended beneficiaries. Groups that are successful with their applications are required to complete a project report form and provide receipts to show how the grant money has been spent.

Generally, the charity's appeals funds have two rounds of small grant giving in the year in order to improve accessibility of funding and cash management of the charity. Operationally, in order to reduce the pressure on the volunteer grant panel GCap Charities staff have and will continue to undertake more sifting of applications prior to panel consideration. These revisions will form the basis of policy and procedure outside London, although the charity will remain flexible to respond to particular local needs.

The categories that the charities funds under are:

- community and playgroups
- young people
- social and leisure
- health
- refuge
- language and literacy.

Grantmaking 2006/07

During the year the charities had assets of £1.6 million and an income of £3.1 million. Grants were made across the charities' geographical areas of benefit totalling £1.2 million. Grants to organisations working with children and young people account for most of the charities' charitable expenditure.

Commenting on the year the charities made the following observations:

During the period the charities gave out 683 grants with a combined value of £1.2 million. Grants awarded helped to fund the purchase of play and special needs equipment, sport and leisure activities, youth clubs, refuge and homeless projects, holiday playschemes and activity breaks in the UK, and educational programmes. It is estimated that over 87,000 children, young people and disadvantaged adults have benefited from grants awarded to various groups across the charities' network of operations.

Help a London Child grants

Help a London Child has the biggest grant programme within the group. It made 411 grants totalling £667,000 under its small grants (under £3,000) programme. The level of funds available was reduced in line with an expected decrease in income, and applicant groups were advised to reduce the amounts requested. Subsequently, the average grant fell in the current year to £1,623 from £1,959 in 2005/06.

159

Regional grants

The charities' other funds distributed grants to 271 groups in the year with a total value of £501,500. It is estimated that 27,000 children, young people and disadvantaged adults benefited from these grants. One hundred and thirty grants were given to community groups, 17 were awarded to groups focusing on youth initiatives, 19 grants supported social and leisure projects, 91 grants were made to health and special needs projects, seven refuge groups were awarded money and seven grants were given to language and literacy projects.

Several large, one-off grants were awarded to groups across the regional network. These included £20,000 distributed from Southern FM's Help a Local Child to the Rockinghorse 'New Alex Fund', helping to provide a piece of interactive play equipment in the entrance hall to the new Royal Alexandra Hospital for Sick Children in Brighton. Reading Canoe Club's 'MOTOR-vate' project received £15,000 to support young canoeists, and £14,000 was awarded to Plymouth Sound Unite's 'Light Up a Life' appeal raising funds for a white light sensory room at Woodlands School for physically disabled children.

The trustees continue to aim to increase the number of applications received. Grant application forms and guidelines are continually reviewed to ensure groups are as clear about the criteria as possible before applying. GCap Charities' representatives also attended funding fairs, helping to increase awareness of the charities and assess any important developments in the funding requirements of potential recipient groups.

Information available

Accounts were on file at the Charity Commission.

Exclusions

Each individual branch has specific exclusions, generally, however, the charities will not fund:

- individual children or families
- retrospective funding
- statutory funding, such as schools and hospitals
- salaried posts
- deficit funding
- medical research
- purchase of minibuses
- trips abroad
- distribution to other organisations
- distribution to individuals
- religious activities
- political groups
- general structural changes to buildings
- projects which are part of a larger charity organisation and not separately constituted
- core funding for a national or regional charity.

Applications

If you have any queries, please contact the allocations team at the Help a London Child office (Tel: 020 7054 8395/8396) who should also be able to help you with enquiries regarding regional applications.

J Paul Getty Jr Charitable Trust

CC no. 292360

Contact

Elizabeth Rantzen, Director,
1 Park Square West, London NW1 4LJ
Tel: 020 7486 1859;
website: www.jpgettytrust.org.uk

Areas of work: Social welfare, arts,
conservation and the environment.

Total grants: £2.5 million (2007)

Youth grants: £467,000

Beneficial area: UK.

General

The trust funds projects to do with
poverty and misery in the UK, and
unpopular causes in particular.

Grants, usually for running or project
costs, are often for three-year periods and
can be for up to a usual maximum of
about £30,000. There are also a large
number of small grants of £2,000 or less.

Few projects are supported in London.
The grants for heritage and conservation
are few and small.

The trust has continued to increase its
level of grantmaking, taking the view that
it should start assuming a long-term level
of total return on its investments that will
ignore short-term fluctuations, especially
in gains or losses of capital. Nevertheless
the trust remains heavily oversubscribed,
with a success rate of less than 10%, no
doubt the result of its own accessibility to
those working in fields few others are
interested in funding.

Background

*The J Paul Getty Jr Charitable Trust
started distributing funds in 1986. Since
then nearly £35 million has been given to
over 3,000 worthwhile causes all over the
UK.*

*The trust was funded entirely by Sir Paul
Getty KBE, who died in April 2003 in
London, where he had lived since the
1980s. He took a close interest in the trust,
but also continued to make major personal
gifts to the arts and other causes in
England (£50 million to the National
Gallery, £3 million to Lord's Cricket
Ground, £17 million to the British Film
Institute, £1 million towards the Canova
Three Graces, and £5 million towards the
restoration of St Paul's Cathedral). These
were personal gifts and had no connection
with this trust.*

*Nor has this trust any connection with the
Getty Trust in the USA, to which J. Paul
Getty Senior left his money, and which
finances the J. Paul Getty Museum in
California. These two trusts, one very large
and one small by comparison, should not
be confused by people who apply to us!*

In 2007 the trust had assets of
£57.2 million and an income of over
£2 million. Grants were made totalling
£2.5 million, with 137 new awards being
made.

Guidelines for applicants

The following guidelines are taken from
the trust's website.

*We set out below guidelines for the
majority of our grants, which should be
followed by those making unsolicited
applications. From time to time the
trustees invite selected charities to make
applications which may not entirely fall
within these guidelines. They may also
invite selected charities to make
applications for larger grants.*

There are four main beneficial areas:

- *social welfare*
- *arts*
- *conservation*
- *environment.*

*Most of the funding is given to social
welfare. Please check under the headings
below for details of types of projects funded
in each category. We do not generally fund
projects falling outside these areas.*

*We only fund organisations which are
registered charities or of comparable
constitution, and do not make grants to
individuals.*

Social welfare

Mental health in a wide sense. This includes projects for:

- *mentally ill adults*

- *drug, alcohol and other addictions, and related problems*

- *support groups for people under stress, e.g. battered wives, victims of abuse, families in difficulties, etc.*

- *offenders, both in and out of prison, men and women, young offenders, sexual offenders*

- *communities which are clearly disadvantaged and trying to improve their lot, particularly projects to do with helping young people in the long term*

- *homelessness, particularly projects which help prevent people becoming homeless or to resettle them*

- *job creation projects or ones aimed at making long-term constructive use of enforced leisure time, particularly those set up by unemployed people*

- *ethnic minorities involved in the above areas, including refugees, particularly projects aimed at integration.*

Arts

We fund a limited number of arts projects, and have an interest in those linked to our social welfare priorities described above.

Conservation

Conservation in the broadest sense, with an emphasis on ensuring that fine buildings, landscapes and collections remain or become available to the general public or scholars. Training in conservation skills. Not general building repair work.

Environment

Mainly gardens, historic landscape and wilderness.

Grantmaking in 2007

The level of narrative reporting on the trust's activities in 2007 has reduced significantly on previous years, however the following breakdown of grants by category is provided:

	%	Amount
Children and young people	19%	£467,000
Offenders	16%	£413,000
Drugs and alcohol	15%	£387,000
Heritage and conservation	11%	£235,000
Homelessness	9%	£218,000
Mental health	8%	£213,000
Ethnic minorities	6%	£145,000
Women	5%	£134,000
Families	4%	£103,500
Communities	4%	£91,000
Environment and landscape	2%	£53,500
Other social welfare	2%	£47,000
Other	1%	£13,500
Arts (not related to social welfare)	0.2%	£2,000

Beneficiaries during the year, which were uncategorised, included: Tanyard Youth Project – Pembroke (£90,000); Broadreach House – Plymouth (£69,000); Kaleidoscope – Newport (£60,000); Watts Gallery – Guildford (£50,000); Home-Start Oxford (£45,000); Young Enterprise North East – Gateshead (£33,000); Edinburgh Cyrenians (£30,000); Handel House Trust Ltd – London (£25,000); Lancaster & District YMCA (£20,600); Lizard Outreach Trust – Cornwall (£18,000); Conservation Volunteers Northern Ireland (£10,000); St James Community & Support Centre – Birmingham (£6,000); Pestalozzi International Village Trust (£2,000); and National Osteoporosis Society – London (£1,000).

Information available

Accounts were available from the Charity Commission, which include less detail on grant-making activities than previous years. The trust also has a basic website.

Exclusions

Grants are not given for:

- older people

- children

- education

- research
- animals
- music or drama (except therapeutically)
- conferences or seminars
- medical care (including hospices) or health
- medical equipment
- churches or cathedrals
- holidays or expeditions
- sports or leisure facilities (including cricket pitches)
- residential or large building projects
- replacement of lottery or statutory funds
- national appeals
- grant-making trusts or community foundations
- individuals.

Headquarters of national organisations and 'umbrella' organisations are unlikely to be considered.

Past recipients are not encouraged to reapply.

No applications for projects outside the UK are considered.

The project must be a registered charity or be under the auspices of one.

Priority is likely to be given to projects in the less prosperous parts of the country, particularly outside London and the South East, and to those which cover more than one beneficial area.

Please remember this trust has no connection with the Getty Foundation in the USA.

Applications

Applications can be made to the director at any time. There are no 'closing dates', and all letters of appeal should receive an initial response within six weeks. Please write a letter of no more than two sides long detailing:

- the purpose and nature of the project
- intended beneficiaries
- budget
- existing sources of finance
- other funding applications, including those to statutory sources and the lottery
- whether you have previously applied to us, successfully or otherwise.

Please do not send videos, DVDs, CDs, tapes or bulky reports. They are unlikely to be reviewed and cannot be returned.

Annual accounts will be requested if your application is going to be taken further.

If a project is shortlisted for taking forward for a grant over £2,000, it may be visited by the director before an application is considered by the trustees.

The trustees usually meet quarterly. There is a shortlisting process, and not all applications are put before the trustees. Three months is the least it usually takes to award a grant.

The KPMG Foundation

CC no. 1086518

Contact
Jo Clunie, Director, KPMG, Salisbury Square House, 8 Salisbury Square, London EC4Y 8BB email: kpmgfoundation@kpmg.co.uk; website: www.kpmg.co.uk/about/ foundation

Trustees
John Griffith-Jones, Chair; Gerry Acher; Sir John Cassels; Chris Hayes; Helena Kennedy; Robin Oakley; Dr Ashley Steel; Neil Sherlock.

Areas of work: Refugees, young offenders, children and young people who have been in care, children and young people with dyslexia/literacy difficulties

Total grants: £3 million (2006/07)
Youth grants: £3 million
Beneficial area: UK.

General

The following information is taken from the foundation's website.

The focus of the KPMG Foundation is on education and social projects for the disadvantaged and under-privileged, with particular emphasis on unlocking the potential of children and young people, up to 30 years of age, who for primarily social reasons have not fulfilled their educational potential.

In particular, the trustees have chosen to support four very distinct groups within this broad umbrella of 'disadvantage'. Those groups are:

- *refugees*
- *young offenders*
- *children and young people who have been in care*
- *children and young people with dyslexia/literacy difficulties.*

Grantmaking in 2006/07

In 2006/07 the foundation had assets of £6.8 million, an income of £2.2 million and made grants totalling over £2.4 million. Grants to organisations working with young people were broken down as follows:

Young offenders – £647,000 in 16 grants
Youth at Risk (£134,000); University of Cambridge – Institute of Criminology (£81,000); Kids Company (£50,000); Fairbridge (£49,000); Youth Enterprise Scotland (£48,000); Safer London Foundation (£45,000); Exeter Community Initiatives (£42,000); De Paul Trust – Birmingham Last Chance Project (£35,000); Coldingly Crime Division Scheme (£25,000); the Amber Foundation (£22,000); Turning Point Scotland (£20,000); and Watts Gallery (£11,000).

Young people in care – £67,000 in three grants
Helena Kennedy Foundation (£37,000); British Association for Adoption and Fostering (£28,000); and Tate Gallery (£3,000).

Young people with literacy difficulties – £2.3 million in three grants
Every Child a Reader (£2.3 million); Local Solutions (£57,000); and National Literacy Association (£20,000).

Information available

Accounts were on file at the Charity Commission.

Applications

Application forms can be downloaded from KPMG the website in PDF and Word formats.

The KPMG Foundation considers applications for the general grants programme once a year. Throughout the year, we capture all organisations keen to apply for funding on a database. When the Trustees agree their funding date at the end of each year for the following year, we write to all organisations on our database providing them with details of the funding date, when applications must be submitted and any specific criteria defined by the trustees. If you would like your details added to our database then please email us at kpmg@kpmg.co.uk

The trustees meet four times a year. Once a year the trustees will assess all applications and make their funding decisions. If the trustees are keen to progress your application a project/site visit may be undertaken by either one of the trustees or one of the support team. In addition, the trustees may request that a financial due diligence assessment be undertaken, by the foundation treasurer, of the charitable organisation seeking funding.

John Lyon's Charity

CC no. 237725

Contact
The Grants Office, 45 Pont Street,
London SW1X 0BX
Tel: 020 7591 3330; Fax: 020 7591 3412;
email: info@johnlyonscharity.org.uk;
website: www.johnlyonscharity.org.uk

Trustees
The keepers and governors of the
possessions revenues and goods of the
Free Grammar School of John Lyon.
Grants committee: Nick Stuart, Chair; W
Massey; Mrs J Forman Hardy; T
Walduck; Mrs G Baker; M Edwards.

Areas of work: Children and young
people in north and west London.

Total grants: £4.1 million (2006/07)

Youth grants: £4.1 million

Beneficial area: The London boroughs
of Barnet, Brent, Camden, Ealing,
Kensington and Chelsea, Hammersmith
and Fulham, Harrow and the Cities of
London and Westminster.

General

This is one of the largest local
educational charities in the country,
supporting both formal and informal
educational activities of every sort. Its
budgets vary greatly from year to year for
historical reasons, and from one part of
its beneficial area to another. There are,
however, significant cross-borough
grants.

The charity began in the late 16th century
when John Lyon donated his 48 acre
Maida Vale farm as an endowment for
the upkeep of two roads from London to
Harrow and Kenton. In 1991, the charity
was given discretion to use the revenue
from the endowment to benefit the
inhabitants of the London boroughs
through which these roads passed.

The charity is an independent branch of
the larger Harrow Foundation which also

governs Harrow and the John Lyon
schools. The charity makes over 60
substantial new grants a year, for
amounts normally between £2,000 and
£50,000 and there are a further 50 or so
for amounts of £2,000 or less under its
small grants programme. Larger awards
may be for periods of up to three years.

In 2006/07 the charity had assets of
£187.2 million and an income of over
£5.4 million. Grants were made during the
year totalling £4.1 million, and included
grants committed in previous years.

Guidelines for applicants

The following is taken from the charity's
website and its online document
*Enhancing the conditions of life and
improving the life-chances of young people
through education.*

*The charity's main policy is to enhance the
conditions of life and improve the life-
chances of young people through
education. The charity awards grants to
groups and organisations for the benefit of
children and young adults who are resident
in the beneficial area* [London boroughs
of: Barnet, Brent, Camden, Ealing,
Hammersmith and Fulham, Harrow, the
Royal Borough of Kensington and
Chelsea and the Cities of London and
Westminster. Grants are made in
consultation with these local authorities].

We give grants:

■ *to support education and training,
particularly for young adults*

■ *to broaden horizons and encourage an
appreciation of the value of cultural
diversity through activities such as
dance, drama, music, creative-writing
and the visual arts*

■ *to provide childcare, support for parents,
help where parental support is lacking*

■ *to enhance recreation through sport,
youth clubs and playschemes*

■ *to help young people achieve their full
potential*

■ *to develop new opportunities for young people.*

Grants are given to a broad range of charities. They are intended to be of as direct benefit as possible to young people who are resident in the boroughs listed above.

What we fund:

■ *capital costs (e.g. equipment, furniture)*

■ *revenue costs (e.g. salaries, running costs).*

The maximum length of any grant is normally three years. There are no strict limits on the amount of grant that may be awarded. Some fixed-term grants may be eligible for renewal depending on changing circumstances, records of achievements, and the availability of funds.

The small grants programme

The programme welcomes one-off grant requests of up to £2,000, with no repeat funding. We favour:

■ *one-off small capital grants*

■ *one-off summer schemes*

■ *pump priming funds for small projects that might develop into full grant status.*

If a repeat request is expected in the following year the applicant may be referred to the main grants programme.

Grantmaking in 2006/07

Grants were broken down during the year as follows (with examples of new grants made):

School education and training – £1.4 million

Beneficiaries included: Notting Dale Technology Centre (£250,000), as capital towards the refurbishment of Maxilla Walk Training Centre, North Kensington; London Diocesan Board for Schools (£100,000), for distribution as capital grants to Church of England schools; Cardinal Wiseman School (£50,000), as a capital grant towards the new hospitality and catering kitchen; Kentish Town City Farm (£30,000), each year for three years towards the salary costs of the Education Development Officer; Challenger Trust (£25,000), towards the Learning through Activities schools programme; British Museum Development Trust (£15,000), towards the running costs of the Brent Outreach Project in 2007; Mayor's Thames Festival (£10,000), towards the Puzzle Pathway Project; and National Literacy Trust (£6,000), each year for three years towards the Reading is Fundamental scheme.

Arts in education – £928,300

Beneficiaries included: Royal Court Young Writers Programme (£50,000), towards the Young Writers Festival; Royal Shakespeare Company (£30,000), each year for three years towards the running costs of the Learning Playback schools programme; Opera East Productions (£24,000), over three years towards running costs; Foundling Museum (£20,000), each year for two years towards running costs; Mousetrap Foundation (£13,500), towards the Play the Critic programme; Camden Arts Centre (£10,000), each year for three years towards the running costs of the *Get the Message* project for children and young people from SEN schools; and Sir John Lillie Primary School (£7,000), towards the creation of an arts space.

Youth clubs and youth services – £627,000

Beneficiaries included: Pirate Club (£100,000), towards construction work on the Pirate Castle; Samuel Lithgow Youth Centre (£70,000), towards refurbishments; King's Cross Brunswick Neighbourhood Trust (£30,000), each year for three years towards the youth work programme; Vital Regeneration (£15,000), each year for three years towards the running costs of the

FreqOUT! project; Response Community Projects (£11,000), towards the running costs of the homework clubs; and Castlehaven Community Association (£5,000), towards the Junior Youth Inclusion Programme.

Childcare and support for families – £512,200

Beneficiaries included: Westminster Children's Society (£40,000), as capital for the South Westminster Children's Centre; St Francis Community Church (£25,000), towards refurbishment work; Punch & Judy Family Centre (£20,000), each year for three years towards running costs; Coram Family (£15,000), towards the Music Therapy Service; Venture Community Association (£10,000), each year for three years towards a sports and outreach play worker at Notting Hill Adventure Playground; Barnet After School Provision (£8,000), towards running costs; and Breakaway Holiday Project (£3,000), each year for three years towards support worker costs.

Counselling – £210,600

Beneficiaries included: Brent Centre for Young People (£30,000), each year for three years towards a specialised therapy programme for young people aged 18–23; West London Centre for Counselling (£20,600), each year for three years towards services for young people; SW5 (£20,000), each year for three years towards the running costs of the Resettlement Programme for young men; Women's Therapy Centre (£12,000), each year for three years towards therapy sessions for young women; Rephael House (£10,500), towards salary costs; and Harrow Council for Racial Equality (£10,000), towards the running costs of the Mentoring and Advocacy Programme.

Sport in education – £172,500

Beneficiaries included: Westminster Sports Unit (£100,000), as capital for a new sports centre on Compton Street;

West London Sports Trust (£50,000), each year for three years towards running costs, mentoring and bursaries for young athletes; Westway Development Trust (£50,000), towards the extension of the climbing wall; Somerset House Trust (£30,000), for free skating for schools and community groups; Brentford Football Club (£20,000), each year for three years towards the running costs of the inclusion project; The Cricket Foundation (£20,000), each year for three years towards sessional coaching and equipment costs for cricket in schools; Watford Football Club (£20,000), each year for three years towards the Safer Neighbourhoods Football Project in Harrow; and Canons Cricket Academy (£6,500), towards sessional coaching costs.

Special needs and disability – £163,000

Beneficiaries included: Calvert Trust (£25,000), towards the London Getaway Project; Harington Scheme (£20,000), each year for three years towards the salary of a foundations skill team leader; Caxton Youth Organisation (£15,000), each year for three years towards the costs of an administrator; National Autistic Society (£10,000), towards playground refurbishments at Sybill Edgar School; and Turtle Key Arts (£7,000), each year for three years towards the Key Club.

Housing – £65,000

No new grants were listed for the year.

Youth issues – £35,000

Beneficiaries included: Young Foundation(£15,000), each year for two years as a contribution towards the *Mapping Britain's Needs* project.

Information available

Annual report and accounts were available from the Charity Commission. The charity also has a clear and helpful website.

Exclusions

Grants are restricted to the London boroughs of Barnet, Brent, Camden, City of London, City of Westminster, Ealing, Hammersmith & Fulham, Harrow and Kensington & Chelsea.

Grants are not made:

- to individuals
- for research, unless it is action research designed to lead directly to the advancement of practical activities in the community
- for feasibility studies
- for medical care and resources
- in response to general charitable appeals, unless they can be shown to be of specific benefit to children and young people in one or more of the geographical areas listed
- as direct replacements for the withdrawal of funds by statutory authorities for activities which are primarily the responsibility of central or local government
- to umbrella organisations to distribute to projects which are already in receipt of funds from the charity
- for the promotion of religion or politics
- for telephone helplines
- as core funding for national charities
- for advice and information services
- to housing associations.

Applications

The following information is taken from the charity's website.

Main grants programme

John Lyon's Charity has a two-stage application process:

Stage one: initial proposal

Please write to the grants office with the following information:

- *a summary of the main purpose of the project*

- *details of the overall amount requested*
- *the timescale of your project*
- *some indication of how funds from the charity would be allocated.*

[The charity provides helpful information on how to write a good proposal letter, available to download from the website.]

Closing dates for initial proposals

The next closing dates for stage one: initial proposals in 2009 are:

- *Friday 27 February 2009 for the May/June trustee meeting*
- *Friday 31 July 2009 for the Oct/Nov 2009 trustee meeting*

Stage two: application form

If your initial proposal (stage one) is assessed positively, you will be advised whether you will need to complete an application form. Forms are required for all applications to the main grants programme and for requests of over £2,000 to the small grants programme.

If you qualify for stage two you will be advised by your grants officer when your application form must be returned.

Applications by fax or email will not be accepted. Electronic versions of the application form can be made available. The decision of the grants committee is final.

For more information on the application procedure please contact the grants office on 020 7591 3330.

Small grants programme

This programme is designed to provide easier and quicker access to funds. There is no application form. Requests are made by an initial proposal letter. You will be advised if your proposal is suitable for consideration under the small grants programme. Decisions are made at various times throughout the year and we usually aim to hold at least four small grants rounds a year.

The Jack Petchey Foundation

CC no. 1076886

Contact
Andrew Billington, Director,
Exchange House, 13–14 Clements Court,
Clements Lane, Ilford, Essex IG1 2QY
Tel: 020 8252 8000; Fax: 020 8477 1088;
email: mail@jackpetcheyfoundation.
org.uk;
website: www.jackpetcheyfoundation.
org.uk

Trustees
Ron Mills; Ray Rantell; Graham Adams;
Barbara Staines.

Areas of work: Young people aged 11–25
in specific areas of London and Essex and
the Algarve, Portugal.

Total grants: £12.4 million (2007)

Youth grants: £12.4 million

Beneficial area: Specific areas of London
and Essex and the Algarve, Portugal.

General

This foundation was established in 1999
by Jack Petchey and gives grants to
programmes and projects that benefit
young people aged 11–25. Jack Petchey
was born in July 1925 in the East End of
London. From a background with very
few advantages he became a prominent
entrepreneur and businessman. The
foundation is a rapidly expanding trust
that is eager to help young people take
advantage of opportunities and play a
full part in society by broadening their
horizons and strengthening their positive
skills to grow into healthy and
considerate citizens.

The foundation benefits all London
boroughs north of the Thames,
Greenwich, Southwark, Lambeth, Bexley,
Lewisham, Bromley, Croydon, Epping
Forest, Harlow, Uttlesford, Brentwood
and Thurrock. During 2007/08 the

foundation expended its activities as
follows:

South West London expansion
- Achievement awards in schools and
  youth organisations in Sutton,
  Merton, Richmond, Kingston and
  Wandsworth
- Project grants in schools and youth
  organisations in Sutton, Merton,
  Richmond, Kingston and
  Wandsworth.

Essex expansion – schools
- Basildon, Castle Point, Southend-on-
  Sea, Chelmsford, Rochford,
  Braintree, Maldon, Colchester and
  Tendring.

Essex expansion – clubs
- Basildon, Castle Point, Southend-on-
  Sea, Chelmsford, Rochford,
  Braintree, Maldon, Colchester and
  Tendring.

Grants of over £27 million have been
given since the foundation was
established and are given through
different programmes including:
achievement award scheme, leader award
scheme, projects grants and sponsorship.

In 2007 the foundation had assets of
£5.1 million and an income of
£9.9 million. Grants were made totalling
£12.4 million.

Programmes in 2009

The following information is taken from
the foundation's website.

*In July 2008 we celebrated giving
£50 million since the Foundation was
established ten years ago. The Directors,
supported by Jack Petchey, as Patron, have
agreed the following for 2009.*

*The Foundation will continue to focus on
the following programmes that benefit
young people aged 11–25 and will
concentrate their work in the geographical
areas of Greater London and Essex only.
The programmes to be funded are:*

The Foundation will continue to fund its successful Jack Petchey Achievement Award Scheme working with almost 2,000 groups and will invite all state secondary schools/colleges to apply as from January 2009. The Foundation will continue to support Jack Petchey's Speak Out Challenge, now the largest speaking competition for young people in the world. All state secondary schools in London and Essex are invited to participate in this programme in the academic year 2008/09. The Foundation will continue to work with Young Enterprise in promoting the 'Learn to Earn' 2008/09 programme in 200 schools in London and Essex involving 30,000 young people. The Foundation will continue to support the Step Into Dance programme with the Royal Academy of Dance. This programme will be offered in 100 secondary schools in London during the academic year 2008/09. The Foundation will continue to support our existing Out of School Hours/Study Support programmes (in Newham, Tower Hamlets, Barking & Dagenham, Waltham Forest, Havering, Greenwich and Islington) in the current academic year 2008/09. Currently JPF supports approximately 600 clubs and courses through this scheme.

Information available

Accounts were available at the Charity Commission. The foundation's website includes guidelines, specific areas of benefit, application forms and good general information.

Exclusions

The foundation will not accept applications:

■ from applicants who have applied within the previous 12 months

■ that directly replace statutory funding

■ from individuals or for the benefit of one individual (unless under a sponsorship scheme)

■ for work that has already taken place

■ which do not directly benefit people in the UK

■ for medical research

■ for animal welfare

■ for endowment funds

■ that are part of general appeals or circulars.

The foundation is also unlikely to support:

■ building or major refurbishment projects

■ conferences and seminars

■ projects where the main purpose is to promote religious beliefs.

The foundation only contributes to building or major refurbishment projects in exceptional circumstances.

Applications

Application forms for each of the grant schemes can be downloaded from the foundation's website. There are no deadlines for applications but they should be made in 'good time' before the money is needed. The foundation holds monthly management meetings and aims to give a decision within six weeks.

The Prince's Trust

CC no. 1079675

Contact
Nicola Brentnall, 18 Park Square East, London NW1 4LH
Tel: 020 7543 1234; Fax: 020 7543 1200; email: nicola.brentnall@princes-trust.org.uk; website: www.princes-trust.org.uk

Trustees
Diane Louise Jordan; Patrick Passley; Charles Dunstone; Mrs H J Hancock; Sir Fred Goodwin; Michael Marks; Dr David Dobbin; Simon Fuller; Mick Matton; Shonaig MacPherson; Lloyd Dorfman.

Areas of work: Youth.

Total grants: £1.4 million (2006/07)

Youth grants: £1.4 million

Beneficial area: UK.

Information available

Accounts were available from the Charity Commission. The trust also has a helpful website.

Exclusions

The Prince's Trust aims to change the lives of young people, helping them to develop confidence in themselves, learn new skills and get practical and financial support.

In 2006/07 the trust helped over 40,000 individuals. Around 5,500 of these young people were awarded cash grants and funding to develop their skills and employability, and help devise and deliver their own community projects. Cash grants and funding are available in the following forms:

- The business programme provides low-interest loans and grants to 18 to 30 year olds who wish to start their own business. To be eligible for this programme, applicants must be either unemployed or working less than 16 hours a week and have limited access to any other sources of funding.

- Development awards of between £50 and £500 for young people aged 14 to 25 are offered to help facilitate education or training or to secure employment.

- Group awards are also given to groups of young people who want to set up their own projects that will benefit their local communities.

In 2006/07 the trust had assets of £36 million, an income of £45 million and a total expenditure of £41 million. Approximately £1.4 million was given in grants to individuals.

The Rank Foundation

CC no. 276976

Contact
Jan Carter, Grants Administrator,
12 Warwick Square, London SW1V 2AA
Tel: 020 7834 7731;
email: jan.carter@rankfoundation.co.uk;
website: www.rankfoundation.com

Areas of work: Christian communication, youth, education, general.

Total grants: £4.9 million (2007)

Youth grants: £3.2 million

Beneficial area: UK.

General

The charity was established in 1953 by the late Lord and Lady Rank (the founders). It was one of a number established by the founders at that time and to which they gifted their controlling interest in The Rank Group plc (formerly The Rank Organisation plc), best known as a film production company, although this was only one of its commercial interests. The Rank trusts and foundations all share a Christian ethos.

Summary

This a heavily proactive foundation, with offices around the country, and much of whose grants are committed to ongoing programmes; because of this only about one in four of unsolicited appeals are supported.

It concentrates on:

- the promotion of Christian principles through film and other media
- encouraging and developing leadership amongst young people
- supporting disadvantaged young people and those frail or lonely through old age or disability.

Large grants are typically part of a three or five year commitment and very seldom result from an unsolicited application. Small grants (less than £5,000) are usually one off. Local charities are unlikely to get recurrent funding or multi-year awards.

Grantmaking in 2007

In 2007 the foundation had assets of £243.7 million and an income of £10.1 million. Grants were committed during the year (including multi-year awards) across various programmes totalling over £8 million, including £1.3 million to the Foundation for Christian Communication (founded by Lord Rank). Grants were broken down by category as follows:

Category	Amount
Youth (including education)	£3.25 million
Community service programme	£2.89 million
Promotion of Christian religion	£1.9 million

Grants paid during the year totalled £4.9 million.

The foundation's excellent annual report provides interesting details on its areas of interest and activities during the year. Details of the foundation's youth programme are reproduced here:

Youth programme

Annually, three major business conferences take place.

- *The launch conference for all new projects, usually held in the spring.*

- *A recall and review conference for all new workers and managers who have had our investment for five or six months, usually held in mid-winter.*

- *Our annual business conference for the entire network, usually held in September.*

For all involved we publish in partnership with the George Williams YMCA College an agency handbook, which will be revised on an annual basis. As before, over 250 people from the network have been involved in the conferences.

The main theme for this year has been looking forward to the 21st anniversary of the Youth or Adult? programme, the formation of a steering committee and the launch of 'YARN', the Youth or Adult? Rank Network. All details of The Rank Foundation youth work initiatives and all details of YARN will be on a website www.rankyouthwork.com. Over 21 years a considerable network has been developed which already has a wide range of achievements and ongoing activities, including the residentials mentioned above, publications, seminars, charity evenings with the fellowship, help with the Gap Scheme, think tanks, etc.

Research and development

Action and research always inform our work and its continuing organic development. This has been the busiest year for all enquiries, researches, visits and general demand and has necessitated an even clearer focus and qualitative investment and development. 2007 has also seen one of the largest batches of new projects supported throughout the UK. This activity has been further augmented by our involvement with our partners in The Joseph Rank Trust.

Youth or Adult? Scheme

This remains the flagship programme, founded in 1987, and it is the longest and largest programme of its sort in the UK.

The results represent a high degree of matched funding and sustainability, and an achievement of 100% employment for those who have successfully gained their professional qualification. The foundation has supported over 230 initiatives and helped qualify over 260 full-time youth workers under the auspices of Youth or Adult? and allied initiatives.

This scheme also incorporates thousands of part-timers and volunteers. Through researches for the development of YARN we estimate that there is a potential network of around 500 people with an active network of 300. We are delighted to say that the full-year honours degree programme is now integral to all new projects and workers coming into Youth or Adult? The first year Foundation Studies programme, which is transferable to other areas of activity such as community development will remain the access into university part of the initiative and the following four years is an honours degree programme. 16 new students have joined the foundation level students – eight from The Rank Foundation and nine from The Joseph Rank Trust. Ten trainees have successfully completed the Foundation Studies level, seven gained their higher education diploma and seven degrees. This included a distinction, two merits and a first degree.

There is at least an 80% sustainability rate with projects we have worked with which continue to have a significant influence in their areas. Various projects have come on board this year; projects focusing on rural development, community development within a housing association, youth clubs, work in the inner city of Sheffield, a town centre project acting as a centre for different youth groups, and a focus on sexual health, education and relationships.

Key workers

The review in 2006 has partially paid off. However, priorities and consideration given to this area require difficult decisions. Whilst there is a shortage of core funding for projects, a disproportionate amount of initiatives fail to see the potential of investment and the 'pebble in the pond' philosophy. Whilst The Rank Foundation does not demand new work just for the sake of it, it does demand the workers to have vision and to put that vision into developmental action on the front line, including training, development and leadership. This has been particularly disappointing at the initial research phase. It also has its negative repercussions in the certain lack of involvement and commitment to the network and a rather parochial stance. Nevertheless, over 20 key worker initiatives are currently being supported, some of which overlap with small Investing in Success programmes as well.

A number of new initiatives have started under this heading, including an arts development in Wolverhampton with a community development agency, and a leadership, training and development qualification focusing on Wakefield but spread on a wider basis throughout West Yorkshire.

In the north of the UK, Volunteer Development East Lothian has commenced a progressive programme of growing a cohort of young leaders over a 12 month period and identifying potential apprentices to be further trained using the Skills Apprentice Scheme.

Skills Apprenticeship Scheme

The scheme now has over 12 young leaders whose chosen fields range from performing arts to outdoor adventure to work with the young deaf. It would be fair to say that this scheme has been more successful at the end of its pilot years than we ever thought. We will be exploring the transferability of this scheme and its strength in growing in-house leaders to other Rank initiatives such as Youth or Adult? This flexibility and open access could be a new way of pointing the way forward. With over 50% of the skills apprentices undertaking degrees and others with a wide range of educational *abilities and achievements, we believe there is huge potential for success in the future. The whole focus of agencies who we know well identifying their own leadership potential within indigenous fields and communities is vast.*

For those just now successfully completing the Skills Apprentice Scheme there is a 100% success rate into further education, higher education or jobs. We have been able to look at extending a number of the skills apprentice initiatives to bring them more in line with the Youth or Adult? programme, hence the transferability potential mentioned above.

Investing in Success

One new Investing in Success initiative has been supported in South Wales, combining the learning from the 'Build It' initiative and its many achievements with local community development and regeneration, including youth work and informal education. Under the aegis of the People & Work Unit their 'Life Support' and 'Build It' initiatives have seen over 50 young people and adults trained and professionally qualified at a national level from degrees in youth work to level 3 in various building trades or national qualifications in health and nursing. This has been one of the highest levels of success of any project that we have supported in Wales over the last two decades. It has seen a great deal of community generation, the creation and development of real jobs and qualifications, and much innovatory developmental and forward looking work. All those involved in these initiatives must be congratulated on these achievements.

In the north of the UK, three initiatives based on past Youth or Adult? Workers vision have begun, one in Middlesbrough, with Community Campus, where housing support and personal development are focused on, another in Girvan on the west coast of Scotland where a refurbished former hotel is nearing completion as a dedicated youth centre and associated outdoor initiative and finally Belfast,

where a Community Enterprise Sports Network in the north and west of the city is identifying sports leaders.

The Rank Volunteer Gap Award Scheme

Overall, the gap scheme has never been busier. The level of success and demand this year has posed its own problems and with the continuing development of the network we had to consider changing the allocation of certain agencies involved with this initiative and have had to give the greater priority and opportunities to newer projects coming on board. We will, of course, be reviewing these priorities from time to time but we hope that those older members of the network can continue to develop their own gap scheme with alternative funding. The reserve lists have got longer but the successes on the scheme have remained at much the same level. There is a 95% success rate over our three year researches of getting those that have completed the gap scheme (at least 1,000 hours of voluntary work and training) into real jobs, further education or higher education. The remaining 5% represents an unknown element as often people have moved on, quite rightly, and are out of touch with their original host agency and indeed ourselves. The gappers have completed work with an organisation called Speakers Bank which helped to enhance levels of public speaking and confidence. A whole day was spent in contributing and creating inputs onto the website for our colleagues at CTVC True Tube. This was a huge success and provoked a great deal of interest amongst the young leaders.

One of the most important launches and pieces of research undertaken was Turning Points where 12 of the young leaders we have supported over the years developed their own piece of action research. This essentially told their stories and the main turning points in their lives to date. All the young people involved had moved on to other things, often within the Rank network, ten had originally been involved through the gap scheme, one through Skills Apprentice and one through Youth or Adult? This project resulted in a mobile exhibition of banners which has been seen by over 2,000 people at various events including the graduation at the YMCA George Williams College last autumn.

'Produced' was a DVD containing a summary of stories from all 12, an audio track with the complete stories of six of the leaders, and a brochure of the stories of all 12. To quote our summary, 'Perhaps to understand where we're going we sometimes need to reflect on where we've been. These 12 young leaders in local communities have all touched other people's lives and their lives have been touched by other people. In all cases they've shown enormous courage and bravery, often demanding vision and determination and equally often, against many odds, they crossed the road and made that extra effort.

Their words emphasise the importance of role models and respect in times of extreme prejudice. Theirs is a vision of dialogue, sensitivity, democracy and diversity. This initiative has involved the oral tradition of storytelling going back thousands of years and now perhaps neglected as a method in youth work, community work and informal education. Everyone has a story to tell and most have their turning points.

Bursaries

The schemes have enjoyed another fully subscribed and successful year. The Tall Ships Youth Trust, in which we have invested over £1 million since 1980, has recently celebrated its Golden Jubilee.

The Outward Bound Trust has continued to promote high endeavour and challenge for the individual and is about to open its new outdoor centre at Howtown, in the Lake District, to accommodate its growing schools' work.

School Leadership Award

The chief objectives for 2007 were to increase the number of good applicants for the award, to continue to promote the concept of leadership among the award holders and to develop their understanding and experience of working with charitable causes.

The number of applicants increased as new schools came into the scheme and an active dialogue developed between heads and the new administrator.

The Fellowship held its third 'leadership day' attended by the 16 current Leadership Award holders. A team-building exercise involved the assembling of bicycles which were then donated to the charity JUMP.

Reports from the Community Action Placements undertaken by the award holders attested to the dramatic impact these residential placements had on their confidence and their outlook.

Rank Fellowship

The main objectives in 2007 were to further the connection between individual fellows and charities, to develop the regional reach of the fellowship and to open up connections between the fellowship and organisations from other countries with similar charitable objectives.

The second Fellowship Charities Evening was held at the RSA in November. Seventy fellows and their guests attended, along with the representatives of 14 charities, trustees and Rank staff members. This successful event produced a significant number of volunteering offers and very positive feedback from the charities involved.

Two fellowship dinners were held in the North West in June. A steering group is now planning a Manchester Charities Evening for 2008.

Close links were established between the Fellowship and the Fundacao Estudar (Brazil) and the London Maghreb Society (Tunisia, Morocco and Algeria), organisations which share the same objectives as the fellowship. *Representatives from these two organisations attended the Charities Evening and joined the steering committee in 2007.*

Information available

Annual report and accounts were available from the Charity Commission. The foundation has an informative website.

Exclusions

Grants to registered charities only. Appeals from individuals or appeals from registered charities on behalf of named individuals will not be considered; neither will appeals from overseas or from UK-based organisations where the object of the appeal is overseas.

In an endeavour to contain the calls made upon the foundation to a realistic level, the directors have continued with their policy of not, in general, making grants to projects involved with:

- agriculture and farming
- cathedrals and churches (except where community facilities are involved)
- culture
- university and school building and bursary funds
- medical research.

Applications

Applications should be addressed to the general appeals office.

There is no formal application form, but for administrative purposes it is helpful if the actual appeal letter can be kept to one or two sides of A4, which can be supported by reports, etc. General appeals, including unsolicited appeals relating to youth projects, should include:

- charity registration number
- full details of project and total cost involved

- amount already raised
- the most recent audited set of accounts.

Preliminary enquiries are welcomed. Unsolicited appeals are considered quarterly. All appeals are acknowledged and applicants advised as to when they will be considered. The trustees meet quarterly in March, June, September and December.

The Francis C Scott Charitable Trust

CC no. 232131

Contact
Chris Batten, Director, Suite 3, Sand Aire House, New Road, Kendal, Cumbria LA9 4UJ
Tel: 01539 741610; Fax: 01539 741611; email: info@fcsct.org.uk; website: www.fcsct.org.uk

Trustees
Susan Bagot, Chair; Richard Boddy; Ian Pirnie; Joanna Plumptre; Alexander Scott; Madeleine Scott; Don Shore; Clare Spedding.

Areas of work: Disadvantaged young people in Cumbria and north Lancashire.

Total grants: £1.4 million (2007)

Youth grants: £1 million

Beneficial area: Cumbria and north Lancashire, comprising the towns of Lancaster, Morecambe, Heysham and Camford.

General

The trust was created in 1963 by Peter F Scott CBE, then Chairman of the Provincial Insurance Company. Peter Scott, together with his parents Francis and Frieda Scott and his sister Joan Trevelyan, endowed the trust with a significant holding of Provincial Insurance Company shares.

It supports registered charities addressing community deprivation in Cumbria and north Lancashire, and is principally concerned with meeting the needs of young people from 0–19 years. It seeks to target its funds where they can be most effective and can make a real difference to people's lives.

Grantmaking in 2007

In the nine months to the end of 2007 the trust had assets totalling just over £30.6 million and an income of £699,000. There were 95 grants paid during this period, including commitments from previous years, totalling over £1.4 million. There were 50 grants committed totalling just under £1.3 million, broken down as follows:

	No.	Amount
Young people	21	£547,000
Families and children, women and men	20	£454,000
Communities and charity support	5	£205,500
Disabled, chronically ill and older people	3	£21,000
Other	1	£20,000

The following information is taken from the trust's website.

What we fund

The majority of our grants are multi-year revenue grants (i.e. salaries and running costs), however trustees will also fund capital projects that make a tangible difference to a local community.

Whilst we prefer to fund organisations that are registered charities, we will consider offering grants to organisations that are pursuing charitable objectives providing their aims/constitution are clearly not-for-profit. We will only consider applications from national organisations where the beneficiaries and project workers are based within our beneficial area.

Preferred areas of support

In broad terms, trustees are looking for projects that are responding to identified needs from a specific group or community. A project or service does not need to be new or innovative to receive funding support – the most important consideration is whether it is effective. The bulk of our grants are for revenue funding (running costs and/or salaries) over a number of years – please refer to our eight-year funding model for details [see below].

Within our overall aim of supporting charities that are addressing the needs of 0–19 year olds in the most deprived communities in Cumbria and north Lancashire, the following are our key priority areas:

- *Early years/family support work: The nurturing and development of 0 to 5 year olds and those who are caring for them.*

- *Children's work: Within the 6 to 13 age group, we are particularly keen to support projects that are assisting children with the transition from primary to secondary school.*

- *Youth work: This trust has long supported developmental work with teenagers and will continue to fund those projects addressing the needs of the most disadvantaged within this age group.*

Eight-year funding model

Following a strategic review process conducted in 2003, the trustees have adopted the following approach to revenue funding for those projects/organisations they believe require extended investment in order to become established. Appeals for capital or bursary funding are considered separately. [See table on page 178.]

Grants in 2007

Young people

Two large capital grants were made during the year, to Brathay Hall Trust (£275,000) and Whitehaven Harbour Youth Project (£250,000). Other beneficiaries receiving grants during the year included: Brathay Group Sponsorship Fund (£40,000); Millom Youth Partnership and YMCA – Lancaster & District (£20,000 each); Aspatria Dreamscheme and Mirehouse Amateur Football Club (£15,000 each); Community Projects Carlisle and Mobex Cumbria (£10,000 each); Carlisle (Young) Carers Association (£8,000); Practical Alternatives to Custody and Quondam Arts Trust (£5,000 each); and Carlisle One World Centre (£2,000).

Families and children, women and men

Beneficiaries included: Living Well Trust (£30,000); Lancaster & District Homeless Action Service (£25,000); Barrow Dads Group (£18,000); HomeStart Barrow (£16,000); SAFE Domestic Abuse Team – NSPCC (£15,000); ContinYou (£11,000); Cumbria Alcohol & Drug Advisory Service (£10,000); Visitors'/Children's Support Group (£5,000); and Samaritans of Barrow, Furness and South Lakes (£3,000).

Information available

Accounts were available from the Charity Commission; the trust has a good website.

Exclusions

The trust does not consider appeals:

- from individuals
- from statutory organisations

- from national charities without a local base/project
- from charities with substantial unrestricted reserves
- from medical/health establishments
- from schools/educational establishments
- from infrastructure organisations/ second-tier bodies
- for projects principally benefiting people outside Cumbria/north Lancashire
- for retrospective funding
- for expeditions or overseas travel
- for the promotion of religion
- for animal welfare.

Applications

The trust is always pleased to hear from charities that need help. If an organisation thinks that it may come within the trust's criteria it is invited to contact the director to request an application form. Application forms are also available to download from the trust's website. Initial applications should be made on the trust's standard form which should be completed and returned with the latest set of accounts.

The trust welcomes potential applicants to telephone the director or one of his colleagues for an informal discussion before submitting an application.

The Francis C Scott Charitable Trust

Phase	Year	Focus	Objective
1	up to 1 year	Research	Define area of need and then seek organisations to address it.
2	1–3	Core funding	Provide running costs (some or all) and actively support with staff time to ensure the project's early success.
3	4–6	Project funding	Foster a more strategic approach to funding and target project development.
4	7–8	Scale down funding	Withdraw funding over an agreed time period and attract other funders (especially statutory).
5	8+	Cease funding	Remain a background advocate for the project, but move on.

Grants below £5,000 are decided on a monthly basis, with larger appeals going to the full trustees' meetings in March, July and November.

The whole process of application to receipt of a grant may take up to four months. An application form is available from the correspondent and should be returned with the latest set of audited accounts.

The Henry Smith Charity

CC no. 230102

Contact
Richard Hopgood, Director, 6th Floor, 65 Leadenhall Street, London EC3A 2AD Tel: 020 7264 4970; Fax: 020 7488 9097; website: www.henrysmithcharity.org.uk

Trustees
Jamie Hambro, Chair; Mrs Diana Barran; Nicholas Acland; Mrs Anne Allen; The Rt Hon. Clare Al M Countes; Tristan Millington Drake; The Rt Hon. Max Egremont; Ms Marilyn Gallyer; Miko Giedroyc; Mrs Carola Godman-Law; Ms Merlyn Lowther; Noel Manns; Mrs Anna Mcnair Scott; Mark Newton; Ronnie Norman; P Smallridge; Gordon Lee Steere; Sir Richard Thompson.

Areas of work: Social welfare, older people, disability, health, medical research.

Total grants: £26.2 million (2007)

Youth grants: £4.7 million

Beneficial area: UK. Specific local programmes in east and west Sussex, Hampshire, Kent, Gloucestershire, Leicestershire, Suffolk and Surrey.

General

The Henry Smith Charity was founded in 1628 with the objects of relieving and where possible releasing people from need and suffering. These objects continue in the grant-making policy today. The Henry Smith Charity makes grants totalling over £20 million per annum for a wide range of purposes across the UK, funded from investments.

In 2007 the charity had assets amounting to £772.4 million and an income of £24.9 million. Grants were made totalling £26.2 million.

There are three types of grant made:

- **'Special list' grants** – grants made on a one-off basis which relate to a specific project for which applicants have requested support. This could include purchase/refurbishment of a building, purchase of specialist equipment, other similar capital expenditure, or one year's running costs. Requests must be for £10,000 or more for one year only.

- **'General list' grants** – annual grants made for more than one year, and up to three years. They are usually for a specific item in the applicant's budget such as a salary, or towards the costs of a particular project. Grants can be used for core costs. Requests must be for £10,000 or more, per annum.

- **'Small grants'** – grants are given to organisations with an annual income of less than £150,000. Applications can be made for amounts up to £10,000. Grants can be for one-off capital items such as equipment purchase; these grants must be used within six months of being awarded. Grants can also be towards one year's running costs. Grants are one-off payments although repeat applications can be considered.

The charity also awards 'major' grants. These consist of a programme of grants in a specially selected area. Their aim is to make a significant impact in the chosen field. For the period 2006–2009 grants were made in east Lancashire, although this is now closed to new applications. A new initiative will be announced by the charity in 2009.

Grants, other than for the small grant schemes, are generally large. Few are for less than £20,000 and some are for £100,000 or more.

Programme areas

The following programme areas are specifically aimed at young people:

Young people

Projects that provide support to young people at risk, particularly those living in areas of considerable deprivation.

Family services

Projects which provide support to families at risk.

Holidays for children

Projects which provide holidays or outings for children from areas of considerable deprivation or children with a disability, aged 13 or under. For more information on this programme please call the Information Line on 020 7264 4970.

Information available

Annual report and accounts available on the charity's website.

Exclusions

What will not normally be considered for funding:

- arts or educational projects, except those specifically for the rehabilitation and/or training of the disabled, prisoners or young people at risk

- leisure or recreational activities, except those specifically and solely for the rehabilitation and/or training of disabled people, or holidays and outings for children from areas of considerable deprivation or children with a disability

- environmental projects whose primary purpose is conservation of the environment

- projects which promote a particular religion

- community centres, except those in areas of considerable deprivation, where those served are primarily in special need of help (e.g. older people, those prone to drug or alcohol misuse or homeless people), and where the staff involved in the project have appropriate qualifications

- capital appeals for places of worship

- youth clubs/projects, except those situated in areas of considerable deprivation

- playgrounds, except where a substantial element of need is involved, e.g., disabled children or children in an area of considerable deprivation

- local authorities

- umbrella or grant-making organisations

- universities and colleges, and grant maintained, private or local education authority schools or their parent teacher associations, except if those schools are for students with special needs

- charities applying on behalf of individuals

- general requests for donations

- running costs under £10,000 per annum except as specified under the small grants programme

- professional associations and training of professionals

- projects which are abroad, even though the charity is based in the UK

- expeditions or overseas travel

- campaigning organisations or citizens advice projects or projects providing legal advice

- community transport projects

■ general counselling projects, except those in areas of considerable deprivation and with a clearly defined client group.

Applications

Special and general list application guidelines

There is no application form, but trustees suggest that the following guidelines be used:

Applications should be no longer than four A4 sides, and should incorporate a short (half page) summary.

In addition applications should include a detailed budget for the project and the applicant's most recent audited accounts. If those accounts show a significant surplus or deficit of income, please explain how this has arisen.

Applications should:

■ State clearly who they are, what they do and whom they seek to help.

■ Give the applicant's status, e.g., registered charity.

■ Confirm that the organisation has a child protection policy (where appropriate) and that Criminal Record Bureau checks are carried out on all staff working with children.

■ Describe clearly the project for which the grant is sought answering the following questions: What is the aim of the project and why is it needed? What practical results will it produce? How many people will benefit from it? What stage has the project reached so far? How will you ensure that it is cost-effective?

■ If the request is for a salary, enclose a job description.

■ If the request is for medical research, please see separate guidelines.

■ Explain how the project will be monitored and evaluated and how its results will be disseminated.

■ State what funds have already been raised for the project, and name any other sources of funding applied for.

■ Explain where ongoing funding (if required) will be obtained when the charity's grant has been used.

■ If the request is for revenue funding for a specific item, please state the amount sought.

■ Give the names and addresses of two independent referees.

Keep the application as simple as possible and avoid the use of technical terms, acronyms and jargon. Please do not send videos or CD ROMs.

Applications can be submitted at any time during the year. A letter acknowledging the application will be sent within two weeks of receipt.

Trustees meet quarterly in March, June, September and December to consider applications. Applications must be received at least eight weeks prior to a meeting in order to be considered at the next meeting.

Applicants whose appeals have been considered at those meetings will be informed in writing of the trustees' decision within two weeks of the meeting.

Applicants who are unsuccessful are required to wait a minimum of six months from the date of notification before reapplying. Please note that whilst the appeal might fit the trustees' criteria, owing to the high volume of appeals, not all applicants will be successful.

Applicants whose appeals are outside the charity's objects and/or current policy will be notified within four weeks of receipt of application.

Small grants programme application guidelines

The small grants programme is divided into two strands: the county list for applicants from the counties with which the charity has a historical association, i.e. Gloucestershire, Hampshire, Kent, Leicestershire, Suffolk, Surrey, East Sussex and West Sussex, and the small grants programme for applicants from other areas in the UK.

County list

- Applications from the counties with which the charity has a traditional connection i.e., Gloucestershire, Hampshire, Kent, Leicestershire, Suffolk, Surrey, East Sussex and West Sussex, are under the aegis of a particular trustee who is resident in that county.

- County list grants are available to organisations with an annual income of under £150,000 (exceptions may be made for charities whose activities are county-wide).

- Applications can be made for grants between £500 to £10,000.

- Grants can be for one-off capital items such as equipment purchase; these grants must be used within six months of being awarded. Grants can also be used towards one year's running costs (including core costs).

- County grants are one-off payments.

- The organisations must be based within the United Kingdom.

- Applications are considered by the county trustee and recommendations for grants are subject to approval when the trustees meet in March, June, September and December.

Other areas in the UK

- Small grants are available to organisations from areas outside of the traditional counties which have been registered with the Charity Commission for a minimum of two years and have an annual income under £150,000.

- Applications can be made for grants between £500 to £10,000.

- Grants can be for one-off capital items such as equipment purchase; these grants must be used within six months of being awarded. Grants can also be used towards one year's running costs (including core costs).

- Small grants are one-off payments.

- The organisations must be based within the United Kingdom.

- Small grants applications can be submitted at any time during the year; they are processed fortnightly and are sent to the trustees of the small grants committee. If there is sufficient support, the grant is approved and the applicant is informed by telephone. All applicants will be sent a letter notifying them of the trustees' decision within four to six weeks of receipt of their application.

In addition to those outlined in the exclusions section, the following also apply:

- organisations not registered as charities or those that have been registered for less than two years

- organisations with an annual income of more than £150,000

- pre-school groups

- out of school playschemes, including pre-school and holiday schemes, except those specifically for people who are disabled.

- applications for revenue funding for more than one year

- applications for salary costs for new posts (salaries for existing staff can be considered).

The Tudor Trust

CC no. 1105580

Contact
Anne Lane, Grants Team Manager,
7 Ladbroke Grove, London W11 3BD
Tel: 020 7727 8522; Fax: 020 7221 8522;
website: www.tudortrust.org.uk

Trustees
Mary Graves; Helen Dunwell; Desmond
Graves; Nell Buckler; Christopher
Graves; Catherine Antcliff; Louise
Collins; Elizabeth Crawshaw; Matt
Dunwell; James Long; Ben Dunwell;
Francis Runacres; Monica Barlow.

Areas of work: Welfare, general.

Total grants: £20.4 million (2007/08)

Youth grants: £2.7 million

Beneficial area: UK and sub-Saharan
Africa.

General

The trust meets a range of both capital
and revenue needs, notably including
related building costs, for voluntary and
community groups. Grants can be of all
sizes, very often to be paid over two or
three years. There is no maximum or
minimum grant amount.

Much larger grants can be made, but
these are more likely to be the result of
proactive work by the trust.

Grants for work outside the UK are
targeted and proactive, and therefore
applications are not sought for this
aspect of the trust's work.

Background

The trust was founded in 1955 by Sir
Godfrey Mitchell, who endowed it with
shares in the Wimpey construction
company (making this one of the
extraordinary number of major trusts
with their origins in the building
industry). The shareholdings have now
been wholly diversified, with investments
valued at £290 million in 2008.

The trust spends from both income and
capital, and has so far maintained its
levels of grantmaking despite reductions
both in income and, to a greater extent,
in the value of its investment portfolio.

The trustees include a substantial
number of family members, including
Christopher Graves who is also the
director of the trust.

Grants committees meet every three
weeks and are made up of both trustees
and staff (though grants are the overall
responsibility of the trustee committee,
which also itself considers some of the
more substantial grants).

The staffing is modest for an
organisation spending this amount of
money and doing so through 350 to 400
grants a year (a reduction on previous
years – see below). The 'support costs' of
the grant-making activity represent
around 5% of the grant total. In part this
may be made possible by a substantial
degree of voluntary input from trustees.

Review of grant-making activities
2007/08

The following is taken from the trust's
excellent annual report:

*The board set a flexible budget at the
beginning of the year and agreed that
funds to resource this would be drawn from
both capital and income. While it was the
trustees' intention to make around 350
grants, in the event we made 392
commitments (2007: 397) to a total of
£20.4 million (2007: £17.9 million). To
some degree the fact that we made more
grants than planned reflects the high
standard of applications received over the
year.*

*We received fewer applications this year
than last – 3,199 compared with 3,660 in
2007. This was quite surprising as it had
been thought that opening up the
guidelines would lead to a major increase
in applications received. It is encouraging
to note that the number of 'eligible'*

applications continues to increase: 88% of applications were eligible this year compared with 85% in 2007. Our hope is that clear and straightforward funding guidelines, and easy access to advice over the telephone and via our website, will continue to reduce the number of applications from groups which aren't eligible to apply for funding.

The 392 grants, and two loans, committed over the year addressed our ultimate aim of tackling the social, emotional and financial needs of people on the margins of society in many different ways. Reflecting our continued move away from fixed funding priorities, the work we supported over the year was hugely varied in terms of location, issues tackled, scale and approach – from a horticulture project for ex-offenders in Devon to a community hall refurbishment in Peterhead; from the integration of migrant workers in Norfolk to counselling for the families of alcohol misusers in South Wales.

Some grants grew out of an established interest – for example, we supported a number of community land trusts over the year, building on Tudor's longstanding involvement in the field of affordable housing. Others took us into newer territory: this year we funded more work addressing issues surrounding young people and gang activity, for example, as well as more wide-ranging conflict resolution work in the community.

Where appropriate, our grantmaking is supported by internal research, intended to give staff and trustees a better understanding of new or developing issues, or of the context in which organisations are operating. Over the year research into areas including digital inclusion, women involved in sex work, social enterprise, play and adventure activity for young people, community interest companies and the arts and social inclusion contributed to our policy development and informed our grantmaking.

Although we are a national funder, Tudor recognises the importance of local intelligence and of keeping abreast of regional and national issues across the devolved UK. This year members of the grants team attended the Association of Charitable Foundation's Northern Ireland Conference in Belfast and a meeting of Scottish trusts in Glasgow, which provided some useful insights. Alongside this, when carrying out visits in an area staff also try to arrange a meeting with an infrastructure body providing support to the voluntary sector, to give us a sense of the wider 'climate' for voluntary groups. Last year we discussed the particular issues affecting organisations in the West Midlands, Coventry, Sheffield and the Welsh Valleys.

While we no longer fund under specific remit headings, we continue to code our grants by subject area so that we can maintain an overview of the sort of work we are supporting, and compare projects addressing similar issues or working with specific client groups. The table below gives more detail on how our grants were allocated across various subject headings in 2008. [See table on page 185.]

Over the year a number of special interest groups made up of trustees and staff continued to focus their attention on Tudor's funding response to specific issues. The Africa Group's small capacity building grants programme continued this year, with five small grants being made to enable exchange visits within Africa and attendance on residential training courses. The group made an unusually large capital grant of £200,000 towards a building providing residential accommodation and training rooms for St Jude Family Projects in Uganda, a flagship farmer training centre; complementing this a grant was made supporting the work of Build It International, an organisation which explores appropriate and sustainable building methods with African communities. In total, the Africa Group made 22 grants totalling £728,000 to organisations spreading the concept of sustainable agriculture in sub-Saharan Africa.

The Almshouse Group continued to pursue the idea of creating a building in partnership with an older people's co-housing group and their housing association partner, but there has been slow progress, particularly around the identification of a suitable site. However work is continuing and the group is keen to have a role in taking a development forward.

The Debt Group focused on supporting practical, community-based work to reduce over-indebtedness, making five grants totalling £345,500. While the bulk of the group's grants were made to credit unions it is interesting to note that grants committees also made grants to five credit unions this year. This reflects the transfer of knowledge and expertise from the group to the trust as a whole.

The Criminal Justice Group, meanwhile, concentrated this year on a single issue – support for women offenders in prison and on release – and made five grants totalling £425,000. Towards the end of the year the group decided to wind up, feeling that there was less need for a dedicated group now

that a better understanding of criminal justice issues had spread throughout the trust.

Finally, the Tudor LankellyChase South West Partnership (TLC) entered its third year. The CLINKS South West Development Worker, funded by TLC, continued building the capacity of voluntary sector groups in the criminal justice field, encouraging communication and cooperative working across the South West. Over the year TLC visited and funded a wide range of groups across the South West, agreeing ten grants totalling £597,900 (£298,950 contributed by Tudor). Towards the end of the year under review the boards of both Tudor and LankellyChase agreed that the partnership would be extended for a further two years, with a further budget of £1.2 million allocated over the period – £600,000 from each trust.

Over the year we maintained a balance of reactive and proactive grantmaking across the UK. London continued to receive significant levels of funding, with 25% (2007: 27%) of our grants by value going to organisations based in the capital. However, this figure includes grants made to organisations which are based in London but which work nationally or regionally: adjusting our figures to take this into account gives a reduced percentage of

The Tudor Trust

	No. of grants	%	Value of grants	%
Youth	47	12%	£2,730,500	13%
Older people	13	3%	£806,000	4%
Community	112	29%	£6,060,300	30%
Relationships	38	10%	£2,147,500	11%
Housing	32	8%	£1,344,100	7%
Mental health	40	10%	£2,454,600	12%
Substance misuse	12	3%	£677,500	3%
Learning	12	3%	£546,000	3%
Financial security	12	3%	£722,000	4%
Criminal justice	42	11%	£2,053,000	10%
Overseas	32	8%	£883,000	4%
Total	**392**	**100%**	**£20,424,500**	**100%**

17% (2007: 22%). The table below shows how our grants were allocated by region in 2008.

Guidelines 2008/09

In April 2006 the trust launched new funding guidelines (which will remain largely unchanged for 2008/09), a summary of which is as follows:

The Tudor Trust is an independent grant-making charitable trust which supports organisations working across the UK. We do not focus our funding on specific themes or programmes. Instead we want to fund a wide range of people and organisations working to achieve lasting change in their communities. Our role is to support and enable their visions, trusting the groups we fund to do the work that is needed.

Tudor aims to support work which addresses the social, emotional and financial needs of people at the margins of our society. We are interested in how organisations tackle these needs, and their root causes. We want to encourage growth, progression and development, not just keeping things as they are.

Although we still make grants across our established funding areas (youth, older people, community, relationships, housing, mental health, substance misuse, learning, financial security and criminal justice) we

are also open to hearing about work in areas we have not funded before. [See 'What are we looking for when we make grants?' on page 187].

We receive many more applications than we will ever be able to fund, so we have introduced a two-stage application process. This is designed to reduce the time, effort and resources organisations spend on their first approach to us. All applicants are therefore asked to complete a brief first-stage proposal for initial assessment [see Applications].

There are some types of organisation and work which we will not consider for funding [see Exclusions].

What kind of funder is Tudor?

We know that solutions to the difficulties people face are seldom straightforward or immediate. We are therefore interested in encouraging people to use their own skills and abilities as a resource for change; to find new ways of tackling deep-rooted problems or to cope with and move on from difficult situations. We recognise that this may take time so, if appropriate, we can commit funding over a sustained period.

As an independent grantmaker, an important part of our role is to support work which is untried, which has uncertain outcomes and which may be difficult to

The Tudor Trust				
Grants made by region				
	No. of grants	Value of grants	%	Grant per head (UK only)
East Midlands	16	£1,092,000	5%	£0.26
Eastern	12	£510,000	2%	£0.09
London	91	£5,076,000	25%	£0.71
North East	16	£1,055,000	5%	£0.42
North West	44	£2,329,300	12%	£0.35
Northern Ireland	5	£215,000	1%	£0.13
Scotland	26	£1,210,500	6%	£0.24
South East	31	£1,404,000	7%	£0.18
South West	49	£2,513,000	12%	£0.51
Wales	15	£793,700	4%	£0.27

fund. However, we are not preoccupied with innovation and understand that there is a place for well-founded, practical work which seeks to bring normality and wellbeing into difficult places and situations.

We are most interested in helping smaller, under-resourced organisations which offer direct services and which involve the people they work with in their planning. The groups we fund don't have to be registered charities; we can also make grants to other groups as long as they have established charitable objectives.

We want to fund effective people who work to high standards. We recognise that their organisations are best placed to know what the problems are and what to do about them. We trust these groups to go ahead and do the work that is needed, and want to give them the opportunity and practical tools to do so. We want to respond to ideas and energy. We don't have specific funding programmes designed to advance a particular agenda. Instead, we try to support work which is clearly needed and for which funding from Tudor can make all the difference.

Tudor aims to be a helpful and flexible funder and we want to respond imaginatively to organisations' real concerns and priorities. Organisations dealing with complex issues are seldom themselves straightforward and so we hope to engage with the groups we support in a variety of ways, offering grants, loans, advice and development support.

Grants can take the form of core funding (including salaries and running costs), development funding, project grants or capital grants for buildings or equipment. As we want to fund work which engages with the reality and complexity of people and their problems, we look to support organisations working across sectors and boundaries (whether actual or perceived).

We usually make grants over one, two or three years, but may sometimes work alongside organisations for a longer period. However as we are keen to support a range of organisations, including those which are new to us, our funding cannot continue indefinitely.

We want to offer high levels of support and engagement when this will be helpful and appropriate. Our two-stage application process gives us more time to focus on working creatively with applicants who reach the second stage. Through constructive dialogue and increased understanding we hope to give applicants the opportunity to think about their options and develop proposals which focus on the real needs of their organisations and the people they are working with.

What are we looking for when we make grants?

Tudor's focus is on smaller groups, led by people of vision, which are committed to growth, progression and development. Some of the other characteristics we are looking for when we make grants include:

- organisations which are embedded in and have developed out of their community – whether the local area or a community of interest

- organisations providing direct services to marginalised people

- a focus on building stronger communities by overcoming isolation and fragmentation and encouraging inclusion, connection and integration

- high levels of user involvement, and an emphasis on self-help where this is appropriate

- work which addresses complex and multi-stranded, often difficult, problems in unusual or imaginative ways

- organisations and people who know what difference they want to make and have the energy and vision to make it happen

- *we can only consider making a capital grant for new premises or for building improvements if the organisations using the building display some of these characteristics. Good buildings which contribute positively to their environment are important, but we are most interested in what goes on inside the building and the difference building improvements would make to your work.*

We are more likely to fund groups with an annual turnover of less than £1 million.

How likely are you to receive a grant from Tudor?

We aim to make around 350 grants a year but receive thousands of applications. There is no minimum or maximum grant amount that the trust will consider. It is important to understand that only a small proportion of applicants will receive a grant from Tudor, and that your proposal may be turned down even if your work falls within our guidelines. We do not want applicants to have unrealistic expectations.

This is why we have a two-stage application process. We know that putting together a full funding application places heavy demands on your time and resources, so we are asking all applicants to complete a brief first-stage proposal instead. These will be read by Tudor's trustees and staff, and those we can take forward for detailed discussion with the trustees are asked to complete a full application.

We estimate that only around one in ten applicants will go through to this second stage. Many proposals rejected at the first stage will be for valuable and interesting work; they may be rejected simply because the ideas are not ones that the trustees can take forward at that moment. Because of the numbers of applications we receive, we cannot provide individual feedback on why we are not taking your proposal through to the second stage.

If you are asked to complete a full second-stage application the chances of succeeding will be higher. But not all second-stage applications will receive funding; even at this stage the trustees have to make difficult choices about what they fund.

Recent beneficiaries

The following is a sample of beneficiaries from the third quarter of 2008, and the purposes for which grants were made:

Small Charities Coalition (£150,000), over two years towards the salary of the chief executive and the running costs of this national coalition providing a voice for and coordinating support to small charities; Revolving Doors Agency (£120,000), over four years to build capacity to enable the organisation to influence government policy in relation to vulnerable people with complex needs; Vine Trust – Walsall (£100,000), towards the building costs of a new 'state of the art' youth centre for training advice, recreational activities, alternative education and social enterprise activities; Whitehill Community Association (£85,000), over three years towards the salary of a community development worker to involve young people in Bangor, Co. Down in improving their estate; Revive (£60,000), over two years as continuation funding for the salary of a case worker for an organisation providing support to asylum seekers in Manchester; Prison Dialogue (£30,000), towards piloting a new approach to threshold dialogue for local operational groups with the overall aim of supporting offenders in Dorset and the Midlands; and Giroscope Ltd (£10,000), towards the running costs of an organisation providing affordable rented housing and a community shop in west Hull.

Information available

Excellent annual report and accounts are available from the trust. Website also includes full, clear guidelines for applicants.

Exclusions

The following information is taken from the trust's funding guidelines, which are downloadable from the website.

We want to be clear about areas in which we will not make grants, so we list here the types of proposal we will not consider for funding. Some are self-explanatory while others derive from the Trust's history and experience. To save yourself time and effort please check this section carefully before starting work on your proposal.

1) We do not make grants to individuals.

2) We will not consider proposals from these types of organisations:
- *statutory bodies*
- *hospitals, health authorities and hospices (or towards any sort of medical care, medical equipment or medical research)*
- *universities, colleges and schools (or towards academic research, bursaries or scholarships)*
- *organisations working primarily with children under five*
- *organisations working primarily in the field of: physical disability; learning disability; autistic spectrum disorder; physical illness; sensory impairment*
- *organisations focusing primarily on: adult learning, skills training or employment training; the restoration or conservation of buildings or habitats*
- *animal charities*
- *scouts, guides and other uniformed youth groups*
- *museums, places of entertainment, leisure centres and clubs, social clubs or sports clubs*
- *larger charities (both national and local) enjoying widespread support.*

3) We will not consider funding the core work of:
- *advice and information-giving bodies*
- *community foundations*
- *volunteer bureaux and centres*
- *councils for voluntary service*
- *infrastructure organisations/ second-tier bodies (i.e. organisations fulfilling a supporting, coordinating or development role within the voluntary sector).*

4) Finally, we will not consider funding:
- *the promotion of religion*
- *overseas projects. We run a targeted grants programme promoting sustainable agriculture in sub-Saharan Africa so we don't consider speculative proposals from overseas groups*
- *one-off holidays, residentials, trips, exhibitions*
- *arts and sports-based projects unless there is a particularly strong focus on developing marginalised groups*
- *endowment appeals*
- *work that has already taken place.*

Applications

The first-stage proposal

The first-stage proposal is intended to help us understand what sort of organisation you are and why you are doing the work you are doing. We do not want a detailed description or full costings of the work you are seeking funding for; we will discuss these areas with you if your application goes through to the second stage. Keeping your options open at this point allows us to work together more creatively if you are invited to send us a full application.

A first-stage proposal must include:

1) *An introductory letter, of no more than one side of A4, on your organisation's letterhead.*

2) *A completed organisation details sheet. This sheet can be downloaded from our website: www.tudortrust.org.uk.*

3) *Your answers to the following questions, on no more than two sides of A4:*
   - *What difference do you want to make, and how will your organisation achieve this?*
   - *Why are you the right people to do this work?*
   - *Tell us about the people you are working with, and how you know there is a need for your work.*
   - *How would you use funding from Tudor?*

4) *A copy of your most recent annual accounts, and annual report if you produce one. If your organisation is too new to have annual accounts please send a photocopy of a recent bank statement instead. Please don't send any other supporting documents.*

All first-stage proposals go through an initial assessment process which involves both trustees and staff. In some cases we may phone you to discuss your proposal. We aim to let you know within a month whether or not we are inviting you to submit a second-stage application.

Address your proposal to 'The Trustees' and send it to us by post; we do not accept applications by email or fax. There are no deadlines for sending us your proposal; they are assessed as part of a rolling programme.

The second-stage application

If you are invited to put forward a full, second-stage application a member of the grants team will get in touch with you to discuss the next steps, to discover how best Tudor could support your organisation and its work, and to identify the information we need to move your application forward. A member of staff or a trustee may visit you so that we can gain a better understanding of your organisation and the work you do.

Although your chances of success are significantly higher at this stage, being invited to submit a second-stage application does not guarantee that a grant will be made. Not all second-stage applications get as far as committee stage, and not all applications going to committee are funded.

Tudor tries to consider all applications quickly. We aim to make a decision on most second-stage applications within three months, although in some circumstances we can act more swiftly. Complex applications can of course take longer to develop.

Trustees and staff meet every three weeks to consider applications at a grants committee or trustee committee. They will discuss your application in detail and will usually make an immediate decision on funding, although in a few cases they may request further information or a visit if one has not already taken place.

The Westminster Foundation

CC no. 267618

Contact
Mrs V Parish, Administrator,
70 Grosvenor Street, London W1K 3JP
Tel: 020 7408 0988; Fax: 020 7312 6244;
email: westminster.foundation@
grosvenor.com

Trustees
The Duke of Westminster, Chair; J H M Newsum; Mark Loveday; Lady Edwina Grosvenor.

Areas of work: Church, conservation, youth, education, medical, arts, social welfare.

Total grants: £1.9 million (2007)

Youth grants: £73,000

Beneficial area: Unrestricted, in practice mainly UK. Local interests in central London (SW1 and W1 and immediate environs), North West England, especially rural Lancashire and the Chester area, and the Sutherland area of Scotland.

General

The foundation was established in 1974 for general charitable purposes by the fifth Duke of Westminster and continues to make grants to a wide range of charitable causes. In 1987 the Grosvenor Foundation, a separately registered charity, transferred all its assets to the Westminster Foundation.

The foundation makes over 100 grants a year, mainly for welfare and educational causes but with substantial support for conservation and rather less for medicine and the arts. Grants appear to be all for UK causes and perhaps half by number, though less by value, are in the areas of church, conservation, youth, education, medical, arts and social welfare.

Grants can be for very large amounts, but generally all but a handful are usually for amounts of not more than £60,000 and most are between £5,000 and just a few hundred pounds. About half of the beneficiaries were also supported in previous years.

The foundation has previously noted that:

It is usual that the trustees have knowledge of, or connection with, those charities which are successful applicants. The trustees tend to support caring causes and not research.

Grants are directed towards geographical areas in which the Grosvenor family and

Grosvenor Group have a particular connection. For example, Grosvenor Group are major stakeholders in the redevelopment of the Paradise Street site in Liverpool [completed in September 2008]. The trustees have previously committed £500,000 over a period of five years to the Liverpool One Foundation [previously known as the Liverpool Paradise Foundation], a registered charity set up by some of the stakeholders involved in the Liverpool development, and this money will be distributed to a wide range of charities and organisations in the immediate vicinity.

This is assumed to be a largely personal trust, created by the present duke. He is well known in the charity world for his active personal involvement in many organisations, and no doubt a significant number of the regular beneficiaries are organisations with which he has developed a personal connection that goes beyond grantmaking.

In 2007 the foundation had assets of £38 million and an income of £3.8 million. Grants were committed to 140 organisations totalling £1.9 million and were broken down as follows:

	No.	Amount
Social welfare	65	£1,310,000
Conservation	13	£484,600
Medical	29	£125,000
Education	10	£80,000
Youth	14	£73,000
Arts	4	£13,000
Church	3	£2,200
Commemorative	2	£1,000

Grants in 2007

The foundation's accounts list grants made of £20,000 or more. Although grants were made under the youth category totalling just £73,000, youth organisations also appear to be supported under the social welfare category.

Social welfare

Beneficiaries included: LandAid Charitable Trust (£103,500 over four years), for the Foundation for Life programme, which helps young homeless people turn their lives around [one of the Westminster Foundation's trustees, Mr J Newsum, is also a trustee of the LandAid Charitable Trust]; and Blacon Community Trust – Chester (£50,000), to support local community improvements, working in partnership with local residents groups and organisations to provide community-based activities and catering for all age groups within the area.

Youth

Beneficiaries included: Army Cadet Force (ACF) Association (£25,000), towards a community initiative run by the ACF in close consultation with social services, local authorities, police authorities and schools. Adventure training is provided for 12–14 year olds who have been selected from underprivileged and vulnerable backgrounds.

Information available

Accounts were available at the Charity Commission, giving details of grants over £20,000.

Exclusions

Only registered charities will be considered. No grants to individuals, 'holiday' charities, student expeditions, or research projects.

Applications

In writing to the secretary, enclosing an up-to-date set of accounts, together with a brief history of the project to date and the current need.

The Garfield Weston Foundation

CC no. 230260

Contact

Philippa Charles, Administrator, Weston Centre, 10 Grosvenor Street, London W1K 4QY
Tel: 020 7399 6565; Fax: 020 7399 6588; website: www.garfieldweston.org

Trustees

Guy H Weston, Chair; R Nancy Baron; Miriam L Burnett; Camilla H W Dalglish; Catrina A Hobhouse; Jana R Khayat; Sophia M Mason; Eliza L Mitchell; W Galen Weston; George G Weston.

Areas of work: General.

Total grants: £51.7 million (2007/08)

Youth grants: £1.9 million

Beneficial area: UK.

General

This huge foundation makes about 1,500 one-off grants a year, typically for amounts anywhere between £3,000 and £1 million. Perhaps helped by the fact that the income of the foundation has been rising rapidly, about half of all appeals result in a grant, though not necessarily for the full amount requested. Awards are regularly made in almost all fields except overseas aid and animal welfare.

Probably more than 85% of the money, and an even higher proportion for the largest grants, is for capital or endowment projects.

The published 'criteria' for grantmaking, reported below, are in the most general terms. Compared with the general run of trusts described elsewhere, there are relatively few grants to unconventional causes, or for campaigning or representational activities, and more for institutions such as independent schools and charities connected with private hospitals. Nevertheless, almost all kinds of charitable activity, including the radical, are supported to some extent. Grants are rarely given to major charities with high levels of fundraising costs.

The foundation is one of the few which can consider very large grants.

In 2007/08 the foundation had assets standing at over £3.7 billion. Its income totalled £42.7 million. As in previous years, grants were made far exceeding income, totalling £51.7 million.

Grantmaking criteria

The trust describes the criteria by which applications are assessed as follows:

- The financial viability of the organisation.
- The degree of need for the project requiring funding.
- The amount spent on administration and fundraising as compared with the charitable activities.
- The ability to raise sufficient funding to meet the appeal target.
- Whether the aims of the organisation meet the trustees' aspirations.
- Whether the organisation has the right priorities.
- Where possible, the ability of the organisation to meet its goals.

Grants for youth

In 2007/08 the foundation made grants to 189 organisations working with young people totalling almost £1.9 million. A description of these activities in given in the foundation's annual report:

The two largest grants in this category were for the Outward Bound Trust and the Marine Society & Sea Cadets, both of which received £100,000. The Outward Bound Trust is at the forefront of challenging and innovative outdoor learning and has centres located in Fort William, Aberdovey and Ullswater. Young people are introduced to both physical and mental activities, and are encouraged to

try new things in a safe and controlled environment. The trustees recognise that outdoor adventure makes a significant contribution towards the development of young people.

The Sea Cadets is the nation's most enduring maritime youth charity, with 400 units throughout the UK and 15,000 young people engaged in learning nautical and other skills. Fun, friendship, adventure and the acquisition of new skills is at the core of the organisation. This year's grant helped to acquire a new training vessel.

There were several grants of £50,000, mostly for charities organising a range of activities for young people. The Woodlarks Camp Site Trust in Farnham is redeveloping some outdated support buildings, the Rona Trust in Southampton is replacing one of its yachts and TocH in Aylesbury is being supported in its work encouraging young people to volunteer. Lodge Hill Trust activity centre near Chichester received £30,000 for refurbishing overnight accommodation.

£25,000 was donated to Skill Force Development for its work with disadvantaged and vulnerable young people. It aims to build confidence and self-esteem, and also to develop team work, problem solving and leadership skills. It takes place largely within schools and complements the statutory provision. This grant was in support of the ongoing delivery of their work in Islington and Greenwich.

Kids' City received £15,000 to help maintain and grow its frontline work in the inner city boroughs of Lambeth and Wandsworth. Activities range from martial arts to arts and crafts, keeping children engaged and active. An extensive volunteering and training programme for young people and adults with limited work experience has also been introduced.

£15,000 was also received by the Exodus Project in Barnsley, which runs activity clubs for children aged 8 to 11 and separate

clubs for older youths. It also visits children and their families in their homes in order to support parents and carers as well as the wider community.

The trustees considered a wide range of projects of varying scale, demonstrated by a £1,000 grant made to Holiday Support in Cheltenham, which provides respite holidays for children living in women's refuges in Gloucestershire. Similarly the 21st Hartshill Scouts was supported with £1,000 for new camping equipment.

Information available

Excellent descriptive annual report and accounts with an analysis of a selection of grants, large and small, and a full list of beneficiaries.

The Yapp Charitable Trust

CC no. 1076803

Contact
Mrs Margaret Thompson,
Administrator, 47a Paris Road, Scholes,
Holmfirth HD9 1SY
Tel: 01484 683403;
email: info@yappcharitabletrust.org.uk;
website: www.yappcharitabletrust.org.uk

Trustees
Revd Timothy C Brooke; Peter G
Murray; Mrs Stephanie Willats; David
Aeron-Thomas; Annette Figueiredo.

Areas of work: Social welfare.

Total grants: £504,000 (2006/07)

Youth grants: £92,600

Beneficial area: England and Wales.

General

The Yapp Charitable Trust was formed in 1999 from the Yapp Welfare Trust (two-thirds share) and Yapp Education and Research Trust (one-third share). However, rather than combining the criteria for the two trusts, the trustees decided to focus on small charities,

usually local, rather than UK-wide charities. The trust now accepts applications only from small charities and organisations with a turnover of less than £60,000 in the year of application. The objects are restricted to registered charities in England or Wales and cover work with:

- the care or housing of older people
- the welfare of children and young people, including youth clubs, hostels and similar institutions
- the care or special education of people who have learning difficulties, or are physically disabled or suffer from mental health problems
- the advancement of moral welfare
- the advancement of education and learning, and of scientific and medical research.

Applications from outside these areas cannot be considered. Grants are given towards running costs and salaries but not for capital equipment.

In 2006/07 the trust had assets of £6.7 million and an income of £308,500. There were 85 grants made during the year totalling £504,000. Grants explicitly for children and young people totalled £92,600.

Guidelines

The following information is taken from the trust's website.

We make grants to small registered charities to sustain their existing work with:

- *elderly people*
- *children and young people aged 5–25*
- *people with disabilities or mental health problems*
- *people trying to overcome life-limiting problems of a social, rather than medical, origin – such as addiction, relationship difficulties, abuse, a history of offending.*

We also make grants to sustain small registered charities' existing work in the fields of:

- education and learning (with a particular interest in people who are educationally disadvantaged, whether adults or children).

We are not able to fund work which does not come into one of the above categories.

Size and type of grant

We give grants for running costs and salaries for up to three years. Grants are normally for a maximum of £3,000 per year. Most of our grants are for more than one year because we give priority to ongoing needs. Like most other funders we have many more applications than we can fund. We find we are able to give a grant to only about one in ten of the applications we receive. In 2009 we expect to give about £300,000 in about 50 grants.

Criteria

Within our charitable objects, the trustees focus on making grants to small charities registered and working in England and Wales. Applicants must have a total expenditure budget of less than £60,000 a year for the whole charity. We concentrate on sustaining existing work rather than funding new work because many funders prefer new projects.

We are happy to fund the core costs of small charities whose work falls totally within our objects.

The trustees give priority to charities:

- tackling work that is unattractive to the general public or unpopular with other funders
- helping to improve the lives of marginalised, disadvantaged or isolated people
- able to demonstrate effective use of volunteers.

In practice only charities whose work meets at least one of the above priorities are likely to receive a grant.

Grants in 2006/07

Examples of grants awarded during the year are broken down as follows (with most being given over two or three years):

Children and young people – 16 grants totalling £92,600

Beneficiaries included: Wythenshawe Youth Theatre (£9,000); Freshwaters Contact Centre (£8,000); Norbrook Youth Club (£7,500); Somali Welfare Trust (£6,000); Teenbridge Project (£4,300); Falmouth Youth Club (£3,000); and 1st Shoeburyness Girls Brigade Company (£1,500).

Information available

Accounts were on file at the Charity Commission. The trust also has a clear and helpful website.

Exclusions

The following information is taken from the trust's website.

We do not accept applications from:

- Scotland and Northern Ireland – your charity must work in England or Wales
- charities whose total annual expenditure is more than £60,000
- charities that are not registered with the Charity Commission in England & Wales. You must have your own charity number or be excepted from registration. Industrial and provident societies and community interest companies are not eligible to apply
- branches of national charities. You must have your own charity number, not a shared national registration
- new organisations – you must have been operating as a fully constituted charity for at least three years, even though you may have registered as a charity more recently.

We do not make grants for:

- new work – we provide continuation funding to sustain existing work that

has been happening for at least a year.
We do not offer grants to launch new or
additional activities nor to put on
special events

- *creating new paid posts even if the work is now being done by volunteers*
- *capital-type expenditure – equipment, buildings, renovations, furnishings, minibuses*
- *work with under-5s*
- *childcare*
- *holidays and holiday centres*
- *core funding of general community organisations such as community associations, community centres and general advice services, because some of their work is outside our charitable objects*
- *bereavement support*
- *debt advice*
- *community safety initiatives*
- *charities raising money to give to another organisation, such as schools, hospitals or other voluntary groups.*

Applications

We have a simple application form which we ask you to send in by post, together with a copy of your most recent annual report and accounts and any other information you wish to send.

Applications are processed continuously. When we receive your application we will be in touch, usually within two weeks:

- *to ask for more information*
- *or to tell you the application will be going forward to the next stage of assessment and give an idea of when you can expect a decision*
- *or to let you know we can't help.*

The time it takes to process an application and make a grant is usually between two and six months. We always write to let you know the decision.

Previous applicants

We will accept an application only once each year and you can have only one grant at a time from us. Current grantholders may make a new application when their grant is coming to an end. If we refused your last application you must wait a year before applying again.

The application form and guidelines can be downloaded from the trust's website or obtained from our administrator. Phone or email if you prefer to receive a pack by post. Electronic forms are available in Word (for those who like to fill in forms on a computer) and in pdf format (for those who prefer to fill in forms by hand). Use the eligibility check before downloading. The pack is also available from the administrator in large print.

Case study

YouthBank

In 1999, a group of five organisations came together to develop YouthBank: the British Youth Council, Changemakers, the Community Foundation Network, the National Youth Agency and The Prince's Trust. These organisations helped to set up pilot YouthBanks in Bristol, Bradford, Highlands and Islands of Scotland, Northern Ireland, Northumberland, Tyne and Wear and Wales and are now YouthBank UK's 'Consortium Partners'.

YouthBank is an innovative UK-wide grant-making initiative run by young people for young people. Local YouthBanks provide small grants to projects led by young people, of benefit to the community and that also benefit the young people taking part. It is young people themselves who make decisions about how local YouthBanks are managed and run and, through a board of young people, also direct the UK-wide programme.

YouthBank is more than just a way of giving out grants – it is about supporting and training young people to enable them. Through grantmaking and related activity, YouthBank supports and trains young people to benefit their peers and their community, as well as themselves. It builds on young people's skills and experiences to enable them to reach their full potential and to play a full part in their own communities.

Young people come together to form the YouthBank; they decide how grant applications will be assessed and who receives the money. They are supported by local organisations that help with training, administration and provide support to the young people involved.

YouthBanks offer a range of development opportunities for young people; opportunities to learn about and participate in their own communities, to develop new skills and have new experiences, and to travel to meet other young people involved in YouthBank across the UK. It provides a positive role for young people in their communities and in turn can improve the community's perception of them. YouthBanks directly contribute to the regeneration of communities and, by putting money into the hands of young people, ensure their priorities are being met.

YouthBank projects are already established in a number of locations across the UK and it aims to become established UK-wide, with local projects linked into a regional and national network. *continued...*

Twice a year, young people from all over the UK come together to celebrate their involvement in YouthBank and to swap ideas and experiences. They have the opportunity to get and give support to each other, find out more about the organisation's philosophy and learn new skills.

Information taken from www.youthbank.org.uk

Case study

The Prince's Trust
Who cares?

Overcoming the twin challenges of leaving care and unemployment won eight young people from Chelmsford the NatWest Community Impact Award.

All eight had been in care and were drifting. With no jobs, few qualifications and little confidence, their futures were looking bleak. But together, and with financial help from The Trust, they embarked on a life-changing project to help other young care leavers.

They formed the Young People's Participation Group (YPPG), with the aim of helping other care leavers understand their rights and give them a voice with the decision makers whose policies affected their lives.

By staging workshops featuring music, dance and drama to get their messages across to local young people and members of the county council alike, they transformed both their futures and those of others around them. All of the YPPG are volunteers on other local youth projects, with three of them aiming for careers working with children. And their success has spawned five more projects supporting young people in Essex.

9 Raising money from the National Lottery

The National Lottery (the Lottery) was launched in 1994 and rapidly established itself as a key funder of the voluntary sector. Since it began, £22 billion has been raised and more than 300,500 grants given out for good causes (2008 figures). However, it takes time and effort to put together a good application and the assessment process is a rigorous and demanding one. Many organisations commit a substantial part of their fundraising resources in applying for grants from the various Lottery distribution bodies.

The National Lottery currently funds four good causes:

- charities, health, education and the environment (jointly)
- sports
- arts
- heritage.

In this chapter we give an overview of how Lottery money is spent, who distributes the money to the four good causes, how the various distribution bodies operate, details of current programmes to which groups can apply and information on the Big Lottery Fund (BIG) thinking consultation process.

How Lottery ticket money is distributed

The company in charge of running the game, Camelot, collects the money from the sale of tickets. Camelot was reappointed by the National Lottery Commission (an independent body set up by the government to monitor the integrity of the Lottery – www.natlotcomm.gov.uk) to run the Lottery from 2009 to 2019.

The following is a breakdown of where money goes from each £1 ticket sale:

Lottery winners	50p
Good causes	28p
HM Revenue & Customs	12p
Individual retailers	5p
Camelot	5p

Each 28p for good causes goes initially to the Department for Culture, Media and Sport (DCMS), which is also responsible for the Lottery's policies and the structure within which the distribution bodies work. DCMS has no decision making powers on how Lottery money is given out and grants should be made independently of government departments.

Distribution bodies

Distribution bodies or Lottery funders are the organisations that distribute the good causes' money to local communities and national and international projects. They cover arts, heritage, sport, community and voluntary groups as well as supporting projects concerned with health, education and the environment. They will also be funding the 2012 Olympic Games and Paralympic Games in London and until at least 2012, the diversion of Lottery funds to the Olympics means that there will be less new Lottery money available.

In England the funding bodies are:

- **Arts Council England.** Arts Council England is the national development agency for the arts in England, distributing public money from government and the Lottery.
- **Awards for All.** Awards for All England was a joint Lottery grants programme supported by Arts Council England, the Big Lottery Fund, the Heritage Lottery Fund and Sport England. However, this programme has closed and has been replaced by the funding agencies' small grants progammes. See details on page 214.
- **Big Lottery Fund.** The Big Lottery Fund (BIG) is committed to improving communities and the lives of people most in need.

- **Heritage Lottery Fund.** The Heritage Lottery Fund uses money from the Lottery to give grants for a wide range of projects involving the local, regional and national heritage of the UK.
- **NESTA.** NESTA (the National Endowment for Science, Technology and the Arts) is a non-departmental public body investing in innovators and working to improve the climate for creativity in the UK.
- **Olympic Lottery Distributor.** The Olympic Lottery Distributor's remit is to support the delivery of the London 2012 Olympic and Paralympic Games. The Olympic Lottery Distributor is not currently running any open funding rounds.
- **Sport England.** Sport England invests in projects that help people to start, stay and succeed in sport and physical activity at every level.
- **UK Film Council.** As the lead agency for film, the UK Film Council aims to stimulate a competitive, successful and vibrant UK film industry and culture, both now and for the future.
- **UK Sport.** UK Sport works in partnership to lead sport in the UK to world-class success.

The Lottery distribution bodies are independent; however, because they distribute public funds, their policies are subject to a level of statutory control from government. Their grantmaking is also under close public and media scrutiny and is often the subject of wide-ranging debate.

Currently Lottery funding is allocated to the good causes in the following way:

- charities, health, education and the environment – 50%
- sports – 16.67%
- arts – 16.67%
- heritage – 16.67%.

Big Lottery Fund (BIG)

BIG was launched in 2004 and given legal status on 1 December 2006 by way of the National Lottery Act 2006. It was brought about by the merging of the Community Fund and New Opportunities Fund, and the transfer of residual activities and assets from the Millennium Commission.

BIG is the largest of the Lottery distributors and is responsible for giving out 50% of the money for good causes raised from the Lottery, which provides a budget of about £630 million a year. Funding covers health, education, environment and charitable purposes.

Since its launch it has distributed over £2.7 billion to thousands of projects across the UK.

Its mission is to be 'committed to bringing real improvements to communities and the lives of people most in need'. To do this, it has identified seven values. They are:

- fairness
- accessibility
- strategic focus
- involving people
- innovation
- enabling
- additional to government.

The Act of 2006 also includes powers for BIG to distribute non-Lottery funding and to make loans. Much of BIG's funding is given in grants made directly to successful applicants, particularly those in the voluntary sector. However, for some programmes such as Children's Play in England, funds are awarded to local authorities that have the responsibility for developing children's play strategies in their areas. There is a requirement that proper partnership arrangements are in place with voluntary and community organisations to deliver the outcomes set. BIG can also make funding available through its 'award partners' – expert intermediaries who act on BIG's behalf. The Changing Spaces programme in England (see page 203) is one example.

In response to complaints about the short-term nature of its funding, a number of BIG's programmes now provide funding for up to five years. Projects are required to provide a realistic exit strategy that plans out how the project will continue after the funding from BIG has finished. One effect of this is that requests for larger amounts and for longer periods are made, which, over time, might lead to BIG funding fewer projects.

Current BIG programmes in England

Changing Spaces

The Changing Spaces programme will invest around £200 million in environmental projects in England, including schemes to improve green spaces, grow local food and help community groups to reduce the amount of energy they use.

BIG is working with five organisations that have the skills and experience to run an effective environmental programme on its behalf. Each organisation is running an England-wide, open grants programme.

Changing Spaces: Community Sustainable Energy Programme

Summary

The Community Sustainable Energy Programme (CSEP), run by the Building Research Establishment (BRE), opened in April 2008. The programme will help community-based organisations in England reduce their environmental impact through the installation of energy saving measures and microgeneration technologies. The scheme will also fund development studies that help community organisations to find out if a microgeneration and energy efficiency project will work for them.

Grants available

This programme will award grants of between £5,000 to £50,000 and will provide £8 million to community-based organisations for the installation of microgeneration technologies (producing heat or electricity on a small scale from a low carbon source).

The grants are broken up as follows:

- Capital grants – projects can apply for up to £50,000 or 50% of the project cost (whichever is lower).
- Project development grants – maximum grant available is £5,000 or 75% of the study cost (whichever is lower).

Deadlines

Capital grant funding rounds:

Funding round	Application deadline (5pm)	Selection panel meeting
1	**Friday 16 May 2008**	**w/c 23 June 2008**
2	**Friday 15 August 2008**	**w/c 22 September 2008**
3	**Friday 7 November 2008**	**w/c 8 December 2008**
4	**Friday 30 January 2009**	**w/c 9 March 2009**
5	*Friday 1 May 2009*	*w/c 8 June 2009*
6	*Friday 7 August 2009*	*w/c 14 September 2009*
7	*Friday 30 October 2009*	*w/c 7 December 2009*
8	*Friday 29 January 2010*	*w/c 1 March 2010*
9	*Friday 7 May 2010*	*w/c 7 June 2010*
10	*Friday 30 July 2010*	*w/c 6 September 2010*
11	*Friday 29 October 2010*	*w/c 29 November 2010*

NB The dates shown in italics are to be confirmed. Please check the website www.communitysustainable.org.uk for the most up-to-date information and where details of all aspects of the grant application process can be viewed.

Capital grants will be awarded on a competitive basis at quarterly selection panel meetings. Project development grants will be awarded on a first-come first-served basis until all funds are spent.

Eligibility

CSEP will only award grants to not-for-profit community-based organisations in England. This includes: community groups governed by a written constitution, registered charities and trusts, parish councils, schools and colleges, charitable companies with a community focus, mutual societies, church-based and other faith organisations.

Changing Spaces: Ecominds

Grants: £20,000 to £250,000. This programme is for groups that want to encourage people with experience of mental distress to get involved in environment projects.

Summary

Mind has received funds from BIG to run a £7.5million grant scheme as part of the Changing Spaces environmental initiative over five years. This programme is for a range of groups that want to encourage people with experience of mental distress to get involved in environmental projects, such as improving open spaces and wildlife habitats, designing public art and recycling.

Ecominds has been designed 'to help reduce the stigma surrounding mental distress and help create a society that treats people with experience of mental distress fairly, positively, and with respect'.

Grants available

The programme will award grants of up to £250,000. Four levels of grant are available:

- small – up to £20,000
- medium – from £20,001 up to £60,000
- large – from £60,001 up to £150,000
- flagship – from £150,001 up to £250,000 (approximately five grants will be awarded within this category).

Deadlines

Ecominds is a rolling programme (it expects to have two funding rounds each year). All projects must be delivered by December 2012.

Eligibility

The following England-based groups may apply to Ecominds:

- mental health, environmental and community groups
- commercial organisations running projects on a not-for-profit basis, including community interest companies and social enterprise companies where project profits are reinvested solely into the Ecominds project.

Exclusions

This programme will not fund individuals, statutory authorities (although applications from organisations working collaboratively with them are welcomed), projects aligned with or co-funded by pharmaceutical companies and applicants and projects based outside England.

For more information on this programme and full details of the application process, please visit the Ecominds website: www.ecominds.org.uk. Please note there are two sets of guidance notes for this programme.

Changing Spaces: Local Food

Summary

Local Food, run by RSWT (Royal Society for Wildlife Trusts), opened in March 2008. It funds a range of organisations that want to carry out a variety of food related projects to make locally grown food more accessible and affordable to local communities.

Grants available

This programme will award grants of between £2,000 and £300,000.

Three types of grants are available (small, main and beacon), ranging from £2,000 to £500,000. NB Beacon grants closed for applications in June 2008:

small grants between £2,000 – £10,000

main grants between £10,001 – £300,000

beacon grants between £300,001 – £500,000.

Deadlines

Small and main grants are available on a rolling basis. All funded projects must be completed by March 2014.

Eligibility

Grants will be awarded to not-for-profit community groups and organisations in England, including schools, faith-based organisations, health bodies (such as primary care trusts) and universities.

See RSWT's website for more information and full details of the application process – www.localfoodgrants.org.

Changing Spaces: Community Spaces

Summary

Community Spaces is a £50 million open grants programme managed by Groundwork UK on behalf of an experienced national consortium.

The programme empowers community groups to improve public spaces in their neighbourhood. 'It responds directly to people's aspirations to have better places on their doorsteps – more interesting places for children to play, safer places for people of all ages to sit, greener spaces where people and nature can grow and flourish.'

The Community Spaces programme aims to:

- create better local environments
- increase people's access to quality local spaces for interaction, play and recreation
- increase the number of people actively involved in developing and running a practical environmental project that is visible in their community
- improve partnerships between communities, support organisations and local authorities.

Grants available

This programme will award grants of between £10,000 and £450,000. It will fund community groups that want to improve local green spaces such as play areas, community gardens and parks.

Applications

Applications must show that projects will improve local neighbourhoods and environments. Types of projects can include, for example:

- community gardens and parks
- informal sports areas and multi-use games areas
- nature reserves
- squares and village greens
- churchyards
- ponds and projects which improve the local community's access to green space.

This list is not exhaustive and if you are thinking about a project that isn't listed here, it may still be considered, as long as it meets the eligibility criteria.

There will be some crossover with BIG's other funding streams. For example, projects looking at play areas, orchards, city farms and woodlands will be considered as long as they meet the general criteria of the programme, although there are other of BIG's Changing Spaces programmes that will fund these types of projects.

There are two stages to the application process and all community groups that are successful at stage 1 must agree to work with a facilitator – a trained individual who is able to provide specialist advice and guidance to groups. Facilitators will be able to help groups develop their stage 2 application form and may be able to help successful groups develop and deliver their project.

Applications from youth groups for youth projects are welcomed as it is considered important for young people to be fully involved in projects and where possible be leading projects of direct benefit to them. However, the main applicant and alternative contact must both be aged 18 years or over.

For further information on the application process please visit the Community Spaces website – www.community-spaces.org.uk.

Eligibility

Community Spaces will provide funding for community groups across England that hope to create and improve their local environment. To be eligible to apply for funding groups must meet the following criteria:

- Applications must be from community groups – defined as 'people living in one particular area or groups of people focused on a neighbourhood who are considered as a unit because of their common interests, background, nationality or other circumstances'.
- Projects must be in England.
- Projects must meet the Community Spaces outcomes – see the project outcome/s document provided on www.community-spaces.org.uk. Consideration of your application will depend on your stated outcomes.
- Projects must be within a two mile radius of a residential area.
- Projects must be open to the public 'most of the time' – please see the 'Definitions' page on the community spaces website.

Community Spaces is a majority capital-funding programme designed to ensure that money is spent on making physical and lasting improvements to people's neighbourhoods. You will be expected to split your project costs into revenue and capital expenditure. Small and medium grants will need to ensure that any revenue expenditure does not exceed 25% and capital expenditure is at least 75%.

Deadlines

Community Spaces' small and medium grants will be open for applications until January 2011 and decisions will be made on regular basis throughout the programme's life.

Exclusions

Community Spaces will not fund:

- individuals
- sole traders
- local authorities
- parish or town councils
- schools
- health bodies
- profit-making organisations and other statutory bodies that have not been mentioned above.

Community groups will not be able to apply for funding for the following:

- costs incurred or monies spent on a project before being awarded a Community Spaces grant
- projects without reasonable physical access for the general public
- activities that promote religious or political beliefs
- the purchase, construction, refurbishment of or access to buildings
- the purchase of land
- formal sports pitches
- projects on school grounds
- the purchase of animals
- projects on commercial property
- vehicles for transporting goods or people
- projects based on statutory allotments
- anything that is the legal responsibility of other organisations
- road improvement projects.

Examples of funding

Group name – The GOAL Group (Greasby Outdoor Activity and Leisure)
Project name – Coronation Park Multi-use Games Area
Project – Playground
Grant awarded – £32,392

Group name – Fern Gore Residents Association
Project name – Fern Gore Community Wildlife Area
Project – Recreational activities
Grant awarded – £49,419

Changing Spaces: Access to Nature

Summary

Access to Nature, launched in April 2008, is run by Natural England on behalf of a consortium of major environmental organisations. It is a £25 million grants programme to encourage people from all backgrounds to understand, access and enjoy our natural environment.

It aims to encourage more people to enjoy the outdoors, particularly those who face social exclusion or those who currently have little or no contact with the natural environment. It funds projects in urban, rural and coastal communities across England.

The programme awards grants of between £50,000 and £500,000 to support projects that deliver one or more of the programme's main outcomes. In addition the programme will make a small number of larger grants of over £500,000 for projects that have a national significance or impact.

Grants available

This programme will award grants of between £50,000 and £715,000.

Applications

Before applying for funding for your project, you are advised to read the Access to Nature general guidance notes document to check that what you are planning to do fits the programme. These guidance notes give information on the types of project that will be considered for funding, the types of grants available and full details of the application and assessment processes. The guidance notes should be read in conjunction with the Regional Targeting Plans, which explain the priorities for each region; both can be found on Natural England's website.

All projects must meet outcome 5 (see page 212) and at least one other outcome. For more information on outcomes and these targets, refer to www.natural england.org.uk/ourwork/enjoying/outdoorsforall/accesstonature/outcomes.aspx.

The application process is in two stages:

Stage 1 – Outline proposal form

All applicants should initially submit a stage one application form to provide basic information about their project and organisation and there is guidance on the website to help you with this. Receipt of your application form should be acknowledged within five working days. A regional adviser will then contact you within 20 working days to discuss your project in more detail. Applicants should go to the online system at www.naturalengland.org.uk/leisure/grants-funding/how-to-apply.htm.

Please note that section 4 (the 'Declaration Form') requires original signatures and will need to be posted in hard copy form. Photocopies, fax and email versions will not be accepted and assessment will not begin until the signed declaration has been received.

Stage 2 – Full application form

If your organisation is eligible to apply and your project is something that might be supported, the regional adviser will tell you how to submit a stage two application form. You should read carefully the stage two guidance notes, which can be found on the website and which explain how to complete the form. A grants officer will assess your application and it will then be considered by the project board (for grant applications up to £100,000) or by an independent grants panel (for grant applications over £100,000), who will decide whether to award you a grant.

Deadlines

Grants: June 2010. For up-to-date information on closing dates for the national and flagship projects see Natural England's website.

Eligibility

Access to Nature will only award grants to not-for-profit community-based organisations in England. This includes: community groups governed by a written constitution, registered charities and trusts, parish councils, schools and colleges, companies with a charitable purpose and community focus, mutual societies, church-based and other faith organisations.

Funding will focus on three main themes:

- community awareness and active participation
- education, learning and volunteering
- welcoming, well-managed and wildlife-rich places.

Within these themes, grants will be awarded to organisations which can demonstrate that their project will deliver one or more of Access to Nature's five main outcomes:

1) A greater number and diversity of people having improved opportunities to experience the natural environment.
2) More people having opportunities for learning about the natural environment and gaining new skills.

3) More people being able to enjoy the natural environment through investment in access to natural places and networks between sites.

4) Richer, more sustainably managed, natural places, meeting the needs of local communities.

5) An increase in communities' sense of ownership of local natural places, by establishing strong partnerships between communities, voluntary organisations, local authorities and others.

For more information on this programme, please visit the Access to Nature website: www.naturalengland.org.uk/leisure/grants-funding.

Contact for all Changing Spaces programmes

Call the Changing Spaces Advice Line helpline on 0845 3 671 671 (opening hours 8am to 7pm Monday to Friday) for further details of any of the Changing Spaces programmes.

Fair Share (UK)

Some parts of the UK have missed out on Lottery funding in the past. The Fair Share Programme aims to help provide a better balance in funding.

Fair Share received £50 million of Lottery money, which was put into a trust – the first Lottery model of its kind. The funding is secure and any interest earned on the original sum covers the management costs, which means that the total £50 million will be spent as grants in the Fair Share Trust areas.

Since launching in 2003, the Fair Share Trust (the trust) has established itself in 81 neighbourhoods across the UK through the work of local delivery partners – 'local agents'. The programme in England runs until 2013.

The trust is entirely managed by Community Foundation Network (CFN), the UK's largest independent community charitable grantmaker, which has set up partnerships with its members – community foundations – and other local grant-making bodies to manage the programme locally. These local agents work with the trust communities to prioritise and agree spend, in line with the guidance for delivery.

Selected neighbourhoods in each area are receiving targeted support from these agents in order that local people have the opportunity to make decisions on where the funding goes.

The Fair Share Trust programme aims to:

- build capacity and sustainability – by involving local communities in decision making about Lottery funding

- build social capital – by building links within and between communities to promote trust and participation
- improve liveability – by improving the living environment for communities.

Each local agent set up a local advisory panel, involving people from the communities receiving the funding, to agree local priorities, drawn from neighbourhood assessment documents, based on local strategic partnership data highlighting local community needs and issues.

Once the local priorities were identified, the local agents and local panels began identifying potential funding recipients. Each local agent would vary in their approach of identifying projects for funding, tailoring the approach in line with local circumstances. The initial setting up phase has been completed, grants have been made and now the outcomes are being gathered through monitoring and results evaluated.

For more information on the Fair Share Trust, please visit the CFN website – www.communityfoundations.org.uk.

Reaching Communities: England

Grants: £10,000 to £500,000. This programme has been extended and will run until at least 2010.

Reaching Communities will fund projects that help people and communities, identified by those communities and who are most in need, particularly those people or groups that are hard to reach. Projects can be new or existing activities, or be the core work of your organisation.

This programme is designed to achieve changes in communities as a result of funding. For example:

- people having better chances in life, including being able to get better access to training and development to improve their life skills
- strong communities, with more active citizens, working together to tackle their problems
- improved rural and urban environments, which communities are better able to access and enjoy
- healthier and more active people and communities.

Eligibility

You can apply to Reaching Communities if you are:

- a registered charity
- a voluntary or community group
- a statutory body, (including schools)
- a charitable or not-for-profit company
- a social enterprise – a business that is chiefly run for social objectives, whose profits are reinvested in the business rather than going to shareholders and owners.

Applications

There have been high levels of interest in this programme and BIG states that it has had to turn down some very good projects. You should consider contacting BIG before embarking on work for this programme to discuss whether there is another programme to which your project might be better suited. This programme is under regular review to ensure it is meeting those communities most in need.

Contact

National helpline for advice on 0845 410 20 30.
Email – general.enquiries@biglotteryfund.org.uk.
Lottery Funding Helpline on 0845 275 00 00 or go to www.lotteryfunding.org.uk.

Small Grants Programme – formerly Awards for All

It is anticipated that new money available for small grants in 2009–10 will be comparable to money that was available to community groups through Awards for All in 2008/09.

Each distributor will run its own small grants programme as follows.

- BIG will launch a new small grants programme on 1 April 2009, awarding grants of £300 to £10,000 to local communities in 2009/10.
- Sport England will provide small grants for sports ranging from £300 to £10,000 from 1 April 2009.
- Arts Council England will provide small grants through the existing 'Grants for the arts' programme, supporting awards between £1,000 and £100,000.
- Heritage Lottery Fund small grants will be provided through the existing 'Your Heritage' (£3,000 to £50,000) and 'Young Roots' (£3,000 to £25,000) schemes.

Community Assets

The Community Assets programme is not funded by the Lottery, the funding is provided by the Office of the Third Sector. However, the programme is delivered by BIG, because it was considered to have the necessary expertise. The aim of the programme is community empowerment. It offers capital grants for third sector organisations and local authorities to refurbish local authority buildings in England for third sector ownership.

Community Assets aims to empower communities by facilitating the transfer of genuine assets from local authorities to third sector ownership for the benefit of the community. Genuine assets will generate operational, financial and other benefits for third sector organisations without significant liabilities, over a long-term period. The deadline for the Community Assets programme passed on 15 November 2007 and it is not known whether the programme will re-open at a later date – for any new information visit BIG's website.

Arts Council England

Arts Council England is the national development agency for the arts, supporting a range of artistic activities including theatre, music, dance, literature, photography, digital art and crafts.

'Grants for the arts are for individuals, arts organisations and other people who use the arts in their work. They are for activities carried out over a set period and which engage people in England in arts activities, and help artists and arts organisations in England carry out their work.' Grants for the arts are funded by the Lottery.

Between 2008 and 2011 Arts Council England will invest in excess of £1.6 billion of public money from the government and the Lottery.

The Council has recently simplified its application form and improved its guidance on how to apply. For more details on the plan for 2008–11 and the Council's priorities for the future visit: www.artscouncil.org.uk/plan. An enquiries team is available on 0845 300 6200.

NESTA

'NESTA is the National Endowment for Science, Technology and the Arts – a unique body with a mission to make the UK more innovative.' It invests in early-stage companies, informs and shapes policy, and delivers practical programmes 'that inspire others to solve the big challenges of the future'. For more details visit NESTA's website – www.nesta.org.uk.

Olympic Lottery Distributor

The Olympic Lottery Distributor is an independent body set up by Parliament, its remit is to support the delivery of the London 2012 Olympic and Paralympic Games and their legacy.

> *When making grants, we will seek to ensure that the principles of a lasting legacy, environmental and social sustainability, as set out in the bid which won the Games for London, are put into practice. We are part of a family of organisations concerned with the funding of the Games and to date have grant funded the Olympic Delivery Authority (ODA) and the London Organising Committee of the Olympic Games and Paralympic Games (LOCOG). We will monitor grants to ensure that they are spent effectively and will work with our partners towards a successful London 2012.*

The Olympic Lottery Distributor is not currently running any open funding rounds.

Sport England

Sport England is the government agency responsible for 'developing a world-class community sport system and creates opportunities for people of all ages and abilities to play sport in the community'. In June 2008 a new strategy was launched to help community sport make the most of the opportunities presented by the London 2012 Olympic and Paralympic Games.

Sport England has published the following targets to be achieved by 2013.

- One million people taking part in more sport.
- More children and young people taking part in sport for five hours every week.
- More people satisfied with their sporting experience.
- Twenty-five per cent fewer 16 to 18 year olds dropping out of five sports.
- Improved talent development in 25 sports.

Sport England invests in projects that help people to start, stay and succeed in sport and physical activity at every level. For further information on Sport England and its application processes, visit the website – www.sportengland.org.

UK Film Council

The UK Film Council works with the film industry and government, awarding funds from the Lottery and making policy on issues surrounding film; it aims to stimulate a competitive, successful and vibrant UK film industry and culture, both now and for the future.

Every year the Council distributes around £27 million from the Lottery and the same amount from government to support: script development, film production, short films, film distribution and export, cinemas, film education, culture and archives, festivals, audience support schemes, skills training and national and regional film agencies.

Over 1,600 funding applications per year have been received for Lottery funding since 2000, 80% of which have been unsuccessful. The Council has a target time of 40 days where final approval or rejection is made.

Funding priorities for the three-year plan of 2007–10 have been set and you can find information on these at the Council's website, where related policy and strategy papers are also available – www.ukfilmcouncil.org.uk.

UK Sport
Established by Royal Charter in 1996, UK Sport works in partnership with the home country sports councils and other agencies to 'lead sport in the UK to world-class success'. UK Sport is responsible for managing and distributing public investment and is a statutory distributor of funds raised by the Lottery.

Through its World Class Events Programme, UK Sport distributes approximately £3.3 million of Lottery funding each year to support the bidding and staging costs of major events on home soil, as well as providing specialist support to organisers. For more information visit: www.uksport.gov.uk.

BIG thinking consultation process for funding in 2009–15

BIG thinking is a consultation process initiated by BIG to discover where its contribution can best be made. By shaping its funding programmes for 2009–15 it hopes to ensure that it acts in a way that promotes social, economic and environmental sustainability.

BIG thinking ran until the end of February 2009 with events being held across the UK to debate the issues. The results will be analysed and fed into BIG's strategic framework and separate country plans for 2009–15. BIG states that responses to the consultation process will be summarised and published separately.

It is not appropriate to detail in this guide all the information available before the consultation has been evaluated and finalised. However, it might help you to know the ten statements that were made by BIG as a preface to each of its consultation questions, the results of which will help BIG to determine how its funds will be spent in the next round of programmes. These statements will give you some idea of BIG's thoughts and proposals.

1. 'Transitions' and 'isolation' emerge from evidence and experience as themes that we should adopt in 2009–15. We think that they are a useful starting point for all our funding.

2. BIG has a powerful role to play in helping those most in need, including the most marginalised people in society. In the period 2009 to 2015, we expect to increase the focus of our funding on this group. But we also want to continue to reach a wider audience – ensuring everyone gets the opportunity to benefit from the Lottery in some way. We will achieve this through a mix of funding approaches.

3. Our best results have often come from partnership working across sectors, where projects encourage people to achieve what was not previously possible working alone. For this reason, we will use our influence to encourage and broker links between our grantholders and partners in the voluntary and community sector, public and private sectors. In particular, we will work harder across this period to establish more extensive and fruitful links with the private sector.

4. The voluntary and community sector is frequently in the best position to make our funding work for communities and people most in need. It is also central to a strong and effective civil society. The large majority of our funding will continue to go to the voluntary and community sector.

5. Our evidence tells us that to achieve greater effectiveness and impact, we must do more than give out grants. We are improving our service to you but want to go further. We think that the additional cost of more support is worthwhile if it improves the impact projects have, even where this might mean making fewer awards. We think this should become an increasing feature of the way we fund.

6. Lottery funding is more flexible than many other public sources of funding. It can give organisations the chance to try out ideas or gain longer-term funding that is not available from others.

7. BIG has a powerful role to play in funding new approaches, taking risks and challenging standard practice. This will form an important element of our funding.

8. BIG is a UK-wide organisation whose funding is devolved predominantly to the country level. However around 10% of our money is managed at a UK level and we expect that to continue.

9. Public engagement in our work helps raise the profile of funded projects and shows what Lottery money can do. It helps attract new groups to the Lottery and inspires communities to do things. We will continue to explore ways of engaging the public in our funding.

10. Since 2006, BIG has had the power to distribute funds other than those that come from the National Lottery. We will take on more of this work, where we think we are the right organisation to do so and where it would help us achieve our mission to support communities and those most in need.

A summary of the consultation responses will be published in summer 2009 and will inform BIG's future funding priorities.

The People's Millions

In 2005 ITV teamed up with BIG to launch The People's Millions, allowing people across the UK to vote for projects in their community to win cash from the Lottery.

Since then a total of 229 awards and £13.6 million has been given out to projects around the UK – including skate parks, sensory play areas, woodlands regeneration and even audio sculptures.

BIG wants to fund projects that help communities to transform or enjoy their environment. That means buildings, amenities, public and green spaces and the natural environment.

Priority is also given to local environment projects that get more people involved in the local community and help people in the community who are most in need and are original and innovative.

Films are shown on ITV regional news programmes and viewers are asked to vote for the project they want to see be awarded a grant. If your group would like to be put forward as a beneficiary of this scheme you should visit BIG's website on www.biglotteryfund.org.uk.

In conclusion

The National Lottery's distributors are well known for their complex and rigorous assessment processes and this can sometimes deter groups from applying for funding from them. The process is long and time consuming for applicants and often dreams for a good, innovative new project for the members of their group (and sometimes people's jobs), are pinned on a 'You have been successful' letter. Rejection can be worse than disappointing, it can alter a group's ability to deliver and some may even fold.

While researching this guide, we have been in contact with staff at BIG, the main distributor, through their helpline and it has been encouraging that they have been more than happy to advise on all questions raised about funding and have gone out of their way to be helpful. This was not the case some years ago when staff were actually prohibited from giving all but the briefest guidance.

BIG and the other distributors do want to award the monies that are available, it's their job to get the money out into our communities. However, they are, rightly, subject to public and governmental scrutiny over what they fund and need to ensure that their policies and procedures are transparent and open and that the money they are responsible for goes to sound organisations with a worthwhile and practicable project to deliver.

There is a lot of information available through the Lottery distributors' individual websites and help and advice lines. You should make good use of these resources before you embark on the long road of collecting information and evidence for your bid.

Be imaginative and creative, do your research and collect your evidence and, hopefully, the only luck you will need is that they haven't run out of funds for that round.

10 Winning company support

Why apply to companies?

Although grant giving by companies is not as significant as that of individuals, government or grant-making charities, it is still a funding source that should be considered both on local and national levels.

Before applying to companies you should understand why and how they give. Their support will be different from that of other funders. They are ultimately responsible to their shareholders and answer to them as to how they spend any surplus profits. They will not be motivated primarily by philanthropy or by a desire to see new and pioneering voluntary activity. In many cases, they will be looking to improve their image and their economic position in relation to their competitors, whether at a local, regional or national level.

There is, however, among some businesses a desire to be seen to be giving something back to their communities or society in general and some companies have now set up their own charities which, while having close ties to and receiving assets from the company, are a separate legal entity. Whether these foundations are truly independent of the company in their giving is a matter of debate but they are self-governing and set up for charitable purposes for the benefit of the public.

The relationship you have with any company that donates to your cause, whether by cash, gifts in kind, staff time or other resources is a two-way association. While you will be pleased to receive funding, the company will also benefit from the good publicity, awareness of local issues which it may not have previously had and a boost in morale for its staff. As with any relationship, your group needs to be selective about which companies it approaches: you need to feel some pride in the association you're about to establish. Research the company's website, or any other information with this in mind.

How much do companies give?

Company giving is not easy to quantify. Companies can help in a number of ways, including products and services for free, staff time, secondments, advertising, low-cost or free use of facilities, expertise, free equipment and money. In its research for *The Guide to UK Company Giving*, DSC assessed the total community contributions of nearly 500 featured companies to be £808 million, of which £500 million was in cash support (2007/08 figures).

In 2007/08, the top 300 corporate donors gave around £638 million in total community contributions, £492 million of which was cash support. This total support represents 0.38% of these companies' pre-tax profits and accounts for nearly 99% of company giving in the UK. Indeed, the top 25 companies give around 37% of the total corporate support available (or £298 million in community contributions).

Ten good reasons to apply to companies

- Their employees are connected with your organisation.
- They are local and looking for good publicity.
- They are interested in young people.
- Your event will be good for staff to take part in.
- You know the chief executive or personnel officer, or someone in the marketing department helps out in your club.
- Young people buy their product.
- You're asking for something that's easy for them to give.
- They've given to you before.
- Your activities help their business.
- They like you.

Ten good reasons to think again about applying

- You know nothing about the company.
- It is not successful.
- It is not located in your area.
- Its business is not connected in any way with young people.

continued...

- It has a stated policy of never giving to unsolicited appeals.
- You have received well-publicised sponsorship from a rival firm.
- You are asking for £10,000; the company's total budget is £500.
- Its policies, product, image, etc. is not compatible with your work with young people.
- Your supporters would be against having its support.
- Its charitable giving is already fully committed for the next two years.

Why companies give

Some companies give because they see the benefit that will come to them from being seen to be a good corporate citizen. The more they see the donation as a business opportunity for them, the more likely they are to work with you. The onus is on you to give them good reasons to support your organisation.

These are some of the main reasons why companies give.

Creating goodwill

Companies want to be seen as good corporate citizens in the communities where they operate and as caring by society at large.

Cause association

Companies like to be associated with causes which relate to, or are potentially impacted by, their business. For example, mining and extraction companies might support environmental projects; banks, economic development projects; retailers and insurance companies, projects working with young people and crime prevention; and so on. One motive for this might be to enhance their image, but it could also help build contacts and gain market intelligence and therefore increase sales and consequently profits.

Government pressure

There can be pressure put on companies from the government to support particular initiatives which contribute to government policy.

Expectation

There can be peer pressure among companies in a particular sector of business where each company is concerned to see that the quantity and quality of its giving is appropriate to its status as a company.

Personal interest

It can be very helpful if the chair or other senior directors are interested in your cause (and perhaps support it personally). Even with some large companies that have well-established policies and criteria for their giving, you are more likely to be successful if you can persuade a friend of the managing director to ask on your behalf, even if it does not exactly fit into the company's criteria. Often, you do not need to do the asking yourself; the key is to find the right person to do it on your behalf. Recruiting an eminent local businessperson onto your fundraising committee and persuading them to approach their colleagues saves you time and resources and raises more support; peer to peer asking is often the most effective way to influence a company's giving.

A history of giving

Some companies have a long history of philanthropy and continue to give, following their traditions.

Persistence

Persistence can pay: if a charity persists in its approach to a company eventually the company may not want to keep refusing a worthwhile cause. Although if you are turned down you should consider whether you can improve your application, ask through another method or ask for something else.

Tax reasons

Giving to a charity can be done tax-effectively. This will be an added benefit for the company, but seldom a determining factor.

Privately-owned or family-controlled companies

Privately-owned or family-controlled companies' giving is often little different from personal giving. For public companies, where it is the shareholders' funds that are being given away, the company will want to justify its charitable support. You can help them to do this by telling them not just why you want the money, but why supporting you should be of interest to them. You can also tell them about any benefits they will get in return for their money and about the impact that their donation will make on your work.

Remember too that companies like thanks, recognition and good publicity for their support, whether in newsletters, your annual report, by having their branding on your materials, or through media coverage.

/ Case study \

Lakehouse – Safety, Environment and Careers in Schools Programme

Lakehouse, formed in 1988, is an established service provider with a key focus of working in the affordable housing, education, community and healthcare sections in many of the most deprived areas of the UK. By contributing to local education, the company has reduced unemployment and raised aspirations and enthusiasm in the communities in which it works.

Lakehouse's Safety, Environment and Careers in Schools Programme was designed to support the company's aspirations for sustainable growth and expansion by providing added-value services to clients, community, staff and suppliers. Additionally, it adds value to the communities Lakehouse works within by providing a quality infrastructure, employment opportunities, education and a robust environment for today and the future.

Lakehouse works in many of the most deprived areas of the UK. By contributing to local education, the company has reduced unemployment and raised aspirations and enthusiasm in the communities in which it works.

The programme aims to work with at least 12 educational establishments each year and focuses in three areas – safety, environment and careers. It targets primary and secondary schools and colleges, tailoring its offering to the specific needs of each establishment. Lakehouse works closely with the Construction Industry Council and the Education Business Partnership to provide school leavers with mentoring, work experience and employment opportunities.

The programme has increased awareness about health and safety, the environment and careers in construction and Lakehouse has created opportunities for some of the most marginalised people, including excluded young people.

It's not all about money

A common mistake when thinking about company giving is to see it as only about raising money. While some companies can and do give large sums to voluntary organisations, the majority will not. You have to think clearly about why you are approaching them, what benefits they will receive from being linked with your group, and whether you can ask for something other than financial help.

Applying for support from companies is time consuming and can be frustrating. More groups than ever before are chasing very limited company resources. Well-known high street companies can receive over 100 applications a day. Many companies end up supporting, at best, one in ten of the applications they receive and most grants are for £250 or less, often tied in with employees' charitable interests. It follows then, that the large majority of applications for company support are unsuccessful, and the large majority of successful applications are for small amounts of money. Company giving can seem small in relation to the amount you are looking to raise.

On the upside, when you are successful, you can have a new source of support that has lots of spin-offs: important contacts; work experience opportunities; management committee members; use of company facilities; in-house expertise provided free or at low cost; staff time; and so on.

What companies like to support

There are trends in what companies like to support. For example, in the 1980s, AIDS/HIV and homelessness were not generally supported, but today companies do support these causes. The following are some of the areas that companies find attractive:

- **important local projects in the areas where the company has a significant presence.** Business in the Community organises 'Seeing is Believing' – events for business leaders, when it takes them to visit local projects to see problems at first hand and explain how they can make a significant contribution.

- **activities that relate to their product** – for example, in 1994, NatWest introduced a schools programme, Face2Face with Finance, promoting financial literacy, and banks in general often target their giving at young people (who are potential customers).

- **economic development projects** – companies like economic development projects because a flourishing economy benefits business. Shell, for example, supports LiveWIRE, an award scheme for new enterprise, and the STEP programme, which provides undergraduates with work experience during the summer vacation.

- **environmental projects.** United Utilities, through its United Futures partnership with the Groundwork Trust, will provide funding for a number of environmental projects in local communities across the UK.
- **educational projects.** Companies like educational projects because education and training are an investment in future employees.
- **events, competitions and other activities** attract keen public interest or mass participation, such as Comic Relief's Red Nose Day or BBC Children in Need Appeal.
- **initiatives that have the backing of very prominent people.** Who knows who is always important in getting support from companies. The Prince's Trust is able to capitalise on this in its fundraising 'finding that doors open for them without having to be pushed'.

What companies don't like to support

There are certain areas that UK companies will generally not support:

- **local appeals outside areas where they have a business presence** – there is no business reason for them to do this
- **purely denominational appeals for religious purposes**, although they may support social projects run by religious bodies
- **mailed appeals** that are printed and sent to hundreds of companies
- **controversial campaigns** that might bring them bad publicity
- **overseas development work**, unless the company has a business presence in that country, when support will more likely come from a local subsidiary – although some companies do support emergency and aid appeals on the basis that these are the sort of issues that their staff are interested in.

Case study

Liberty International

Liberty International is a market leader in UK regional shopping centres and the owner of other prime retail assets including the Covent Garden Estate, central London.

The company aims to promote the prevention of crime and anti social behaviour and the effect of these on communities. They have teamed up with Crime Concern in an awareness programme and are operating with a range of schools and other agencies providing support for vulnerable young people.

The Manchester Arndale 4 Youth project, involving some 60 students from Harrop Fold School, Salford, enabled the participants to form 'company style' groups to put forward novel ideas to address the causes and effects of anti social behaviour in their own community, a local shopping centre and the Manchester Arndale. Five ideas were considered by the judges to merit awards.

One such idea came from five Year 11 students who called their group TIPSY – Teaching Independent Personal Skills to Young People, and involved the making of a film entitled 'Consequences' which focuses on underage and excessive alcohol consumption. 'Consequences' will be shown in schools across Salford to get young people to discuss and understand the issues surrounding alcohol and the consequences of drinking irresponsibly, from putting themselves in danger to behaving in an anti social way. The film's central objective is that, by involving teenagers talking to other teenagers in a language they understand and using a medium they are familiar with, this will have the maximum impact in getting the message across.

Continuing the theme and building on the success of the Harrop Fold project it was agreed to extend the programme to Nottingham where we are working with a selected group of young people from Bulwell Youth Inclusion Project, a specialist agency supporting children deemed at risk from truancy, offending, etc. The Victoria Centre, Nottingham is acting as the sponsor with Nottingham Crime and Drugs Partnership.

Some 40 young people took part in the social enterprise project which was spread over 12 weeks. Nottingham County Cricket Club kindly provided facilities at Trent Bridge cricket ground for the launch

continued . . .

> and finals nights. The participants came up with a number of imaginative ideas for addressing antisocial behaviour in Nottingham city centre, which included secure bicycle stores and a poster campaign to highlight the problems of anti social behaviour.
>
> The most promising young people have been offered short-term 'apprenticeships' with local businesses, enabling them to gain first-hand experience of business life, which should serve as a motivational factor in them gaining full-time employment in their chosen field.

The different types of company that give

Multinational companies

Most multinational companies have global giving programmes, generally tied to areas where they have or are developing business interests. Some multinational companies have an international structure for managing their giving, with budgets set for each country and a common policy for the sorts of activity they are interested in supporting. With others, community involvement policy remains a purely local matter for company management in the country concerned, although some have tried to transfer projects and ideas from one country to another.

Leading national companies

The giving of leading companies is well documented in the *Guide to UK Company Giving*, published by DSC. This gives information on the scale and scope of the company giving programmes of the top 500 corporate donors, with enough information to be able to identify those companies that might be interested in supporting you.

The leading national companies will often support large national charities as well as having their own sponsorship schemes, making smaller donations to local charities, and sponsoring events in the area where they are headquartered or where they have a major business presence.

Business in the Community has established the CommunityMark, a new national standard which recognises business excellence in community investment. It was created in consultation with representatives from the London

Benchmarking Group, National Council for Voluntary Organisations, Charities Aid Foundation, the Office of the Third Sector and Volunteering England.

It is open to companies in the UK of all sizes and from all sectors. Companies need to demonstrate the long-term positive impact that they are having in their communities. It is given on the basis of independent evaluations of management processes as well as impacts on the community and the company.

Case study

B&Q

B&Q was awarded a Jubilee Award by Business in the Community, which recognises its long-term positive impact on the communities in which it operates.

B&Q received this award in recognition of its continued commitment to the local community through its Better Neighbour Grants and You Can Do It Awards. Its community focus has been an integral part of B&Q's overall corporate social responsibility (CSR) strategy that focuses on the environment and has been in place since the early 1990s.

In 2008 the scheme was relaunched as the B&Q One Planet Living Grants.

The One Planet Living Grants offer between £50 and £500 of B&Q materials for projects supporting at least one of the following themes – environment/ energy saving, natural habitats/wildlife and local culture/heritage.

In addition, B&Q One Planet Living Awards allow community-based projects to secure up to £10,000 of B&Q products across the UK and Ireland. Projects need to demonstrate how their activities will support one of the above listed themes.

Larger local companies

In any city or region there will be large companies that are important to the local economy. They will often feel a responsibility to support voluntary action and community initiatives in those areas, and value the good publicity this provides. If yours is an important project, make it part of your fundraising strategy to develop a good relationship with the larger companies in your area.

There are also companies with a regional remit. The water, electricity and ITV's regional television operators all have a specific geographical area within which they operate, even if they are part of a multinational company; their community support will be confined within these regional boundaries.

Smaller national companies

The larger companies, because of their size but also because their giving is well documented, are often overwhelmed with requests for support. But there are also companies that are less well known and with smaller budgets for giving which receive far fewer approaches. There are also newly floated companies whose giving will only really develop once they have become public. Such companies can provide opportunities for the enterprising fundraiser.

Smaller local companies

Smaller, local companies (known in European jargon as small and medium-sized enterprises, or SMEs) are often overlooked. Almost everyone targets the large companies because good information is available. However, there is a wide range of local companies, from manufacturers on trading estates to accountants and solicitors in the high street. Many of these firms are privately owned, and the approach will often be through the managing director or senior partner. The best sources of information on what companies exist in your area are:

- **the local Chamber of Commerce**, where most of the more prominent local companies will be members
- **the Kompass directory of companies**, which is regionally organised and can now be searched online
- **the local council**: the business department might produce a list of major business ratepayers. The economic development section may have a list of major employers
- **the local newspaper**, which will carry stories from time to time that mention local companies, and may provide information on new companies planning to set up in the area
- **you**: by keeping your eyes open you can often identify local companies that it could just be worth approaching.

It is likely that most of the smaller companies you approach will not have a donations policy in place (if they give at all), and may well make their decisions on the basis of the personal interests of their managing director or senior partners. Some may never have made a charitable donation before and may not know about the related tax advantages available to them, so be prepared to tell them about these opportunities.

Some of these companies may prefer to give in kind – for example, a prize for a raffle or advertising in a souvenir brochure for a fundraising event. It might be easier to approach these companies for this sort of support in the first instance, and later on, once they have given something, persuade them to make a cash donation.

Small- and medium-sized businesses will react quickly to economic conditions. When business is falling, their concerns will be for their staff, and not giving money to charities.

Staff time is also at a premium as numbers are small and people are usually stretched with their workload. Staff volunteering schemes are therefore unlikely to be entered into.

Charitable giving is far more likely to be led by the enthusiasms of the partners or directors, but is also likely to be responsive to causes where staff are involved. One local business gives the following advice:

- Match your request to what the business can afford. If a project is too large and the business can only give a small donation it will see its contribution as being swallowed up and not making any difference at all.
- Lengthy letters take up too much time to consider. It's much better if they're simple, succinct and concise.
- Letters should be typed rather than handwritten.
- A good track record gives the appeal credence.
- Corporate giving is not just about money – partners tend to give of their time and skills through involvement, more so than cash.
- Telephone to make things happen. If this is daunting, either delegate the contact work to someone else (perhaps someone on your management committee who already has links with business people) or try to increase your confidence in some way.

New economy companies

The end of the last century and the early years of this have seen the growth of a new economy based on the IT revolution (the internet, mobile phones, etc.) and also on new ways of delivering utilities and other services to consumers. Many of these companies are too busy developing their business to put any real effort into philanthropy. But some – as well as their founders, who now rank among Britain's leading rich – are attracted by the concept of 'venture philanthropy', which involves a much more hands-on approach to giving. They are prepared to invest substantially in one or more key projects which have the potential to make a real difference and be replicated, providing cash and other support over a longer timeframe and becoming personally involved in the development of the project. Others, as their business and profit base are consolidated, may give in a more traditional way.

Example of new company giving

Dyson Limited manufactures domestic appliances and support is channelled through the James Dyson Foundation. Education is an important focus for the foundation and in particular design and technology – a subject which challenges the young people of the UK to be creative, by using their hands and brains to create things that work.

The foundation supports educational projects by means of bursaries and awards, such as awards to the Royal College of Art's industrial design engineering students. However, the foundation's support extends beyond monetary support – design engineers from Dyson host workshops at schools and universities throughout the country and the foundation provides free resources to design and technology teachers throughout the UK.

Examples of venture philanthropy

SHINE

Support and Help in Education (SHINE) was set up by a group of city people as a vehicle for their philanthropy. Focusing on literacy and numeracy projects, support is given to disadvantaged, disengaged and challenged children and young people (7 to 16 years) in Greater London and Manchester.

Impetus Trust

Impetus Trust is a pioneer of venture philanthropy in the UK. Impetus offers donors the means to make the biggest difference with their money by enabling charities to achieve a positive change in their performance by focusing entirely on an integrated investment package comprising long-term financing of charities' infrastructure, hands-on management support and capacity building.

233

Who decides and who to write to

Larger companies will have a manager who is responsible for dealing with charitable appeals, although a donations committee (which includes senior management) may have the final say. The largest companies may also employ specialist staff to assess the applications and make recommendations.

Some companies such as Richer Sounds (The Persula Foundation) or Lloyds TSB (Lloyds TSB Foundation for England and Wales) operate an independent foundation which sets policy and decides on applications.

With medium-sized and smaller companies, it is nearly always the most senior executive who decides. You should write in the first instance to the person who deals with charitable appeals. Make sure that you have the name and job title correct. If you have a top-level contact, or if one of your members or volunteers is an employee of the company, then use them.

Getting started

You should try to find out as much as you can about the company and about its possible interest in supporting your project, but remember that:

- companies generally have less well defined policies than grant-making charities, although you can often determine a pattern to their giving
- the chance of an application 'out of the blue' getting substantial support is low
- companies are more conservative in their giving, and are less likely to support innovative projects (at least until they get established) or anything that is risky or controversial
- company policies change more frequently than those of grant-making charities, because of mergers, takeovers, or a fall or rise in profits, so ensure your research is up to date. Consulting a directory, or even having a copy of the company's annual report and accounts is not enough; it may have been taken over since then. Check the financial press on a regular basis.

Research tips

Research is important, not just into policies, but also into contacts. Here are some tips.

1) Find out what, if any, previous contact you have had with companies, any previous fundraising approaches you have made, and with what success.

2) Identify and match possible funders with various aspects of your work. In particular, try to find any local companies that are known for their generosity and might have an interest in supporting young people.

3) Find out whether any of your management committee, volunteers or supporters have any personal contact with the companies you plan to approach – and whether they know people who have credibility in the business world who can help you do the asking.

4) Enlist a senior business leader to assist you with your fundraising. This can be someone to serve as chair of a development or fundraising committee, or just to contact a few colleagues and sign a few letters.

5) Contact Business in the Community to find out about its membership or to help you identify local companies through its regional network.

Ethical issues

Receiving support from companies can be problematic if the business values or practice of the company conflict with what your organisation stands for. There are two approaches:

- Some organisations will accept money from anyone, on the basis that the money can be used to do good.

- Others define certain types of company that they will not accept support from. Tobacco, alcohol, gambling, armaments, mining/oil industries, polluters and companies operating overseas that underpay their workforce are all areas of business activity that can cause problems.

An ethical stance is of particular importance where the work of the charity is directly connected with the issue or where the relationship is high profile. Youth groups promoting health would find it hard to accept money from a tobacco or alcohol company; peace and international relations organisations have similar problems with arms manufacturers; and so on.

Decide your ethical policy before approaching companies. It should be agreed by the management committee and minuted. You might want to define and agree a policy in consultation with everyone in your organisation, although sometimes this can be contentious and create divisions. If you think this is likely, it might be better to treat each decision on an ad hoc basis while moving towards some sort of consensus on policy.

Sometimes the issues are clear cut. It is relatively easy, for example, for a health charity to decide whether to accept money from a tobacco company, or a youth charity from a drinks company. The product relationship with the cause is clear, and all the charity has to do is agree a position on the issue.

There are two organisations that chart the ethical behaviour of companies and which can provide you with the information you need to formulate an ethical donations policy.

- EIRIS (Ethical Investment Research Services) researches companies on the FT All-Share Index. Its main aim is to advise on socially responsible investment. A charge is made for its services.
- Ethical Consumer Research Association produces *Corporate Critic*, which rates over 50,000 companies on their ethical performance at www.corporate critic.org.

Ten ideas for getting support from companies

1) Put yourself in the position of the company. Why should it want to give its shareholders' funds to you? Why should it choose your charity, rather than any of the other organisations that make contact? Think about the benefits the company will get from supporting you and mention these in your appeal letter. If you are looking for sponsorship, then these benefits should be at the heart of your proposal.

2) Suggest something specific for the company to support, and in your letter say why it should be interested. It is often best to think of something quite small if you are approaching the company for the first time.

3) Use all the contacts you have in the company to help get your project supported. Do you know the chair, the managing director or any other senior member of staff who may be able to put in a good word for you? Perhaps if you telephone, you can get into conversation with the chair's personal assistant so that he/she becomes interested and enthusiastic about your cause.

continued...

4) Think of all the ways in which the company could help. Cash might not be the best way for the company to give support. Might it be easier to ask for staff time, perhaps giving you some expertise you lack? Or the use of a vehicle? Or access to company staff to circulate an appeal or volunteer in some other way for your group? It is likely that everyone else will be asking for cash. The company may find it easier to give in kind, but once it has done so and got to know you and your work, cash support may be available next time.

5) Consider whether there is a senior executive of the company (the more senior the better) who might become a trustee of your charity – or serve on a fundraising or development committee. They can bring new ideas, good organisation and a wealth of business contacts to your organisation that will be worth many times the value of a donation. Such an invitation, even if refused, may be seen as flattering. If this level of involvement is too much, a request for advice may succeed.

6) Do you have any volunteers who also work for the company? They may be able to help you 'from the inside', and it will do you no harm if you mention their support for your organisation in your appeal letter, though you must remember to check that they are happy to be mentioned first.

7) Don't assume that every company will give. Make parallel approaches to a number of companies.

8) Consider who might be the best person to make the approach or sign the letter. It may not be you but could be a senior business executive from another company which has already supported your organisation generously. Their endorsement of your work can provide a comfort factor for other companies.

9) Every time you buy anything from a company, ask for a discount. This will save you money, but it is also a way of getting them to support you.

10) Check if the company is registered for payroll giving and, if it is, ask if you can promote your cause to employees. You will find more on payroll giving in Chapter 7 *Raising Support From the Public*.

The kind of help companies give

There is a variety of ways in which companies can support charities:

- A cash donation (usually a one-off grant).
- Support in kind, which includes: giving company products or surplus office equipment; and making company facilities available, including meeting rooms or printing or design facilities.
- Secondment of a member of staff to work with the charity, where a member of the company's staff helps on an agreed basis while remaining employed (and paid) by the company.
- Offering 'internships' or work experience to a charity beneficiary or student at an educational institution.
- Contributing a senior member of staff to the charity's management board.
- Providing expertise and advice or training.
- Encouraging and making it easy for employees to volunteer.
- Organising a fundraising campaign among employees, including encouraging employees to give through payroll giving.
- Sponsorship of an event or activity.
- Sponsorship of promotional and educational materials.
- Sponsorship of an award scheme.
- Cause-related marketing, where the company contributes a donation to the charity in return for each product sold in order to encourage sales.
- Advertising in charity brochures and publications.

Companies will always receive more applications than they will have the budget to respond to. Community involvement budgets have not expanded in line with demands for support and many companies now focus their grantmaking quite narrowly. Some larger companies will have set up small grants' schemes in regions or towns where they have a major factory or business presence. Some have matching schemes, where they match money collected or donated by employees. Some will have developed special grants programmes and others will have a 'charity of the year' for their major donation and as a focus for encouraging staff involvement.

Cash donations

This is the most obvious way that a company can be asked to support your organisation, but also the most expensive for them, so most cash donations are small (under £250), although some companies will match their employees' fundraising. You are more likely to be successful if you offer a 'shopping list' of specific items, rather than a vague request for general support.

In the entries at the end of this chapter we try to give an idea of the range of grants available from the large companies and what they like to support. This varies greatly from company to company. Some will have well-defined policies which work in a similar way to grant-making charities. They know what they want to give to, and what they do not. Guidelines are often publicised and applications may be handled by staff with job titles such as corporate affairs director or head of external affairs.

However, the majority of companies – especially the smaller ones – will have an informal approach. Here, any applications will be looked at by anyone from the personnel officer to the managing director, or her/his secretary. They will not necessarily have any special insight into the voluntary sector and they will be doing the community support task on top of their work, and so may have to fit it into the odd Friday afternoon a month. They do not have the time to work through piles of paper or attend lengthy meetings to get to know the issues you are facing and the work you are doing.

A good number of companies will operate on the basis of the chair's six favourite charities and if you are not on the list, you will have to find a way in, as the company giving policy will already be fixed. Inevitably, if you are successful with this sort of company, you may be successful with others, as part of company giving works on spreading the word.

You might stand more chance of success if you can tie your application in with an event or celebration. Anniversaries are useful; your 50th year or your 500th member, which you may be able to find a company to tie in with. It will be particularly attractive if you have a time limit to your fundraising – this gives those working in the supporting company a definite target to work for.

Tax and company giving

The 2000 Finance Act made giving tax-effectively straightforward for companies.

Donations

The company simply pays the full donation to the charity under Gift Aid and then deducts the total amount of its charitable donations from its pre-tax profit calculations at the end of the year. The level of benefit a company can receive in return is restricted on a sliding scale according to the amount of the donation, up to a maximum of £250 in benefits.

Business expenditure

Any expenditure by a company which is wholly and exclusively for business purposes is also deductible against corporation tax liability. This will cover most sponsorship and advertising payments to charity.

Shares

Companies are able to get tax relief for gifts of certain shares and securities to charity. See the HM Revenue & Customs website www.hmrc.gov.uk for more information.

Gifts in kind

Giving things rather than money is often easier for a company. The value of the gift to the charity will always be much more than the cost to the company. Companies might give:

- products for use by the charity
- products as prizes or as lots to be auctioned
- old stock and ends of lines for resale in charity shops
- professional and technical advice *pro bono* (without charge)
- staff time
- facilities such as meeting rooms, conference facilities or training.

If a company donates articles that it makes or sells in the course of its trade, or an article that it has used in its trade (this can include computers and furniture), then this can be treated as a tax-deductible business expense. The 'book value' of donated items (value as given in the accounts) is written off before the donation is made (un-saleable or damaged stock, ends of lines, etc.) also attract full tax relief. There are organisations which act as 'clearing houses' for gifts in kind, such as Kind Direct (formerly Gifts in Kind UK).

What kind of gift is a gift in kind?

Gifts in kind are donations of items or services, rather than the money to buy them. One community investment director with widespread experience of companies and voluntary organisations suggested the following list.

- Donation of coach/airline/ferry tickets.
- Advertising on company websites.
- Use of surplus storage/sports facilities.
- Donation of hotel accommodation.
- Use of telephones for helplines.
- Design and printing of leaflet/poster.
- Donation of surplus food/drinks.
- Access to information on customer demography/attitudes/preferences.
- Vacant sites for recreation projects.
- Free loan of plant, equipment, scaffolding, marquees, portaloos.
- Donation of rubble, tarmac, topsoil.
- Free advertising space on temporarily unused sites.
- Charity leaflet/appeal in a regular business or customer mailshot.
- Free servicing of vehicles.

Some practical tips on how to set about getting support in kind

Make a list of everything you need

In other words, create a 'wish list'. This can include services as well as products (such as the design for a leaflet you plan to produce).

Go through the list and try to identify companies that might have what you require

Personal knowledge is useful but you might also want to use business directories to widen your choice.

Make contact

Writing a letter can act as an introduction but you will probably need to follow it up with a phone call or personal visit. State your request, saying that it is for a charity and

continued...

---

indicating how well used it will be and how important it is to your organisation's future. If the company refuses to donate, it might be able to give you a discount.

Be positive and enthusiastic

It can be very difficult for the company to refuse if it knows what you want and how important it is for you and the local community. It will always cost the company far less to donate the item than it would cost you to purchase it.

Say thank you

If you are successful in gaining company support, report back on the difference the donation has made. Send it your annual report and later, perhaps try to recruit the company as a cash donor.

Employee volunteering and secondments

A major resource that companies can offer is their staff time and this can be provided in a number of ways.

Employee volunteering

Many of the large companies encourage their staff to volunteer, usually out of office hours, on the basis that this enhances the skills of their employees and promotes good community relations. Some companies make matching donations to the projects their employees are involved with. *Cares* is a national campaign run by Business in the Community that aims to engage employees in their communities through volunteering.

Professional skills

Banks, law firms, accountants, advertising and PR companies can all encourage staff to give their professional skills free of charge or to become trustees.

Secondment

This is where the company loans you a member of staff full time for an extended period. There needs to be a good reason why the company would do this, as it is an expensive form of support.

Employee volunteering is not only valuable in itself, but is strategically important since you will be building a relationship with a member of staff who can then act as an intermediary in asking the company for other forms of support at a later date, including cash donations.

Asking companies to advertise

Companies will sometimes take an advertisement in a publication – possibilities include:

- your annual report
- programmes produced specifically for fundraising events
- conference folders, pads and pens
- leaflets aimed at your service users and others
- posters, including educational wall charts.

However, you do need to think through whether you actually want an advertisement or company logo to appear prominently on your materials.

Advertising can be broken down into two categories:

Goodwill advertising

Where the primary purpose of the advertiser is to support a charity and to be seen supporting a good cause; this creates goodwill for the company rather than selling its products.

Commercial advertising

Where the advertiser wishes to reach the audience that the charity's publication goes to, and the decision is made for purely financial considerations.

What are you offering to advertisers?

Before trying to sell the advertising, you need to recognise what you are offering. If it is goodwill advertising, then the prestige of the event, the nature of the audience, the location and any celebrities who will be present will be major incentives. Price is less of an issue than the work of the charity, although the advertiser will want to know the circulation and readership of the publication, any special characteristics of that readership and any particular connection between it and the advertiser's product. If it is commercial advertising, these details become much more significant.

Pricing the advertising

The first consideration when pricing the advertising is the format of the publication. A lavish souvenir brochure is different from an annual report, and this in turn is very different from a single colour newsletter produced on your computer. There are two factors to consider when deciding the cost of the advertising.

- How much you want to raise? Divide this target by the number of pages of advertising to get a page rate.
- How much are advertisers prepared to pay? For commercial advertising this is especially important. Try to define the value of your audience to them.

Once you have decided a page rate, then you can then set prices for smaller spaces that are slightly higher than pro rata. For example, if the page rate is £250, then a half page might be priced at £150, a quarter page at £85, and eighth page at £50. You can ask for higher sums for special positions, such as the back cover, the inside front cover and facing the contents page. For a regular publication, you could offer a series discount for taking space in several issues.

You might consider producing a rate card which contains all the information that the advertiser needs to know, including:

- deadline for agreeing to take space
- deadline for receipt of artwork and address where it is to be sent
- publication size
- print run
- use of colour on cover and inside pages (four-colour, two-colour, black and white)
- page rates, including special positions, size of advertising space, and whether VAT is chargeable
- payment details.

A simple brochure or covering letter which sets out the reasons for advertising is useful, but posting copies out will generate little response. The way to sell advertising is on the telephone, where you make a call to follow up a letter you have sent. For larger advertisers, you might try to arrange a personal visit. The majority of people you approach will probably say 'no' but your job is to persuade a significant proportion to buy a space.

Business sponsorship

Sponsorship needs to be carefully defined. It is not a donation and the fact that you are a charity is largely irrelevant, it is a business arrangement. The charity is looking to raise funds for its work and the company wants to improve its image, promote and sell its products or entertain its customers.

The sponsor's contribution is usually money, although it could be a gift of goods (such as football kits), or services (such as free transport), or professional expertise (such as promotion or marketing consultancy), or the use of buildings (such as an exhibition centre), or free promotion (such as media coverage in a newspaper).

Many companies will provide much more in sponsorship than they would as a donation, but only so long as the commercial benefits warrant it. Developing links with the major national and local corporate sponsors could be an investment in your future that is well worth making now.

Most sponsors are commercial companies. There are four main options for sponsorship:

Businesses that want to promote themselves

Businesses want to promote themselves to create a better image or generate awareness in the local communities where they operate. This includes those companies with an 'image problem' – for example, mining and extraction companies associated with the destruction of the environment that want to project a cleaner image by being associated with a conservationist cause.

Businesses that want to introduce or promote a product or service

This could include a new brand of trainers or shampoo, or a supermarket opening in the area. Public awareness is important if a product or service is to get accepted, so companies may be open to proposals that give a product or service more exposure.

Companies looking for entertainment opportunities

Companies look for entertainment opportunities to influence customers, suppliers, regulators, the media and other opinion formers. They may be interested in sponsoring a concert, a theatrical event, an art exhibition or a sporting event, which would provide them with an appropriate entertainment opportunity and the opportunity to meet and mingle.

Companies that are committed supporters of your organisation

You may be able to offer them something that they would like to sponsor, even if it is partly for philanthropic reasons.

What are companies looking for?

Youth organisations should be able to offer at least some of the following:

A respectable partner

An organisation to be associated with that has the right image.

A real partnership

What involvement is being looked for from the sponsor and how well does this opportunity meet its needs?

A proven track record and a professional approach

Your proven track record would preferably be in securing and delivering sponsorships. Have you as the applicant approached the business of getting sponsorship in a professional way, and can you demonstrate a similar professionalism in the running of the organisation?

An interesting project and initiative

The project should be interesting at least to the company management and possibly also company staff. Does the sponsorship represent a new initiative, something that would not happen without the company's support? Is it interesting and lively?

Continuity

Is there scope for a continuing relationship (over the next few years), or is the activity or event just a one-off?

Genuine value for money

What are the benefits and how much money is being asked from the sponsor? How does this rate as compared with other possible sponsorships that the company might consider? The relationship of cost to return and the importance of the return to the company are the dominant factors affecting the decision to sponsor.

Visibility

How 'visible' will the event be, and what specific publicity and PR benefits will accrue to the sponsor? Will the company name be given a high profile?

Appropriateness

Is the activity or event appropriate to the sponsor? Also, are you approaching the right company?

Targeted audience

This could lead to direct marketing, for example, by providing the company's fair trade coffee at a reception for young entrepreneurs.

Other tangible benefits

For example, good publicity; media coverage; a link with brand advertising; entertainment opportunities for company directors and staff; access to VIPs; involvement of company employees or retirees; and training or experience for employees.

Why companies like sponsorship
- It helps them get their message across.
- It can enhance or change their image.

- It can reach a target audience very precisely.
- It can be very cost-effective advertising or product promotion.
- Further marketing opportunities may develop from the sponsorship.
- It generates good publicity for the sponsor, often of a kind that money can't buy.
- It generates an awareness of the company within the local community in which the company operates and from where it draws its workforce and customers.
- Sponsors can entertain important clients at the events they sponsor.

What can be sponsored?

There is an extremely wide range of things that can be sponsored, including:

- cultural and sporting events
- mass participation fundraising events, such as a marathon or fun run
- the publication of a report or a book, with an attendant launch
- the production of fundraising materials, leaflets and posters, or the sponsorship of a complete fundraising campaign
- conferences and seminars, especially to specialist audiences (such as doctors) where promotional material can be displayed
- vehicles, where the acknowledgement can be painted on the side
- equipment such as cars or computers produced by the company
- competitions, awards and prizes
- scholarships, bursaries and travel grants.

The bulk of corporate sponsorship money goes to sport, with motor racing, golf, tennis, athletics, football and cricket all receiving huge amounts. These offer extensive media coverage, good opportunities for corporate entertainment and an association with a popular activity.

Arts organisations will know that the arts is another big recipient of sponsorship – business support for the arts runs at around £150 million a year. Arts sponsorship is promoted by Arts & Business, which describes itself as acting 'as a crucible where businesses and arts organisations come together to create partnerships to benefit themselves and the community at large'.

As a charity you will not be competing for a share of these budgets; however, social sponsorship is much smaller by comparison and is a growing area. The 'market' is less crowded and there are all sorts of imaginative ways in which companies can sponsor events and activities run by charities.

Who to approach

The company

You need to be selective when you decide on which companies to approach and then find out who you should contact within the company. The choice of company will depend upon what connection you have with them.

- Have they supported you before?
- Do they have a stated interest in young people or a project such as the environment that you are organising?
- Are they local to your community?
- Are you consumers of their service or product?
- Do they need better publicity in the community and could you offer that with a link?
- Do your activities contribute to improving the business environment?
- Is the company a large employer in the area with an interest in the current and future workforce?

The person

Once you have decided on the company, you will need to find out how it is organised and who makes any decisions about charitable giving. Where a company has a number of branches or operating units throughout the country these may have some autonomy in grant decisions. There is usually a maximum amount that they can decide, over which the application will be passed to the next level, regional or national. If you can find this out beforehand it will save time in the long run.

You need to tailor your request to the level you are asking at and which budget it might come from, it may not necessarily be from the company's charitable giving budget but possibly marketing or personnel. Once you have established the budget source and level, you will then need to find the right person to talk and write to. Many organisations find this the frustrating part. There is no short cut if you have no inside knowledge of the company.

Be prepared to spend time on the company's website or the telephone, particularly if the company has no decided policy on giving. If there is no policy, there is not likely to be a name on the website or at reception. You may have to go through a number of different departments and repeat your request a number of times before you find someone who knows what the company can help with. You should eventually get through to someone who knows and can give you a name to write to. With all 'cold' applications you must have a name to write to and the right job title.

Send a summary proposal to see if it generates any interest and follow this up with a phone call a few days later to try and arrange a meeting. There may be an advertising agency or marketing consultant who will introduce sponsorship opportunities to sponsors. They will sometimes charge you a fee; more usually they will receive a commission from the sponsor. It depends who retains them, and in whose interests they are acting.

Getting sponsorship – ten practical tips

1) Before you begin, think about an ethical code. Are there some companies you wouldn't wish to be associated with?

2) Identify the right person in the company to contact. You need their name and job title. This will often be the marketing manager.

3) Stress the benefits of the sponsorship to the potential sponsor. This should be done often and as clearly as possible and backed up with statistics or other supporting information.

4) The size of the payment will be dependent upon the value of the sponsorship to the sponsor, not the cost of the work for you.

5) Help companies use their own resources to make the sponsorship work. Suggest, for instance, that they might like a picture story in their house magazine or in the trade press. Most are very keen to impress their colleagues and their rivals, but few think of this without prompting.

6) Sponsorship, especially long-term deals, is all about working together. Promise only what you know you can deliver, and always try to deliver a little bit more than you promised.

7) Remember that most sponsorship money comes in sums of under £10,000 and that you are planning a local, not an international event.

8) Get into the habit of reading adverts. Look particularly at local papers and trade press. Who has got money to spend on promotion? What kind of image are they trying to promote? Who are they trying to reach? How can you help them?

9) Mention another company that supports you. One satisfied sponsor can help you get another.

10) Keep trying. It is hard work but sponsorships can be really valuable.

Your sponsorship package

It is not enough to offer 1,000 contacts to a company if it sponsors your event. Most of them may be irrelevant to the company. You need to say which 1,000 people will be involved and how.

Think of each group that you reach in some way. Estimate an annual number for each. The following are general groups of people to get the process started but there may be more specialised areas that you are in contact with. Some groups will overlap. The more you can define your different groups of contacts, and the more information you can give about them, the more help it will be to you and potential sponsors.

Group	Number
Adults	....
Men	....
Women	....
Young adults	....
Teenagers	....
Children	....
Consumers	....
(what, how and where people buy – drinks, clothes, transport, which shops, areas, etc.)	
Businesses	....
(who do you use for products, services, etc.?)	
Schools	....
Clubs	....
Employed	....
Unemployed	....
Trainees	....
Agencies	....
Local authority	....
Central government departments	....
Quangos	....
Health authority	....
Learning and Skills Council	....
Other	....

Contractual issues

Sponsorship involves giving something in return for the money you are receiving, so you need to agree terms through a contract. This can be set out in a legal agreement (for larger sponsorships) or in the form of a letter. You need to be clear about the following factors.

How long the arrangement will run

Is it for one year – requiring you to find a new sponsor next year – or can you get a commitment for several years? What happens at the end of this period – does the sponsor have a first refusal on the following year's event? Most successful sponsorships last for several years, and the benefit builds up over the sponsorship period. But companies don't like being tied to sponsoring something indefinitely – their sponsorship programme would begin to look stale.

The fee to be paid, and when the instalments are due

What benefits are to be delivered in return for the fee. These should be specified as clearly as possible, so that you know precisely what you are contracted to deliver.

Whether VAT is chargeable

This will depend on whether your organisation is registered for VAT and the extent of the benefits offered to the sponsor. If VAT is chargeable, this should be discussed at the outset, and the fee agreed should be exclusive of VAT.

Who will pay for what costs

Who pays for the additional publicity the sponsor requires is something that is often forgotten. There needs to be a clear agreement as to who is responsible for what, so you can ensure that everything is covered and there are no misunderstandings later on.

Who is responsible for doing what

You will need to clarify who will do the public relations, who will handle the bookings, who will invite the guests, whose staff will receive the guests, and so on.

Any termination arrangements

In the event of the activity having to be cancelled.

Who is responsible for managing the sponsorship

You should have a named person on both sides.

Whether the sponsor is a 'commercial participator'

Under the terms of the Charities Act 2006, when the requirements of the Charities Act will apply (see page 253).

If everything is written down and agreed, there will be fewer problems later – and it ensures that everything has been properly thought through at the outset.

Joint promotions and cause-related marketing

Many larger charities are involved in promotional activity to help market a commercial product – this is often known as cause-related marketing (CRM). This can bring in large amounts of money and expose the name of the charity (and sponsor) to literally millions of people. The same idea on a smaller scale can also be adapted for use by local charities through local promotions.

Commercial promotions can include, for example, on-pack and licensing promotional deals, affinity credit cards, competitions and awards and the use of phone lines. What they have in common is that they present an opportunity to raise money for your cause and to project your charity to new audiences, but they require that you work with the company and on its terms to achieve this.

This arrangement benefits both the charity and the commercial partner. It differs from sponsorship in that you are promoting the company's product or service (in return for a payment) as the primary purpose of the arrangement. But, as with sponsorship, you will need to make a business case for it.

Getting started with promotions

Joint promotions are quite difficult to arrange and you must first talk about the possibility of your developing promotional links with companies with someone who has experience of this or with a marketing or advertising agency (but be careful of the cost).

You need to decide whether you are the type of charity that can expect a commercial link of this sort. It has been generally accepted that national household-name charities and those addressing popular causes (such as helping children) are more likely to benefit from this area of fundraising than the less well-known charities or those addressing less 'popular' causes.

You should take the initiative yourself by contacting companies that might be interested in your work. You can also contact promotion agencies (that are not retained by you) to make them aware of the opportunities you are offering which they could include when appropriate in their sales pitch to companies.

If you are approached by a promotional agency pitching for business, this does not mean that anything is certain. It may be working independently, hoping that a good idea that involves your charity can then be sold to a company. In nine out of ten situations, these ideas come to nothing, and you may find you have put in considerable effort without getting any payback.

Issues with sponsorships and joint promotions

Sponsorship involves a close working relationship with a company. Therefore you will need to be sure when you enter into any sponsorship agreement that this relationship will benefit your organisation and will not damage your charity's reputation. With commercial promotions the relationship is even closer. The charity is actively promoting the products of the company, so it is important that the product you are associated with is good value and good quality. With both arrangements it is important that you have no ethical problems in associating with that company. You should develop an ethical donations policy before you apply for any sponsorship or suggest a joint promotion – agreeing in advance which types of company you are happy to work with and which you are not. (See *Ethical issues* on page 235)

There is also the question of who will benefit most from the arrangement. How much you should expect to receive from a sponsorship or commercial promotion is also a difficult question. It may be worth a great deal to them to be linked with you. Any negotiation should start from what you think the association is worth to them. Your need for money should not dim the value of your commercial worth.

Finally, there are important legal issues arising from the 1992 Charities Act (and still applicable following the Charities Act 2006). The 1992 Act defines a 'commercial participator' as 'any person who carries on for gain a business which is not a fundraising business but who in the course of that business engages in any promotional venture in the course of which it is represented that contributions are to be given to or applied for the benefit of a charity'. In other words, high street shops often promote products on the understanding that part of the sale price will go to charity – for example charity Christmas cards published commercially state explicitly that for each pack sold a certain sum will go to charity. The Act also covers advertising and sales campaigns or other joint promotions by companies with charities. If the activity falls within the provisions of the Act, this then requires:

- a written agreement in a prescribed form between the charity and the commercial participator
- the public to be informed how the charity will benefit from its involvement, which shows what part of the proceeds or profits are to be given to the charity. This is a matter for professional advice.

The Charity Commission also suggests that trustees should consider the following points before allowing the charity's name to be associated with a particular business or product.

- The relationship is appropriate and will not damage the particular charity or the good name of charity as a whole.

- The proposed fundraising venture is a more effective way of raising money than others that might be considered and the terms of the arrangement are generally advantageous to the charity.

- The arrangement is set out in some detail and kept under review, such that the charity's name is not misused or improperly exploited, and that the charity has the right to prevent future use of its name if the arrangement proves unsatisfactory. It may be worth taking legal advice in drawing up the terms of the arrangement.

Which companies support youth organisations?

Rather like grant-making charities, the good news is that there are a large number of potential supporters of work with children and young people in the corporate sector. Potentially any company can give to your organisation so long as:

- you make a connection between you and them
- you show them the good commercial reasons why they should support you
- the company does not have a stated exclusion on support for youth organisations.

Following are the details of 20 companies that from the 2008 research for DSC's *The Guide to UK Company Giving* expressed a preference for supporting young people. They represent a cross-section of the various types of youth-related causes that companies support, but are in no way an exhaustive list; there may be many more local opportunities for support from companies that are based near you.

In each entry we give the company's latest annual cash donations figure and, where available, that for total community contributions, which includes in kind support such as gifts in kind and employee volunteering. We have also attempted to give some indication of how much of the total cash support went towards youth projects. In some instances this has been provided by the company. In the main, however, we have had to calculate a figure based on a list of beneficiaries (where provided).

In certain cases it is probable that we have understated the level of the company's support for young people due to a lack of clear information, while in others it has not been possible to give any sort of guide at all.

AOL UK Ltd

Contact
Head of Corporate Responsibility,
62 Hammersmith Road,
London W14 8YW
Tel: 020 7348 2500; Fax: 020 7348 8002;
email: ukcharity@aol.com;
website: www.aol.co.uk

Year end: 31/12/2006

Turnover: £177,552,285

Pre-tax profit: £282,543,858

Nature of business
Launched in the UK in 1996, AOL UK is
an interactive service company and a
division of AOL Europe – the internet,
online and e-commerce services
company.

Main UK locations
London

Cash donations: 2006 £76,676

Community support policy

AOL is a leading provider of interactive
services. In the UK, these are marketed by
AOL UK Ltd which also sells advertising
space and operates the company's
website. AOL UK has longstanding
relationships with a number of UK
charities in order to extend the benefits
of the internet to their users. Its priority
areas are young people and people with
disabilities. To meet these aims the
company may provide direct funding
and/or advice and support in kind to
charities and community groups going
online to demonstrate innovative use of
the medium. In 2006, AOL made
charitable donations in the UK of
£76,676. The main beneficiaries of this
included its established charity partners –
John Grooms (Liveability), NCH,
Mencap, Citizen's Online and CAF. No
further details were available.

In kind support

AOL supports GiveNow.org which is
hosted by CAF (Charities Aid
Foundation) and the Time Warner
Foundation. GiveNow.org is the UK's
first website to enable donors to give
both their time and money to the
charities of their choice.

Employee-led support

AOL UK offers each employee up to two
days' paid leave per year to volunteer for
good causes, be it AOL's partner charities
or their own chosen charity. There is also
an annual Time Warner Volunteer Day
(Time Warner owns AOL), with past
projects including planting trees,
painting playgrounds and working on a
city farm.

AOL UK also helps employees to raise
funds for their chosen charities by
offering matched funding for individuals
and teams. Recent fundraising initiatives
range from completing the Great North
Run to organising a secondhand book
sale, climbing Ben Nevis to competing in
World Cup fantasy football.

Payroll giving

The Give As You Earn scheme is offered
by the company, enabling employees to
donate to good causes directly from their
salary, before tax is deducted.

Exclusions

No funding or support for individuals
(including, for example, overseas events
and marathons), advertising or
sponsorship in charity brochures
(including calendars and ball
programmes).

Applications

AOL UK does not accept unsolicited
applications.

BAA plc

Contact
Caroline Nicholls, Director, BAA
Communities Trust, 130 Wilton Road,
London SW1V 1LQ

Tel: 020 8745 9800;
email: caroline_nicholls@baa.com;
website: www.baa.co.uk

Year end: 31/12/2007

Turnover: £2,247,000,000

Pre-tax profit: £747,000,000

Nature of business

BAA plc is one of the world's leading airport companies and owns and operates seven UK airports: Heathrow, Gatwick, Stansted, Aberdeen, Edinburgh, Glasgow and Southampton. Each airport is run by a separate operating company.

Main UK locations

Heathrow, Gatwick, Edinburgh, Glasgow, Southampton, Stansted, Aberdeen

Cash donations: 2007 £1,376,238

Grants to youth: £450,000

Community support policy

The company has its own charitable trust, the BAA 21st Century Communities Trust: (Charity Commission no.1058617), which provides grants in the areas surrounding the company's airports. Support is concentrated on projects which will be of community benefit, mainly in the areas of education, youth development and environment. In 2007, cash contributions from the company totalled £1,376,238 of which £569,796 went to the BAA Communities Trust. The BAA 21st Century Communities Trust gave a total of £566,430 in grants in 2007. Grants were generally in the range of £2,000 to £10,000, although some larger amounts were granted. Recipients included: VSO Global Xchange programme (£158,000); Young Engineers (£51,750); 21st World Scout Jamboree (£30,000); Gatwick Environment Centre (£28,000); East Potential (£25,000); Scottish Council Foundation, Surrey Education Business Partnership, and Surrey and Sussex Youth Games (£10,000 each); Scotland Junior Golf Coaching Scheme (£5,000); and The Box – Youth Project, Essex

(£2,000). In addition to the above, support has included: the second year of a three-year partnership with the youth volunteering charity 'v', with £450,000 committed in total; and the final year of a three-year partnership with YouthNet valued at £75,000, enabling more young people to access volunteering opportunities through the internet.

Employee-led support

The company matches employee giving on a pound for pound basis, and employee fundraising to a maximum of £250. Staff are also given time off to volunteer.

Payroll giving: The company operates the Payroll Giving in Action and the Give As You Earn schemes.

Exclusions

No support is given to circular appeals, advertising in charity brochures, animal welfare, appeals from individuals, the arts, older people, fundraising events, heritage, medical research, overseas projects, political appeals, religious appeals, science/technology, sickness/disability or sport.

Support for a 'charity of the year' is not considered.

Applications

Applicants are advised to contact the community relations manager at their local airport.

BAA Aberdeen: Aberdeen Airport, Dyce, Aberdeen AB21 7DU (0870 040 0006; Fax: 01224 775845).

BAA Edinburgh: Edinburgh Airport, Scotland EH12 9DN (0870 040 0007; Fax: 0131 344 3470).

BAA Gatwick: Gatwick Airport, West Sussex RH6 ONP (0870 000 2468).

BAA Heathrow: Heathrow Airport, 234 Bath Road, Hayes, Middlesex UB3 5AP (0870 000 0123; Fax: 020 8745 4290).

BAA Southampton: Southampton Airport, Hampshire SO18 2NL (0870 040 0009; Fax: 023 8062 7193).

BAA Stansted: Stansted Airport, Enterprise House, Bassingbourne Road, Stansted, Essex CM24 1QW (0870 000 0303; Fax: 01279 662066).

Information available: Written guidance is provided in letter form in response to requests. The company also produces a social responsibility report.

British Land Company plc

Contact
Sarah Cary, York House,
45 Seymour Street, London W1H 7LX
Tel: 020 7486 4466; Fax: 020 7935 5552;
website: www.britishland.com

Year end: 31/03/2008

Turnover: £645,000,000

Pre-tax profit: (£1,609,000,000)

Nature of business
Property investment and development, finance and investment.

Main UK locations
London

Cash donations: 2008 £36,000

Total contributions: £1,036,000

Community support policy

The company states that:

British Land builds constructive relationships with the communities in which it operates. It does this by supporting selected local initiatives through staff volunteering, skills mentoring and financial assistance. Larger national programmes may also be supported where they benefit communities neighbouring British Land's investments. British Land is strongly committed to investing in the future through education, the arts and sport, with particular emphasis on helping young people.

In 2007/08, British Land made total community contributions in the UK of just over £1 million. This comprised £850,000 to good causes through sponsorship, nearly £30,000 in time, £120,000 in gifts in kind, and £36,000 in cash donations. This benefited a range of organisations and people including: youth projects – British Land Chess Challenge and Reading is Fundamental; arts – Create; sports – Capital Kids Cricket.

During the summer of 2007, and in partnership with West Euston Partnership's Integrated Youth Project and Diorama Arts, a group of 14 young people from West Euston participated in the arts project, 'The Future is Now, The Future is Here'. This not only helped develop their art and IT skills, but also encouraged them to think about local regeneration and diversity.

In kind support

Education
The following information is taken from the company's website.

In 2007, the team at the Peacocks Centre worked with Surrey Education Business Partnership and local secondary schools on business games, foreign language workshops and town planning exercises. They mentored over 300 Year 10 and 11 students from Bishop David Brown, Winston Churchill and Jubilee High Schools, providing an insight into the world of work, and hosted mock interviews followed by constructive, personalised feedback.

Training
In 2007, St Stephen's Shopping Centre in Kingston-upon-Hull became the first UK shopping centre to work with The Prince's Trust and a range of retailers to offer disadvantaged young people the chance to participate in the 'Get into Retail' job scheme. Seven St Stephen's retailers provided 16 work placements as part of the

Trust's intensive three week programme, which culminated in job interviews. All learners gained Level 2 health and safety qualifications and five learners went on to get jobs.

Employee-led support

British Land offers all its employees volunteering opportunities and encourages the management teams at its properties around the UK to get involved in local initiatives.

In 2007, the company's head office team spent almost 400 hours volunteering, while 26% were involved in volunteering initiatives during 2007/08. Examples include: a team of British Land volunteers helped to dig, clear and prune shrubs in a meadow at Waterlow Park in Camden; and Meadowhall Shopping Centre volunteers converted a storage room at the local Phillimore Primary School into a comfortable room for staff to work with children and their families on social issues including low self esteem, behavioural issues and family problems.

Exclusions

The company will not provide support for political purposes.

Applications

In writing to the correspondent.

Information available: The company's 2007/08 corporate social responsibility report is available online.

BT Group plc

Contact
Steve Kelly, Corporate Responsibility Team, BT Group Communications, 81 Newgate Street, London EC1A 7AJ Tel: 020 7356 5000; Fax: 020 7356 5520; website: www.btplc.com

Year end: 31/03/2008

Turnover: £20,704,000,000

Pre-tax profit: £1,976,000,000

Nature of business
The group's principal activity is the supply of communications services and equipment.

Main UK locations
London

Cash donations: 2008 £2,500,000

Total contributions: £22,300,000

Community support policy

BT donates money, time and expertise to make a difference to the communities where it operates. The company's community investment (including charity donations, volunteering and in kind support) is focused on activities that inspire people to make a better world through the power of communication skills and technology. The majority of these activities focus on helping young people and supporting arts and culture.

Through its 'Better World Campaign', BT gives disadvantaged young people the skills they need to succeed in life and to improve their world. A significant part of this comes under the theme of 'Giving Young People a Voice'. This contains a number of strands, including the following. **Big Fat Voice** – a website that is being designed, developed and managed by a panel of 17 young people to discuss and debate their views on issues that affect and matter to them. **Big Takeover** – on 7 November 2008, young people across England had the chance to take the reins of schools, businesses and even government departments. BT promoted the event by encouraging employees to mentor a young person for the day. **Schools Question Time Challenge** – open to all UK secondary schools and colleges. Twelve schools are chosen as finalists from the hundreds of applications and the students produce their own debates based upon the popular BBC Question Time format.

In 2007/08, BT made total worldwide community contributions of £22.3 million, including £2.5 million in cash donations. No figures were available regarding the amount contributed in the UK or towards youth projects.

In kind support

BT gives in kind support to ChildLine, such as strategic and technical advice. Its support has included the donation of premises for several years, large-scale promotions and staff fundraising initiatives, and sponsoring the annual BT ChildLine Awards for Services to Children.

Employee-led support

Employee involvement

In 2008, through the BT Community Champions scheme, 842 grants were made worth £200,000.

Through the BT Volunteers programme, employees have the chance to contribute to the company's Better World Campaign by teaching lessons on communication skills in schools and youth clubs. Three thousand current and former employees volunteer in over 150 clubs around the UK. In 2008 they delivered lessons on communication skills to over 146,000 young people.

Payroll giving

BT's commitment to Give As You Earn enables employees to donate to the charity of their choice.

BT has one of the largest payroll giving schemes in the UK. In 2008 employees gave just under £2.4 million which was matched with an extra £1 million contribution from BT.

Exclusions

No response to circular appeals. No denominational appeals, political appeals, appeals from individuals or brochure advertising.

Applications

Decisions on major grants are made at head office by the Board Community Support Committee which meets quarterly. Smaller grants can be made by staff of the relevant community unit at their discretion. Local appeals should be sent to the appropriate BT local office. (Each BT zone has its own community affairs staff operating a programme which reflects the needs of that area.)

Contacts

Voluntary Sector Programmes – Beth Courtier (023 8082 3340); Education and Employment Partnerships – Dave Hancock (0121 230 7855).

Cattles plc

Contact
Community Investment Officer, Kingston House, Centre 27 Business Park, Woodhead Road, Birstall, Batley WF17 9TD
Tel: 01924 444466; Fax: 01924 448324; email: cr@cattles.co.uk; website: www.cattles.co.uk

Year end: 31/12/2007

Turnover: £822,200,000

Pre-tax profit: £165,200,000

Nature of business
Provision of financial services such as secured and unsecured personal loans, hire purchase credit facilities and merchandise.

Main UK locations
Oxford, Manchester, Leeds, Hull, Glasgow, Nottingham, Cleckheaton, Birstall

Cash donations: 2007 £409,946

Total contributions: £456,745

Community support policy

Cattles plc provides financial services to consumers and businesses. The company states in its online document *Cattles approach to community investment* that its community investment is achieved through: 'A practical set of deliverable programmes and activities comprising colleague engagement and external partnerships that enable us to mix business skills, time and resources with the needs of the community'. This is done in three ways: developing partnerships with a small number of key charities or community organisations whose work relates to Cattles' business activities and which follows its main themes to raise the standards in financial education; to improve the general welfare of young people and alleviating social disadvantage involving staff in community and charity work and favouring projects where colleagues have a particular interest contributing to charitable initiatives; and through cash donation and gifts in kind (including time and resources).

In 2007, the company donated £410,000 in total in support of the above. No separate figure was available to show how much went towards youth projects, but the examples below give some indication of the areas likely to be considered for support. The company works with Credit Action and DebtCred to help educate young people about money management and supports employee volunteering on the Leeds Project through a 'CashMatch' scheme. The project gives schoolchildren from disadvantaged areas in Leeds the opportunity to participate in a five-day residential programme of activities to promote self-confidence and personal development. Cattles has also participated in the Employability Programme for Young Learners in Nottingham – a pilot scheme to encourage young people to undertake vocational qualifications.

In kind support

The company may occasionally provide support through gifts in kind.

Employee-led support

The following is taken from the Cattles' online publication *Shared Growth.*

Employee volunteering

We promote colleague volunteering [through] 'Hands Up', our volunteering initiative, [which] encourages colleagues at all sites to make an impact in their local communities. We work closely with Business in the Community's national employee volunteering programme, Cares...

However, we are increasingly sourcing our activities through the 'Hands Up' committees at our main office locations, because they can develop closer links with local communities and better understand their needs.

In 2007, our colleagues undertook 2,644 hours of volunteering – an increase of 28% on 2006.

CashMatch

This initiative gives colleagues the opportunity to double their fundraising for charitable and community activities. We will contribute an equal amount, up to £500, provided certain criteria are met. In 2007, we 'CashMatched' 22 projects with contributions totalling £7,420.

We continue to support the Leeds Project, brokered by Outward Bound. This gives schoolchildren from disadvantaged areas in Leeds the opportunity to participate in a five-day residential programme of activities to promote self-confidence and personal development.

We have also participated in the Employability Programme for Young Learners in Nottingham. This is a pilot scheme to encourage young people to undertake vocational qualifications.

Payroll giving

The Cattles 50/50 Club is a scheme is operated by the company.

This is our Give As You Earn (GAYE) scheme. Colleagues' contributions are matched by the company and donated to five charities selected by colleagues' online votes on our intranet. Colleagues who participate are also entered into a monthly prize draw.

In July 2007 we donated £10,600 to each charity: Macmillan Cancer Support, The Children's Variety Club, Promise Dreams, Mencap and Henshaws Society for the Blind. Over 700 people now participate in the scheme – 15% of all our colleagues.

Exclusions

No support for general appeals, fundraising events or individuals.

Applications

In writing to the correspondent.

Cheshire Building Society

Contact
Maria Mathieson, CSR & Sponsorships Manager, Castle Street, Macclesfield, Cheshire SK11 6AF
Tel: 01625 613612; Fax: 01625 617246; website: www.thecheshire.co.uk

Year end: 31/03/2007

Turnover: £45,000,000

Pre-tax profit: £7,200,000

Nature of business
Building society provider of competitive investments, mortgages, and complementary financial services.

Main UK locations
Bolton, Macclesfield, Mold, Wigan, Stockport, Warrington, Chester, Crewe, Buxton, Accrington

Cash donations: 2007 £196,000

Community support policy

The Cheshire states that its aim is to: 'Improve the way in which we offer support to our local community, making it more transparent and sustainable and easier for charities to apply'. To this end, it established the Cheshire Foundation, which makes decisions on funding applications through a board of foundation members made up of staff, members and people from the local community.

The foundation meets quarterly to consider applications for funding above £150 and, for smaller projects, has introduced a new Community Contribution Award which enables local branch managers to support projects in their area. Support falls into five areas: education; community support; social inclusion; grassroots sport; and financial education. Of these, only the grassroots sport category specifically mentions assisting young people. However, it is feasible that support may also be available under each of the other categories.

In 2007, the society donated £196,000 to the development of its social responsibility agenda, which in turn helped to generate extra revenue of just under £75,000 for the organisations concerned. The Cheshire Foundation provided funding for 64 projects, including: Cerebral Palsy Sport – Boccia training weekend; Children's Adventure Farm Trust; and Careline. During the year, the society continued to work in conjunction with other organisations to develop and deliver educational programmes, which encourage young people to act responsibly when dealing with their finances both now and in the future. In December 2008 the Cheshire Building Society merged with the Nationwide Building Society.

Employee-led support

Staff members raised over £13,000 for their chosen charity partners – the Children's Adventure Farm Trust, Scope North West, Guide Dogs for the Blind, Barnardo's North West and the Donna Louise Trust.

Exclusions

No support for political, religious or military organisations, overseas charities, appeals from individuals, third-party funding or NHS funding

Applications

For the *Cheshire Foundation* you can download an application form and guidance notes from the society's website.

Please remember that the foundation/ society adhere to a strict policy of funding only registered charities that are either based in the North West or have a project or event taking place in our branch operating region.

The foundation meets on a quarterly basis in January, April, July and October. No funding decisions will be made outside these dates so please take this into consideration when applying.

For the *Community Contribution Award*, your organisation must still fall into one of the categories supported by the society, but it is not necessary for your organisation to be a registered charity.

You can download an application form as above, or pick one up from your local branch.

If you require any further information about either of the above, please contact the society's corporate social responsibility team on 01625 652466, who will be happy to provide you with advice and guidance.

The Co-operative Group

Contact
Sarah Kleuter, Senior Community Manager, 8th Floor,
New Century House, Corporation Street, Manchester M60 4ES
Tel: 0161 834 1212; Fax: 0161 833 1383; email: sarah.kleuter@co-operative.coop; website: www.co-operative.coop/ corporate/

Year end: 12/01/2008

Turnover: £9,075,500,000

Pre-tax profit: £149,900,000

Nature of business
The major activities of the Co-operative Group include food retailing, funerals, travel agents, pharmacies and farming. It is the parent organisation of Co-operative Financial Services, whose operating subsidiaries, the Co-operative Bank plc, smile and Co-operative Insurance Society, provide an extensive range of banking and insurance products. Within these financial statements, results are allocated into three key segments – trading, banking and insurance.

Main UK locations
Manchester

Cash donations: 2007 £8,300,000

Total contributions: £10,000,000

Grants to youth: £131,000

Community support policy

In general, the Co-operative Group's community investment strategy targets support at cooperative, self-help and community groups in the areas in which it trades. Within this, support is specifically given to 'young adults', but may also be available under other categories such as homelessness, learning and development, sport and leisure, offenders/ex-offenders and socially excluded/disadvantaged.

In 2007, the group made total community contributions of nearly

£10.0 million (2006: £5.2 million) in the UK of which £8.3 million was in cash donations. This was broken down as follows: financial support (£8.3 million); employee time (£1.5 million); gifts in kind (£200,000); and management costs (£400,000). Around 25% of contributions went towards supporting the work of the Co-operative Foundation and the Co-operative Community Fund, both of which give grants to a wide range of causes within the established guidelines.

The Co-operative Foundation awards grants of £500 to £30,000 and seeks to support locally-led groups that can demonstrate evidence of living the cooperative values and principles of self-help, equality, democracy and concern for the community. Projects must fall within the United Region trading area and benefit disadvantaged groups or communities. In 2007, the foundation made grant totalling £895,000. The Co-operative Community Fund's key objective is to support self-help voluntary and community groups. Applicants must demonstrate that their project benefits a local community in which at least one Co-operative Group business trades, has a charitable purpose, and is aligned to the group's values and principles. In 2007, grants totalled over £1 million of which £131,000 went specifically towards supporting 'young adults'. One of the key focus areas involves tackling crime, with a diverse range of initiatives supported in order to: reduce business crime; reduce youth offending; prevent reoffending; support victims of crime; and, empower people to help reduce crime in their own communities. The Co-operative has also recently undertaken a new community partnership with the charity StreetGames.

Over the next five years the Co-operative is supporting StreetGames to develop a new volunteering programme for young people living in some of the most disadvantaged communities. With support from the Co-operative, the young volunteers will gain skills and experience in community and sports leadership, in addition to coaching qualifications, first aid, child protection, equality and diversity, event management, media and lobbying skills.

In kind support

In kind donations are made by the group, but we have no further details regarding this.

Employee-led support

Volunteering

Staff within the group are actively encouraged to volunteer – donating their time, expertise, energy and enthusiasm to their local communities.

Three categories of volunteering activities are available to staff: team challenges, individual volunteering (e.g. victim support volunteers, mentoring, reading or numeracy volunteering in schools) and specialist volunteering (e.g. Prince's Trust Business Mentoring, interview technique training for prisoners, financial education training).

Matched giving

The 'Charity Booster' scheme enables staff who fundraise for charity to apply for a boost to increase the amount of money they raise and, subject to certain conditions, individuals can apply for a £100 boost, and teams up to £400.

Payroll giving

Staff are able to contribute to their chosen charity through the provision of a payroll giving scheme.

Exclusions

Generally, no grants are made towards: projects which are in conflict with the group's ethical policy; funding political parties; religious appeals; the costs of individuals or groups to travel overseas for charitable purposes or fundraising;

funding for individuals, including school fees; sports and arts initiatives (unless it is a project which benefits disadvantaged groups and sports or arts is a means to these ends); equipment for hospitals and schools which would normally be funded by statutory sources; and salaries or running costs.

Applications

Further information can be had by contacting the correspondent, or by visiting the websites mentioned herein.

Application forms and details on applying to the Community Dividend Fund can be found at: www.co-operative.coop/en/community-fund/

Note: Some major changes are being made to the group's grant schemes and at present funding applications are not being accepted. However, it is expected that application for funding will re-open in spring 2009.

Coutts & Co

Contact
Mrs C L Attwater, Administrator, The Coutts Charitable Trust, 440 Strand, London WC2R 0QS
Tel: 020 7753 1000; Fax: 020 7753 1028; website: www.coutts.com

Year end: 31/12/2006

Turnover: £357,911,000

Pre-tax profit: £163,768,000

Nature of business
Banking and allied financial services. Coutts is the private banking arm of the Royal Bank of Scotland Group. The bank's main location is London, but there are 17 regional offices.

Main UK locations
Liverpool, Manchester, Newcastle upon Tyne, Oxford, Nottingham, Winchester, Tunbridge Wells, Bristol, Cardiff, Cambridge, Isle of Man, Jersey, Leeds, Eton, Guildford, Bath, Birmingham, Bournemouth

Cash donations: 2006 £832,956

Grants to youth: £95,000

Community support policy

Coutts & Co. is the UK private banking arm of the Royal Bank of Scotland. To formalise Coutts & Co.'s charitable giving the Coutts Charitable Trust (Charity Commission no. 1000135) was set up in 1987and makes a large number of small donations to a wide range of charities each year. A portion of the charitable budget is, however, used for larger donations.

The trust's main source of funding is derived from the covenant income calculated at 0.5% of profits chargeable to corporation tax of Coutts & Co. for the preceding year. Grants are given by the trust to UK organisations only and it prefers to support organisations in areas where the bank has a presence, mainly London, but also at 22 locations across the UK.

Charities supported include those involved with helping homeless people, rehabilitation and teaching self-help (drug; alcohol; young offenders), disadvantaged adults and children, youth organisations and education. According to the 2006 accounts (the latest available for the company), Coutts donated £832,956 (2005: £552,088) to the trust which made grants ranging from £500 to £750 to UK registered charities 'where a few hundred pounds can make a great difference'. Some larger donations, of £2,000 or more, were also made. In 2007 approximately 1,600 applications (2006: 1,400) for assistance were received by the trust and the trustees identified and made donations totalling £617,663 (2006: £363,187) to 866 charitable organisations (2006: 724). It is difficult from looking at the trust's accounts to wholly quantify the total given in grants to youth causes as support may have be given under a number of the listed categories. However, in round figures we estimate this to have amounted to about £95,000.

Employee-led support

Payroll giving

The company operates the Give As You Earn scheme.

Exclusions

No response to circular appeals. No support for appeals from individuals or overseas projects.

Applications

Applications to the Coutts Charitable Trust should be addressed to the correspondent above, at any time. Applications should include clear details of the purpose for which the grant is required. Grants are made regularly where amounts of £500 or less are felt to be appropriate. The trustees meet quarterly to consider larger donations.

DSG International plc

Contact
Community Relations Manager, Maylands Avenue, Hemel Hempstead, Hertfordshire HP2 7TG
Tel: 0870 850 3333;
email: communityrelations@dixons.co.uk; website: www.dsgiplc.com

Year end: 03/05/2008

Turnover: £7,929,700,000

Pre-tax profit: (£192,800,000)

Nature of business
The company's main activity is the retailing of high technology consumer electronics, personal computers, domestic appliances, photographic equipment, communication products and related financial and after sales services.

Main UK locations
Nottingham, Sheffield, Bury, Hemel Hempstead

Cash donations: 2008 £400,000

Grants to youth: £295,000

Community support policy

DSG International is one of Europe's leading specialist electrical retailing groups and trades in the UK under the Curry's, Dixon's and PC World brands. DSG International has funded charities and communities for many years through its registered charity DSG international Foundation (Charity Commission no. 1053215). Since the foundation was set up in 1996 it has funded various projects in the areas of education, technology and training initiatives, with a preference for those with employees' involvement. More recently, the foundation has supported 'Switched on Communities', DSG's community involvement programme. Launched in June 2006, the programme aims to provide technology and training to those who need it most, especially young people. As part of the programme DSG has four partners: Foyer Foundation; Eco-Schools; e-Learning Foundation; and AbilityNet. In 2007/08, the group made total community contributions of £1,228,000 (2006/07: £1,141,000). Of this, £400,000 (2006/07: £875,000) was donated to the DSG International Foundation which made grants totalling £1,043,000. Out of this, the Foyer Federation, for example, received around £200,000, enabling it to assist homeless 16 to 25 year olds reach their full potential. Other beneficiaries included: e-Learning Foundation (£94,000); Jubilee Sailing Trust (£5,000); and Setpoint (£2,000)

In kind support

The company also gives assistance through seconding staff to enterprise initiatives and gifts in kind.

Employee-led support

Wherever they are based, many of the group's employees give up their time and skills to help support local community activities. In recognition of this commitment, the group provides employees (as individuals, or at a store level) with grants to support their fundraising and volunteering.

Many employees are given the opportunity to take part in team challenges, from decorating a local charity office to supporting Young Enterprise schemes at schools. If you have an idea for a suitable challenge, please email corporate.affairs@dsgiplc.com

Employees are also offered community-related training options for personal and management development including volunteering, mentoring and skills-transfer opportunities ranging from partnering head teachers to working with young offenders.

In 2006/07, the foundation supported 300 smaller charities and gave out 200 employee grants.

Payroll giving

The Give As You Earn scheme is operated.

Exclusions

No grants are made towards: third party fundraising activities; political or religious organisations; projects that should be funded from statutory sources; overseas appeals; community sponsorship of any kind; or animal charities.

Applications

DSG's community programme currently focuses on its four charity partners and in supporting the charitable work of its employees. As a result, it is unable to process requests from other charities and groups. The current 'Switched on Communities' initiative will run until July 2009. DSG anticipates reviewing the programme in early 2009, so please check its website for further developments.

Freshfields Bruuckhaus Deringer LLP

Contact
Bea Malleson, Head of CSR and Community Investment, 65 Fleet Street, London EC4Y 1HS
Tel: 020 7936 4000; Fax: 020 7832 7001; website: www.freshfields.com

Year end: 27/03/2007

Nature of business
International law firm.

Main UK locations
London

Cash donations: 2007 £490,447

Total contributions: £2,537,587

Community support policy

Freshfields Bruckhaus Deringer is a leading international law firm which aims to 'make a positive difference to the communities where we have offices and, more broadly, to some of the wider legal and social issues that concern so many of us today'. Although a large percentage of its community support involves pro bono work, i.e. providing professional legal advice on a low or no fee basis, this is substantial and is complemented by cash and in kind donations. The majority of the total firm-wide contribution is focused on four themes, with each office, together with its community partners, responsible for interpreting these themes in a way that is appropriate to their local community. The most relevant of these involves raising the levels of achievement and aspirations of young people from disadvantaged backgrounds and improving their skills. In 2006/07, the firm made total UK community contributions of just over £2.5 million. This was broken down as follows: cash – £490,447; gifts in kind – £96,668; and time – £1,950,472 (community =

£347,000; pro bono = £1.6 million).
During the year, volunteers from
Freshfields supported young people in a
variety of ways, including: mentoring
GCSE and UK career academy students;
giving interview practice to pupils in
Hackney hoping to attend either Oxford
or Cambridge Universities; and
providing work experience. The firm also
worked in association with Brent Council
and The Learning Trust on the Black
Leadership programme, which aims to
equip young black students from
disadvantaged areas with the skills
necessary to make better personal and
career choices.

In kind support

Through its Ready for Work programme,
Freshfields provides work experience
placements to homeless people. Between
2000 and 2007, 126 individuals
completed successful placements at the
firm, 14 of whom have taken up
permanent jobs there. Others have gone
on to work elsewhere.

In 2006/07, in association with Brent
Council and The Learning Trust, which
has responsibility for education in
Hackney, Freshfields hosted the launch
and graduation of the Black Leadership
programme for 150 pupils from schools
in these areas.

Employee-led support

Freshfields encourages every member of
the firm to take part in an activity to help
a charity or community-related project
by providing time off to volunteer. In
2007, 35% of staff in London took part in
one or more community affairs
programmes surpassing the annual target
of 30% staff participation in each office
set by the entire firm.

The firm's website states that its
philosophy is to promote active
employee participation, rather than
simply fundraising.

Payroll giving
The firm operates the Give As You Earn
Scheme.

Applications

In writing to the correspondent.

Information available: The firm
provides an online corporate social
responsibility report.

Grosvenor Group

Contact
Virginia Parish, The Grosvenor Office,
70 Grosvenor Street, London W1K 3JP
Tel: 020 7408 0988; Fax: 020 7629 9115;
email: virginia.parish@grosvenor.com;
website: www.grosvenor.com

Year end: 31/12/2007

Pre-tax profit: £524,000,000

Nature of business
The group's principal activities are
property investment, development and
fund management in Britain and Ireland,
North America, Continental Europe,
Australia and Asia Pacific.

Main UK locations
Liverpool, Edinburgh

Cash donations: 2007 £2,000,000

Grants to youth: £100,000

Community support policy

Grosvenor is a group of privately-owned
international property development,
investment and fund management
businesses. The group's community
support is, in the main, routed through
the Westminster Foundation (Charity
Commission no. 267618) which gives to
a wide variety of causes. These are: art;
church; commemorative; conservation
(not building); education; medical (not
research); social welfare; and youth. The
group also recently established the
Liverpool One Foundation (Charity
Commission no. 1112697) in connection
with the group's development of a 42-

acre retail site ('Liverpool One') situated in the centre of the city. As part of its remit, the foundation supports the advancement of education and vocational training to establish children and young people in life. In 2007, the group made charitable donations of £2 million, of which £1.6 million went to the Westminster Foundation. A total of £73,000 was donated to youth projects. During the same year the Liverpool One Foundation had an income of £316,000 and made grants totalling £86,000 under the following headings: community (£55,000); training and youth (£18,000); health (£7,500); and education (£5,000). More specifically, the foundation has funded Young Addaction Liverpool since 2006, helping to support young people on a programme of treatment to develop skills and interests that would divert them from drug and alcohol using environments and increase their confidence.

Employee-led support

The group supports staff fundraising efforts up to a specified limit. In 2007, for example, a cycle ride across the British Isles raised £27,800 on behalf of the Martha Trust, £10,000 of which was matched funding from Grosvenor.

Applications

Applications should be made in writing to the correspondent, who will ensure that they are dealt with dealt with appropriately, i.e. passed on to the relevant foundation.

HBOS plc

Contact
Angela Tinker, Head of HBOS Foundation, PO Box 5, The Mound, Edinburgh EH1 1YZ
Tel: 0870 600 5000; Fax: 0131 243 7082; website: www.hbosfoundation.org
Year end: 31/12/2007

Turnover: £21,291,000,000
Pre-tax profit: £5,474,000,000
Nature of business
The group's principal activities are divided into five divisions, namely: retail banking; insurance and investment; corporate banking; treasury and asset management; and international.

Main UK locations
Edinburgh
Cash donations: 2007 £12,740,000
Total contributions: £18,610,660
Grants to youth: £500,000

Community support policy

HBOS plc was formed following the merger of the Bank of Scotland and Halifax plc. All charitable donations are channelled through the HBOS Foundation (Registered Charity no. SCO32942), launched in 2002. Additional support is provided through in kind giving, affinity cards, and the Bank of Scotland and Halifax's extensive corporate sponsorship programme. The HBOS Foundation works on a national and local level to support a wide range of charities.

During 2007, the foundation made charitable donations of £10.8 million of which we estimate around 10% went towards supporting youth programmes. Donations are mainly disbursed through one of two programmes. *Large grants programme* – this supports a mix of one-year and multi-year projects and initiatives across Great Britain and Northern Ireland. A proactive approach is taken to sourcing potential nationwide projects and initiatives that enable the foundation to benefit different parts of the community. Projects tend to be aligned towards the money advice and financial literacy theme but, as the examples below show, this can include support for young people. *Regional grants* – the foundation operate a structure of regional coordinators enabling it to work more closely with local communities and respond to local issues. Through the community action programme local grants of up to £10,000 to support a diverse range of projects can be provided. The two key themes of the programme are money advice and financial literacy, and developing and improving local communities. Example beneficiaries include: YouthNet/Citizens Advice – £300,000 to fund the joint 'Advice Changing Young Lives' which aims to help 16–24 year olds gain access money management support and advice; £110,000 to the National Youth Agency to deliver its 'Money Mastery' seminars around the country; and £100,000 to UK Youth. Note: In January 2009, HBOS became part of Lloyds Banking Group plc which has its own large and well-established charitable foundations. Whether the takeover will have any affect on HBOS's community support policy we do not know, but as yet we have heard nothing to suggest that any of the above will change in the immediate future.

In kind support

Each year the foundation supports the three charities that are shortlisted as charities of the year by offering their pin badges each month for sale to customers and colleagues.

Charities may also be offered collection account facilities in the company's branches enabling them to raise funds for major appeals at low cost.

Employee-led support

Colleagues who regularly volunteer in their own time can apply to the foundation for an award of up to £250 on behalf of the organisation they volunteer with. Team challenge volunteering enables staff to apply for up to £250 per project.

The foundation also matches colleague fundraising up to £500 per colleague per year and colleague payroll giving to the

Million £ Challenge to a maximum of £600 per colleague per year.

HBOS colleagues are occasionally seconded to work in charities.

Payroll giving

The Give As You Earn scheme and Flexible Benefits Charitable Giving scheme are in operation.

Exclusions

The HBOS Foundation will not provide support for: charitable advertising; sponsorship of fundraising events for registered charities; sponsorship of individuals or third party fundraising initiatives; any project or initiative which discriminates on the grounds of colour, race, sex or religious beliefs; political appeals; animal rights groups; overseas projects; or conferences.

Applications

If you are applying for a grant of over £50,000, visit the HBOS Foundation website (www.hbosfoundation.org)for further information and instructions on how to apply.

If you are applying for a grant of under £50,000, further information is also available on the website, including a downloadable application form. Completed application forms should be posted to your nearest or most appropriate regional coordinator. HBOS Foundation regional coordinators are based across the UK and represent the majority of HBOS businesses, including subsidiaries. A map of the UK on the website shows where the regional coordinators are based.

Man Group plc

Contact
Lisa Clarke, Secretary to the Charitable Trust, Sugar Quay, Lower Thames Street, London EC3R 6DU

Tel: 020 7144 1000; Fax: 020 7144 1923;
website: www.mangroupplc.com

Year end: 31/03/2008

Pre-tax profit: £1,039,500,000

Nature of business
The company is a leading global provider
of alternative investment products and
solutions.

Main UK locations
London

Cash donations: 2008 £5,500,000

Grants to youth: £1,900,000

Community support policy

Through its website and various
publications, the Man Group makes
available a wealth of information about
its corporate community investment and
the philosophy behind it. Basically,
though, its community engagement has
three distinct strands: sponsorship;
philanthropy; and what it terms 'our
people's engagement'. For the purpose of
this guide we will look at the
philanthropic aspect only. Unlike
sponsorship, Man Group views its
charitable activities as entirely separate
from marketing and public relations, and
gives on a purely altruistic basis in line
with its core values. The main conduit
for this is the Man Charitable Trust
(Charity Commission no. 275286) which
in particular supports charities that help
young people to develop self-esteem and
overcome problems that prevent them
from reaching their potential. Such
charities may be involved in educational
establishments, the arts, sport or music,
but can also include those working with
young people affected by addiction,
homelessness and health issues. In
2007/08, the group paid out £5.5 million
to 150 charities selected by the trustees of
the Man Group plc Charitable Trust.
Percentage-wise donations were broken
down as follows: young people (35%);
vulnerable (16.5%); other (16%);
international (12.4%); literacy (12%);
and employee-related (8.1%). More

specifically, within the category 'young
people', the arts received £321,000;
disadvantaged people £667,000;
education £407,000; and sport £414,000.
Examples of beneficiaries include:
Sadler's Wells – Connexions Project
(£30,450); Foyer Federation (£30,211);
UK Mathematics Trust (£20,000); and
London Youth Rowing (£140,000). In
2008/09 the group will contribute around
£16 million to charities, the majority of
which will be donated through the Man
Group plc Charitable Trust. This will
enable the group to broaden its
geographic spread, and provide
opportunities for its larger overseas
offices to give more, and to provide a
cushion for multi-year commitments. As
well as money, employees at all levels are
encouraged to invest their time and
expertise in helping others. Charitable
contributions made by employees,
including via the Give As You Earn
scheme, are matched up to an agreed
limit.

Employee-led support

All staff are encouraged to become
involved in charitable activities.
Accordingly, 'In addition to the selected
charities the trustees [of the group
charitable trust] give preference to
charities where a staff member has an
involvement and they will generally
match any sponsorship raised by staff
members for charitable events'.

The trust will match, up to £100 per
person per month, individual employee
fundraising efforts. There are no
constraints as to which charity may
benefit from these donations.

Payroll giving

The Give As You Earn scheme is in
operation. Donations via the scheme rose
to £214,000 in 2007/08 (2006/07:
£112,000) with a further £86,000 being
added through the group's matched
funding. Membership in the scheme rose
from 141 in 2006 to 200 in 2007.

Exclusions

The Man Group plc Charitable Trust does not generally support: large national charities; charities which use external fundraising agencies; animal charities; charities primarily devoted to promoting religious beliefs; endowment funds; requests that directly replace statutory funding; individual beneficiaries; or successful applicants from the previous 12 months.

Applications

In writing to the correspondent.

Information available: Besides producing an annual corporate responsibility report, the group also provides online access to its internal 'Corporate Responsibility Manual'. This provides an interesting insight into why the company does what it does for the community and how. Such levels of transparency are to be welcomed.

Morgan Stanley International Ltd

Contact
Ami Howse, Morgan Stanley International Foundation,
25 Cabot Square, Canary Wharf,
London E14 4QA
Tel: 020 7425 8000; Fax: 020 7425 8984;
email: communityaffairslondon@ morganstanley.com;
website: www.morganstanley.co.uk

Year end: 30/11/2007

Nature of business
Principal activities: the provision of financial services to corporations, governments, financial institutions and individual investors.

Main UK locations
London

Cash donations: 2007 £5,603,363

Grants to youth: £50,000

Community support policy

The company makes a major proportion of its charitable donations through the Morgan Stanley International Foundation (Charity Commission no. 1042671). The foundation makes contributions to non-profit educational, healthcare and social service organisations which provide a benefit to the firm's local communities. In London, this is primarily focused on the boroughs of Tower Hamlets and Newham, and in Scotland on Cumbernauld and Glasgow. According to its latest report (2007), however, from 2009 the foundation will be seeking new charitable organisations to partner and fund with the themes of support being more focused. Education and employability – the foundation will seek to support programmes that can increase access and opportunity to young people up to the age of 21. These will mainly be based in educational institutions and address academic achievement, raising inspiration, aspiration and employability skills. Children's health – investment will be made in healthcare and innovative health programmes supporting young people aged up to 18 years. Potential partners will include charitable organisations, hospitals and community-based initiatives. In 2007, the firm donated £5.6 million to the foundation, which in turn made grants totalling £3.6 million. The major beneficiary was Great Ormond Street Hospital which received over £1.9 million as the firm's 'charity of the year'. Other smaller grants were made to: Eastside Young Leaders' Academy (£16,500); Business Dynamics (£14,000); Street League (£10,000); Community Food Enterprise (£7,000); GOAL UK (£5,308); and Over the Wall (£2,000).

In kind support

Education

As part of the Tower Hamlets Education Business Partnership's 'Take Our Students to Work Day' programme, 30 local students aged 13–14 spent a day in the Cabot Square offices.

Morgan Stanley also provided paid summer internships to two local A Level students as part of the Corporation of London's Business Traineeship Programme.

Employee-led support

The company encourages its employees to get involved with the local community and the chosen 'charity of the year'.

Staff contributions to charities of their own choice are matched by the foundation up to a maximum of £2,000 per employee, per event. Additionally, employees can apply to the foundation for matching of their time in volunteering. The size of the grant is dependent upon the employee's length of service with both Morgan Stanley and the benefiting organisation.

Exclusions

The following is taken from *Guidelines for making charitable donations*, available online.

As a rule, grants will not be made to either national or international charitable organisations unless they have a project in one of these areas. In addition, grants will not be made to either political or evangelistic organisations, pressure groups, or individuals outside the firm who are seeking sponsorship either for themselves (e.g. to help pay for education) or for onward transmission to a charitable organisation.

Applications

All initial funding enquiries should be directed to Louise Ellison at the Morgan Stanley International Foundation (MSIF): louise.ellison@morganstanley.com

There is no pro forma for grant applications. Please send details of the project for which you are seeking funding, along with a copy of your latest report and accounts, to the correspondent.

Grant applications are considered quarterly in March, June, September and December by the MSIF trustees. The trustees are senior representatives from across the firm's divisions.

Please note that the MSIF takes a proactive approach to grantmaking and rarely responds to unsolicited requests.

Nestlé UK Ltd

Contact
Mrs Vicky Whitelock, Consumer Services, PO Box 207, York YO91 1XY
Tel: 01904 604 604; Fax: 01904 603 461; website: www.nestle.co.uk

Year end: 31/12/2007

Turnover: £1,269,000,000

Pre-tax profit: (£62,400,000)

Nature of business
Manufacture and sale of food products and associated activities.

Main UK locations
Hayes, Castleford, Croydon, Dalston, Fawdon, Girvan, Halifax, York, Tutbury

Cash donations: 2007 £1,005,954

Community support policy

Nestlé supports young people (aged 11 to 18) in the following areas: nutrition; health and wellness; out of school childcare; and education. Support is also given to community projects that focus on Nestlé's key strategies of nutrition, health and wellness and sustainability. The company made charitable donations totalling just over £1 million during 2007 (2006: £1.2 million). Details of the specific amounts given to the company's key partners and/or other organisations were not available. However, the examples below outline some of the types of projects supported. The key charity partners are 4Children (formerly Kids'

Club Network), Fareshare, Allergy UK and Purely Nutrition (PhunkyFoods). The single largest charity partner is 4Children with which the company has worked since 1996 and has partnered with the charity in the Make Space campaign, which calls for new style youth clubs for young people. On 1 July 2008 Nestlé launched the Make Space for Health programme which focuses on nutrition, health and wellness awareness among youth workers and promotes healthy lifestyles to young people outside the classroom. Nestlé support schools, charities and community groups local to its offices and factories mainly by way of product donations.

In kind support

Nestlé's main area of non-cash support is gifts in kind – the company providing product, furniture and equipment donations to local good causes.

Employee-led support

The York site has its own employee charitable trust, which raises funds from employees which are donated in small grants to local organisations in which employees hold an interest. The trust is The Nestlé Rowntree York Employees Community Fund Trust (Charity Commission no. 516702). Please contact Jackie Johnson for further information.

Payroll giving

A scheme is operated through an internal company community fund.

Exclusions

No support is given towards student expeditions, individuals, political causes, third-party fundraising events or the purchase of advertising space in charity programmes.

Applications

Applications should be made to nearest local site. Few national financial donations are given.

Provident Financial plc

Contact
Brent Shackleton, Community Affairs Manager, Colonnade, Sunbridge Road, Bradford, West Yorkshire BD1 2LQ
Tel: 01274 731111; Fax: 01274 727300; email: brent.shacleton@provident financial.com;
website: www.providentfinancial.com

Year end: 31/12/2007

Turnover: £669,200,000

Pre-tax profit: £115,200,000

Nature of business
Personal credit and insurance.

Main UK locations
Bradford

Cash donations: 2007 £776,751

Total contributions: £837,982

Community support policy

The company states on its website that:
Our community programme aims to help people who live and work in the areas in which we operate – our customers, agents, employees and the local community. We work with local partners to offer new opportunities and to play our part in the development of neighbourhoods and communities. The aim of our programme is to create new opportunities for young people. The projects and associations we support are wide-ranging and varied. Additionally, through the 'Provident in the Community' programme, support and encouragement is given to employees and agents to initiate and take part in fundraising activities within the communities in which they live and work.

Total community contributions by the company in 2007 were £837,982, of which £776,751 was in cash donations. A further £142,272 was attributed to management costs. We do not know what proportion of this went towards funding youth projects. Major beneficiaries included: Yorkshire Playhouse; Scottish Youth Hostel

Association; L'Ouverture; and Axis Theatre. Further details of some of these are given below.

L'Ouverture

L'Ouverture provides unique opportunities for young people to learn about the arts and the media. Attention is focused on those young people unlikely to find such opportunities elsewhere, including those from deprived inner city areas and those who have fallen between the cracks of the formal education system. Provident's funding helps the organisation work with young people from Lewisham, Tower Hamlets, Southwark and Lambeth in the provision of in-school sessions, holiday and Saturday clubs.

Give us a Break

Give Us a Break aims to provide new opportunities for young people to take part in outdoor activities and so increase their confidence and self-esteem. The company has joined forces with the Scottish Youth Hostel Association (SYHA) and its sister organisation in Ireland, the Irish Youth Hostel Association, to deliver these learning opportunities.

Employee-led support

Provident in the Community

This programme supports and encourages employees and agents to initiate and take part in fundraising activities within the communities in which they live and work. Provident sees it as a direct way of building on the relationships built between its customers and their agents, their families, friends and associates.

Support is provided in the form of financial donations, practical help, materials and advice. Provident believes that its involvement in such projects builds a greater understanding of the communities in which their customers, staff and agents live and work. It also

encourages the development of new skills and creates a sense of pride in what can be achieved.

In the last 12 months employees and agents across the UK home credit businesses gave time and raised funds for more than 200 local good causes through the scheme. Activities undertaken ranged from raffles to fun runs, and from mentoring to DIY skills. Through their efforts community groups and charities benefited from more than £150,000.

Exclusions

No support for appeals from individuals, heritage, medical research, overseas projects, political appeals, or religious appeals.

Requests for 'charity of the year' status are not considered.

Applications

In writing to the correspondent.

N M Rothschild & Sons Ltd

Contact
Annette Shepherd, Secretary to the Charities Committee, New Court, St Swithin's Lane, London EC4P 4DU
Tel: 020 7280 5000;
website: www.nmrothschild.com

Year end: 29/09/2008

Turnover: £402,047,000

Pre-tax profit: £72,286,000

Nature of business
The company and its subsidiaries carry on the business of merchant bankers. The parent company is Rothschild Continuation Ltd and the ultimate holding company is Rothschild Concordia A G, incorporated in Switzerland.

Main UK locations
London, Manchester, Leeds, Birmingham

Cash donations: 2007 £817,000

Grants to youth: £70,000

Community support policy

Rothschild has been at the centre of the world's financial markets for over 200 years. Today, it provides investment banking, corporate banking and private banking and trust services to governments, corporations and individuals worldwide. Rothschild is committed to supporting charities, both in the areas in which it operates and those in the wider community.

A charities committee was established in 1975 to consider the requests received every year from charities seeking financial support. Typically, the majority of cash donated goes to charities working in the fields of social welfare, young people, and healthcare. Around 50% of the money donated each year is in response to requests from Rothschild employees who have a connection with a particular charity. Applications from small, local charities are particularly welcomed.

The sum of £817,000 was charged against the profits of the group during the year in respect of gifts for charitable purposes. Of this, £285,000 was donated in response to the many hundreds of appeals the charities committee receive each year. A total of 234 new donations were made as a result with 24% (around £68,000) given in support of young people.

In addition to the above, support is given to a core group of charities which are reviewed regularly and to staff's 'adopted' charities. Other youth related charities supported included: Middlesex Young People's Club; YMCA England; Trinity Sailing Trust; Depaul Trust; and Music for Youth.

Employee-led support

Requests for support from staff in respect of charitable causes with which they are associated, or have an involvement, are actively encouraged.

Apart from making financial donations, the group also provides charitable support to local schools in the form of employee volunteers. In London, members of staff attend Bow School weekly to take part in lunchtime literacy and numeracy sessions with those students who need extra support, and a group of volunteers visits South Camden Community School fortnightly to lead mentoring sessions with teenage boys. In Manchester, staff take part in a literacy scheme at Manchester Academy. A full-time member of staff has now been employed to oversee and develop corporate social responsibility initiatives, and further volunteering-based projects are planned. The group is also a supporter of the Specialist Schools Trust (promoting a dialogue between educators and financial institutions) and has contributed to the achievement of 'specialist' status in maths, science, technology and computing at several schools in the Leeds area.

Payroll giving

The Give As You Earn scheme is in operation.

Exclusions

No response to circular appeals. No grants for advertising in charity brochures; animal welfare; appeals from individuals; fundraising events; overseas projects; political appeals; religious appeals; or sport.

Applications

In writing to the Secretary to the Charities Committee, which meets quarterly to make grant decisions.

St James's Place plc

Contact
The Secretary, St James's Place Foundation, 1 Tetbury Road, Cirencester, Gloucestershire GL7 1FP
Tel: 01285 640302;
website: www.sjp.co.uk

Year end: 31/12/2007

Pre-tax profit: £103,200,000

Nature of business
St James's Place plc is a financial services group involved in the provision of wealth management services.

Main UK locations
London

Cash donations: 2007 £1,200,000

Grants to youth: £75,000

Community support policy

St James's Place Capital plc channels its cash contributions to charity through the St James's Place Foundation (Charity Commission no.1031456). The objective of the foundation is to raise money for distribution to organisations that meet its main current theme of 'Cherishing the Children'. This theme is aimed at children and young people up to the age of 25 who are mentally and/or physically disabled, or have a life threatening or degenerative illness. The foundation now also supports the Hospice Movement.

Grants are given to qualifying organisations under a number of criteria. These are: major grants programme – up to £50,000 over two years to charities with a turnover of less than £2 million a year (please note that this programme did not run in 2007/08); small grants programme – up to £10,000 to charities with an income of under £600,000 a year; and major projects – funded from the company's matching contribution, a suitable charity is chosen and approached by the foundation's local office allocation – each of the company's 20 office locations is allocated a sum to use for any local charitable cause partner/staff supported projects or partner/staff fundraising on behalf specific UK children's charities.

In 2007, the company donated £1.2 million to the foundation which in turn made 187 grants totalling £1.7 million. Beneficiaries included: Birmingham Centre for Arts Therapies, Noah's Ark Trust, Open Door Youth Counselling, Straight Talking and Willow Foundation (£10,000 each); The Yard Adventure Centre (£9,600); Bag Books (£6,000); SNIP – Special Needs Information Point (£4,000); Youth Action Wiltshire (£2,838); and Friends Unite Newfield (£2,500). The largest grant during 2007 went to the Teenage Cancer Trust, which received £324,500 under the 'major projects' criteria.

Exclusions

No response to circular appeals, and no grants for advertising in charity brochures sponsorship or individuals.

Applications

The foundation will only consider applications from established charities or special needs schools for projects that meet the funding criteria.

The management committee of the St James's Place Foundation considers applications at its quarterly meetings. Application forms can be requested from the secretary.

Stagecoach Group plc

Contact
Stagecoach Group Community Fund, 10 Dunkeld Road, Perth PH1 5TW
Tel: 01738 442111; Fax: 01738 643648;
website: www.stagecoachgroup.com

Year end: 30/04/2008

Turnover: £1,763,600,000

Pre-tax profit: £167,300,000

Nature of business
Principal activity: the provision of public transport services in the UK and North America.

Main UK locations
Ilford, Chichester, Isle of Wight, Exeter, Gwent, Norhampton, Perth, Sheffield, Rugby, Sunderland, Oxford, Manchester, London, Liverpool, Cowdenbeath, Cambridge, Chesterfield, Carlisle, Gloucester, Ayr

Cash donations: 2008 £700,000

Grants to youth: £400,000

Community support policy

The Stagecoach Group operates more than 12,000 buses, coaches, trains and trams throughout the UK and provides funding to charitable and voluntary organisations at local, national and international level. In 2007/08, the company made charitable donations totalling £700,000 with much of the support being focused on education and young people. According to the company's website, it works closely with schools and police on local crime prevention initiatives and educating young people about the dangers and consequences of antisocial behaviour. Support is also given to many local initiatives that help provide opportunities for young people. Examples include long-term support for the Carroll Youth Centre in the South West, sponsorship of youth football, cricket and basketball teams in a range of locations, and involvement in a scheme to assist the rehabilitation of ex-offenders. The company continues to support the educational charity business dynamics which help young people prepare for the world of work.

In kind support

Stagecoach has a national agreement with Guide Dogs for the Blind that allows the dog trainers free travel on its buses and trains.

Employee-led support

The company also supports employees' volunteering/charitable activities by considering, where appropriate, financial help, allowing time off to volunteer, and matching employee fundraising.

Payroll giving
The Give As You Earn scheme is in operation.

Applications

In writing to the Stagecoach Group Community Fund at the above address.

Thales UK Ltd

Contact
Mike Seabrook, Thales Charitable Trust, 2 Dashwood Lang Road, The Bourne Business Park, Addlestone, Surrey KT15 2NX
Tel: 01932 824800; Fax: 01932 824887; email: mike.seabrook@thalesgroup.com; website: www.thalesgroup.co.uk

Year end: 31/12/2007

Turnover: £326,280,000

Pre-tax profit: £14,756,000

Nature of business
Principal activities: The design, manufacture and sale of defence electronic products, encompassing electronic warfare, radar, displays, defence radio and command information systems.

Main UK locations
Belfast, Birmingham, Bury St Edmunds, Glasgow, Doncaster, Stockport, Addlestone

Cash donations: 2007 £166,000

Grants to youth: £25,000

Community support policy

Donations by the company are primarily made through the Thales Charitable Trust (Charity Commission no. 1000162). The trust's policy is to relieve poor, needy, sick and disabled people, and to support those who are engaged in work, including research, to this end. Thus 70% of the budget is spent on health and medical care, 20% on social welfare and 5% on community services. Within these categories, however, support is given to youth projects. Thales donates around £150,000 a year to the charitable trust, all of which appears to be given away in grants. In 2007, the trust gave £25,000 to YouthNet UK in support of TheSite.org which provides young people with access to work and study advice. Support has also been given in the past to young engineers.

Exclusions

No support for circulars, individuals, expeditions, advertising in charity brochures, fundraising events or small, purely local events in areas of company presence. Unless there are exceptional reasons the trustees prefer to deal directly with a charity rather than with intermediaries.

Applications

All appeals for charitable donations should be sent in writing to the correspondent. Grant decisions are made by a donations committee which meets quarterly. No appeals are considered independently of head office as subsidiaries have no authority to respond.

The company has previously stated that it welcomes appeals from charities, but that the volume of mail is getting too large to handle. Thus, applicants should consider the nature and relevance of their appeal and the following advice from the charitable trust. Applicants are advised to apply at the same time every year. No reply is sent to unsuccessful applicants, and it is seldom worth repeating an appeal regularly if it has been rejected.

11 Raising money from local authorities

Local authorities are allocated funds from central government to provide services for communities in their area, including young people, and are an important source of funding for many voluntary groups.

Local authorities have a wide range of powers and duties. National policy is set by central government, but local councils are responsible for all day-to-day services and local matters. They are funded by government grants, council tax and business rates. Funds are distributed from their own budgets in grant form but also, increasingly, by contracting for service delivery and administering grants programmes on behalf of central government departments, notably Communities and Local Government.

Your relationship with the local authority will be made up of many parts: lobbying, profile raising, partnership building and applying for support. You will need to be clear about what you do and what you need and then make sure that the people who matter to you in the local authority become equally clear. When applying for funding you should know the local authority's priorities and what it is looking for from the relationship and be offering 'added value' or something extra. This will all take time and effort but will increase your chances of success.

Local authority funding and support for voluntary organisations

Local authority spending for voluntary organisations varies from authority to authority and comes in a number of forms, including:

- revenue, for what it costs to run your activity, from salaries and telephone calls to sessional youth workers and courses
- rate relief.

Case study

Example of a local authority youth service
The Liverpool Youth service

The Youth Service aims to provide Liverpool's young people with as many opportunities as possible to bring enrichment to their lives.

We place particular emphasis on securing services for those young people who have had least benefit from the education system.

We provide a variety of programmes and opportunities that are either educational or recreational in nature.

In order to be effective, however, we make sure that these opportunities are:

- *responsive to the needs of young people*
- *within easy travelling distance*
- *stimulating and exciting*
- *affordable*
- *good quality.*

The service works in partnership with other agencies including the following:

- *voluntary organisations*
- *Greater Merseyside Connexions Partnership*
- *the police*
- *Liverpool's Youth Offending Team (YOT)*
- *Citysafe.*

Each year the Youth Service presents a plan which is put together after consultation. It takes account of the following considerations:

- *Any progress which was made on the previous year's plans.*
- *Changes which have taken place in the environment.*
- *The identified needs of young people.*
- *The needs of the community in general.*

The bulk of local authority support for young people is through its youth service but support from other areas has been introduced to increase the amount of funding available, or at least to maintain a level of provision. Employment and training agencies, youth justice support, health monies and expanding education funds have contributed significantly to the range of funding sources local authorities use to resource their work with young people.

General grant giving – local authority community chests

As well as the specific departments, most councils will have a general grant-giving committee. Local authority grants to voluntary organisations are discretionary, but this particular source has a wide remit and can give to a range of organisations for events and activities that are not necessarily covered by other departments. The fund is sometimes called the Community Chest and can be applied for by any organisation within the authority's area. Grants vary in amount and you should check your local authority's limits before you apply.

Events such as youth conferences, festivals or tournaments may have authority-wide benefits and may be supported more on the lines of a sponsorship, particularly if there are publicity and increased profile opportunities.

There may be restrictions on how many times a year you can apply for funding. This need not alter your application for a one-off piece of equipment but if, for example, you are applying for volunteers to attend training courses at different times in the year, you will need to plan accordingly. All departmental budgets have allocations to be spent by the end of each financial year. If you apply towards the end of a budgetary period there may be too little money left and you will have to wait until the next financial year. Your council officers should be able to tell you how much money is left within a particular budget and the deadlines for applications.

The Community Assets Programme

Community Assets is funded by the Office of the Third Sector and managed by the Big Lottery Fund. The aim of the £30 million programme is to empower communities by the transfer of assets from local authorities to the third sector for community benefit.

Community Assets is intended to deliver the following outcomes.

1) Local third sector organisations have greater security and independence, and are better able to meet the needs of the communities they serve.

2) Communities have greater access to better facilities that respond to their needs.

3) There is more effective partnership working between local authorities and the third sector.

The Development Trusts Association (DTA) is working with Coin Street Community Builders, Community Matters and the Environment Trust to deliver comprehensive support to 38 'in principle' award winners. The partnerships involved in the programme cover a wide geographic spread and are from a mix of urban, rural and coastal environments.

Each area is benefiting from tailored packages of support from the DTA and partners to progress the transfer of a local authority asset to a third sector organisation. The support is intended to facilitate the development of high-quality capital delivery plans to underpin proposed refurbishment work by each partnership and includes design input; assistance with legal and governance issues; VAT advice; business planning; fundraising and marketing advice; community consultation support; and more generic capacity building activities.

Successful partnerships will start related asset refurbishment work during spring/summer 2009. The following are examples from the shortlist of successful 'in principle' grant offers.

Name of lead organisation	Name of partner organisation	Project name
Ashfield District Council	Ashfield Community Radio & Media Training	The Studio – Acacia Avenue Community Training and Centre
London Borough of Havering	Briar Community Association	Briar Community & Youth Project (BCYP)
Stoke-on-Trent City Council	Mitchell Memorial Youth Arts Centre Ltd	Mitchell Memorial Youth Arts Centre (MMYAC)
West Lindsey District Council	Young and Safe in Gainsborough	Young and Safe in Gainsborough (YASIG)

Support in kind

Local councils may be able to offer you support in kind as well as cash grants: second-hand office equipment and furniture; premises for your use either free or at a low rent; help with transport maintenance; staff secondments; and access to the council bulk-purchasing scheme, which may offer lower prices than elsewhere.

Rate relief

Local authorities can also give valuable indirect support to local charitable organisations through rate relief. The level of relief varies greatly from area to area, but the mandatory rate is 80% and the discretionary allowance can be up to 100%. The amount will be governed by the authority's policy and may depend upon the type of organisation. Rate relief is only given if you apply, and cannot be given retrospectively.

Contact the local authority for further details of its policy and how to apply. Claim while you can as there is an ongoing review of local authority discretionary rate relief.

Youth councils

In the last decade, local youth councils have gained in recognition, popularity and influence, enabling young people's participation in the political decision-making process.

These councils may exist alongside any of the local government tiers (county, district, borough, city, parish etc.). They may have grant-giving powers or have a consultative role with other local authority committees and their primary focus is to give young people a voice in local decisions and policies.

Different approaches are taken in different areas – there are rural and urban models of how a youth council should operate, single issue groupings, on housing or health for example, or shadow councils and other forums in which young people participate.

There are many formats but all youth councils should:

- be democratic – young people representing others and not just voicing their own concerns
- have access to power – to the committees and structures which make the decisions
- be able to act on things that matter to young people and get results.

The British Youth Council has developed a network of local youth councils, enabling young people to have a genuine voice at community level. These offer participants a practical way of expressing their opinions and experiences to MPs, local authorities and the wider community. If you would like to find out more about youth councils in your area and how to take part, contact the British Youth Council (see *Useful contacts and sources of information* on page 371).

Youth parliaments

Youth parliaments work to encourage young people to participate in the political process. They aim to provide a place where a young person's voice can be heard and an environment where young people's views are taken seriously and acted upon. They offer young people a democratic platform that is designed to foster responsibility, enable views to be heard and achieve change. The UK Youth Parliament is run by young people for young people and provides opportunities for 11 to 18 year olds to use their voice in creative ways to bring about social change. For more information visit www.ukyouthparliament.org.uk.

Local compacts

Local compacts have been or are being developed throughout most areas in England. Similar to the national compact, these set out the mutual responsibilities that the local authority and local statutory bodies have with the local voluntary sector. There seems to be a wide variation in the quality and effectiveness of local compacts – local organisations should try to find out how much progress their local authority has achieved so far and whether the agreement seems to be functioning as it should. For more information, including case studies, an information bank, and a register of local compacts, see www.thecompact.org.uk.

How local authorities can help

These are some examples of what local authorities support. Each area and authority will be different, and yours may support work with young people in other ways as well.

- Advice
- Equipment – to buy or loan
- Salaries
- Running costs – heating, lighting, etc.
- Project start-up costs
- Training
- Bursaries   *continued ...*

- Buildings
- Transport
- Refurbishment
- Sessional hours
- Sports and arts activities
- Help with programme development
- Access to other funders and programmes
- Publicity
- Endorsement
- Rate relief

Organisational structure of local authorities

It might make your application to the local authority easier if you understand how the authority is structured and who you need to get to know. There are two main ways that local government is organised, depending on where you live – one-tier or two-tier systems. There have been several reforms over the past 40 years, leading to different arrangements in different areas.

County and district councils

In most of England, there are two levels: a county council and a district council. These parts of the country are known as shire areas.

County councils

These cover large areas and provide most of the public services, including education, social services, public transport and libraries. They are divided into several districts.

District councils

These cover smaller areas and provide more local services, such as council housing, leisure facilities, local planning and waste collection. District councils with borough or city status are called borough council or city council instead of district council, but this doesn't change their role.

Unitary authorities

In the larger towns and cities of England, and in some smaller counties, there is just one level, called a unitary authority or a metropolitan district council. They are responsible for all local services. Some towns also have their own directly elected mayor.

In London, each borough is a unitary authority, but the Greater London Authority (the Mayor and Assembly) provides London-wide government with responsibility for certain services like transport and police.

Unitary authorities may be called borough council, city council, county council, district council, or just council.

Town and parish councils

In some parts of England there are also town and parish councils, covering a smaller area. They are responsible for services such as allotments, public toilets, parks and ponds, war memorials and local halls and community centres. They are sometimes described as the third tier of local government.

Joint services

Some local authorities share services covering a wider area, such as police, fire services and public transport. This may be done to avoid splitting up services when council structures are changed, or because some councils are too small to run an effective service on their own.

It is important for fundraisers to be aware of the organisational structure of their local authority and also the decision makers whose responsibilities are in line with their organisation's priorities.

Make personal contact

Where you are not sure how your local authority is structured, ring your local councillor's office, or arrange a visit, and ask about the local authority and how it works – this will be a useful introduction for your organisation. The chief executive's department will have a directory of local councillors' numbers. Local authorities have websites to publicise their initiatives and to increase accountability and this will also be a useful start to your research.

Contacting the appropriate office in your local authority can be time consuming and frustrating but how your local authority is set up will directly affect who you apply to and what you ask for, so it is worth spending some time getting to know the system and who does what within it.

Council officers will be able to tell you how much is available, if anything, and how it is spent. Councillors may be able to lobby on your behalf. Some parish council meetings are attended by local authority councillors, they may use meetings as a sounding board to find out about the local priorities and if your name is mentioned here and wins support, there may be more note taken at a district level.

The new role of local government

Strong and Prosperous Communities, published in October 2006, is a government white paper on the future role and structure of local government. It sets out many changes, including plans to give people more say on public services and action in their area. The Bill received Royal Assent in October 2008 and so far two implementation plans have been issued with a third and final document expected to follow sometime in the first half of 2009. You can view the latest document published on www.communities.gov.uk/publications/localgovernment/implementationplanprogress.

The main changes are:

- reducing central government control
- setting up the framework for strong and high-profile local leaders
- giving more power to local people and communities
- making sure local services go on getting better and become more coordinated.

Local authorities have a key role in leading the development of local strategic partnerships (LSPs) and the 'joining up' of service delivery plans, which places new responsibilities on local authorities to make connections between community needs and services.

Local strategic partnerships and local area agreements

LSPs are local bodies that bring together the local authority, the voluntary and community sector and the local business sector in a local authority area.

The LSP agrees a vision for the future of the area, called a sustainable community strategy and this vision then informs the negotiation of the local area agreement (LAA), which details specific targets and outcomes to be achieved over a three-year period at a local level.

LAAs simplify some central funding, help coordinate public services more effectively and allow greater flexibility for local solutions to local circumstances.

Through these means, LAAs are helping to devolve decision making and trying to reduce bureaucracy.

LAAs set out the local priorities that have been negotiated between all the main public sector organisations in your area, your local authority and central government. The ideas behind them are to:

- recognise that local services should reflect what local people want
- give more flexibility to local authorities and other public sector organisations in the ways they deliver services for local people
- make local authorities and other public services more accountable to local people
- reduce red tape and improve value for money
- enable local people to get more involved in decisions about local services.

You can obtain details of what the priorities are in your area by visiting www.localpriorities.communities.gov.uk.

LSPs are the mechanism through which community strategies are developed and regeneration and development money is delivered, and will reduce the number of different initiatives and partnerships in any given area.

Between 2001 and 2006, £60 million of funding was provided through the Community Empowerment Fund (part of the Neighbourhood Renewal Programme) to set up and maintain community empowerment networks in the 88 Neighbourhood Renewal Areas in England. These local structures facilitated the voluntary and community sector's (VCS) participation in LSPs in those areas. However, the vast majority of LSP areas have not had any funding specifically earmarked for VCS participation. Given the probability of a tighter fiscal environment in future years, it looks as though funding for the 88 areas will not be extended either.

The 2007 Third Sector Review announced an extra £6.5 million for VCS participation in LSPs, but this is not ring-fenced. Even if they are able to participate effectively in LSPs, there is no guarantee that local voluntary groups will be able to access funding locally in the same way as LAAs become more widespread. The white paper referred to earlier recognises the need to maintain small grants programmes for local organisations. However, there is no guarantee that this will be the case and much of the funding for delivering LAA targets may be in the form of contracts or go to single organisations that are involved in the LSP and are commissioned to run larger projects to fulfil the LAA targets.

The Third Sector Review announced several initiatives to support local groups, but largely avoided addressing the impact of LAAs on the numerous funding streams these groups have come to depend on.

The establishment of LSPs across England and the increasing importance of LAAs means that making contacts and forging relationships with members of these partnerships is also crucial. In many areas, particularly in the 88 Neighbourhood Renewal Areas that received Community Empowerment Fund money, there may be established networks of voluntary organisations set up to represent the voluntary sector on the LSP. In many cases this will be led by an already established support body, such as the local council for voluntary service. If you want to be able to participate in the activities of LSPs and have an influence on the decisions they make, you will need to become actively involved in some way.

Getting in touch

Once you have decided how your local authority is organised, you need to approach the appropriate officials. The named office that has responsibility for youth varies from authority to authority. Youth services may come under education; some include youth provision under leisure services; others will have a wide-ranging function called community services, or cultural and community services where youth services will be found. Where there is one, a key contact will be the principal youth officer.

Whichever way your local authority is organised, find out:

- Who takes the lead in developing and supporting young people? Which council, county, district etc. and then, which departments?
- Who makes the policies which affect young people (for example, councillors or committees)?
- Who makes these policies happen (for example, officers and offices)?

Get to know the key people and policies. It is important for local organisations to keep abreast of changes in the system operating in their authority. The local authority itself should be your first point of call, but the Local Government Association – www.lga.gov.uk – is also a useful resource for information.

Fundraising at any level is most effective when you connect with key people who are enthusiastic about your cause and can support you and it is much more effective to meet them personally, if that's possible, than to write. In local authorities the main people to contact are:

- local authority officers
- local councillors.

You should be proactive in meeting the people who can influence and help your organisation – it is much better to make your group known before you ask for support. If you do not yet know of any local people who have influence in the community, ask your members, parents, volunteers and staff to find someone who does. If there is someone connected with your organisation who has particular experience or knowledge of making things happen locally, use them to make introductions for you and to promote the project themselves.

Local authority officers

Your first point of contact with the authority will usually be an officer within one of the departments or directorates. Officers are paid members of staff employed to implement council policies and can help your project in many ways. In some local authorities a principal youth officer heads up the statutory youth service in the area. In some areas there will be only one youth officer and in others there will be several with their own projects and expertise (maybe in funding or training) or with responsibility for particular youth areas. You should also bear in mind that administrative officers often have detailed knowledge of what is happening and may have the most overall information.

There may also be staff working in other departments who can advise and help. For example, if you are running an after-school club or work with those at risk of exclusion from school, you may find a useful contact within the education department. Where your work involves young people with disabilities, young women and girls or young people from a particular ethnic group, there may be an officer with specific responsibilities for services under these headings.

In all cases you will need to keep officers informed about your organisation and ensure that your activities are promoted within their department. Most council websites are informative and helpful and you should be able to find who you are looking for from these. If you are unsure which officer you should speak to, contact the chief executive's office, which will be able to give you a name as a starting point.

Officers make recommendations to councillors to act upon and you should brief them well and update them regularly. They will want to know how your proposal is to work; what resources (not just money) will be required; whether there is community support; whether there is opposition; and any possible repercussions from supporting your activity.

Like other funders, local authorities may want clear acknowledgement of, and publicity for, the support given by the council and you should have an idea of how you will do this. Your briefing should include an awareness of your local authority's strategic plans and how it is implementing best-value measures within the authority.

When contacting local authority officers and councillors, follow up telephone calls and meetings with a letter with the key points you wish to make; this will be helpful to you both in summarising the current position and any action either party needs to take.

Councillors

Councillors are representatives of their local community; they serve on committees and decide policy following briefings given by local authority officers. The fact that they are local representatives gives you the greatest point of leverage, as their first duty is to represent the people in their ward. If you are working with young people you are contributing to local communities and councillors should be interested in what you are doing. You need to engage with them and make them enthusiastic about your work.

When you need help from a number of departments within the local authority, councillors can sponsor your application and generally help the progress of a proposal. They may help to broker a deal between departments that can give larger funding to a project than could be given by a single department.

If you are looking for county (as opposed to district) funding, councillors can also help to cross district council lines. For this to happen you will probably need to promote the regional benefits of your proposal. Local councillors on your side will help to identify which county officers to speak to and the channels to go through. They can also make a difference on the committees they participate in.

Local councillors are listed in your town hall and local citizen's advice bureaux, which will also give details of their surgery hours. You can also search the *Municipal Yearbook*, published by Hemming Information Services, available in your local library. Some local authorities list councillors and committee members on their websites. You can contact your local ward councillors at their home address (they expect this) or through the local authority. You should write care of the local authority when contacting councillors other than your own.

Be realistic in your approach and consider the scale of your activity and what you are asking for. Remember that, while the chair and vice chair of any committee are obviously central to any decision making, they are also the busiest people.

They will be key contacts, but you will have to work around committed schedules. Many committee meetings are open to the public and publicised daily in the town hall.

Bear in mind that the balance of political power can be very different between the various tiers of local government. It is important to be able to present your case in different ways to attract the support of politicians with different remits. Keeping informed and aware of political and structural change will help your approach.

Promoting your cause may seem daunting at first. However, if you are clear about why the local authority should support you, your enthusiasm and a well-argued case will at least guarantee a hearing. Local authorities are like other funders and will want to know why they should support you and what they are getting for their support. Briefing councillors and officers is part of this process. It may be useful to refer to *Promoting Your Cause*, published by Directory of Social Change (*see Useful contacts and sources of information* on page 371).

When briefing councillors, ensure that what you say is based on facts and argue your case on its merits. Don't assume they have background knowledge of your organisation, the issue or the approach you are taking or of where young people contribute to the community.

Relationships built up with councillors over time will prove valuable, so try to involve them in your work, invite them to meet your group or ask them to address a meeting of your supporters.

Which departments should you approach?

Local authorities organise their departments in different ways. They have various functions; for example, housing, community services, social services and education. Each of these functions includes a number of responsibilities, for example, cultural services (which may be a separate department or be part of community services) will be responsible for parks, gardens, cemeteries, arts and libraries, sports development and recreation, and sometimes the youth service.

Other departments

Depending upon your project there may be departments in the local authority other than the youth service that you could approach. Some are obvious, others less so. In each case you will need to look into their current services, priorities and timetables for applications. Research their budgets, usually available through committee minutes, as it is useful to know how much they have to spend.

You also need to look closely at who benefits from your activities and whether there are other parts of the local authority that may be interested in your proposal. There may be help for those working with young people in the following areas:

- education
- social services
- sports development
- the arts
- opportunities for people with disabilities
- minority ethnic communities
- women
- health promotion
- increasing awareness of the local authority
- urban development and regeneration
- rural isolation
- environmental improvement
- voluntary sector liaison
- community safety.

Where your project fits in with a department's current priorities and concerns, it may welcome your approach. The social services department, for example, may be interested in projects such as:

- after school clubs
- work with young parents
- work with young asylum seekers or refugees
- work with young travellers
- counselling and information services
- work with young gay men and lesbians
- work with young people leaving care
- work with young carers
- reducing youth crime.

The education department may consider projects such as:

- playground activities in schools
- work with those at risk of exclusion from school or non-attenders
- training
- literacy and numeracy support

- play schemes
- work with unemployed young people
- work with young people with special needs
- health education.

Local contacts

For grants and other forms of advice and help, get in touch with the range of local authority officers who are responsible for information and support services relevant to your organisation. In many local authorities there are specialist grants officers with the specific remit of providing funding information to voluntary organisations, so these are the obvious first port of call. Find out if your local authority has such an officer and subscribe to any bulletins on funding or other useful services that are offered.

While it is vital to contact the specialist grants officer (if there is one) or to find the officers who service the committees relevant to your youth work, you should also find out the names of the councillors serving on committees, particularly the chair. Try to enlist the support of your local councillors in the ward where you are working, whether they are from the party in overall control of the council or in opposition and find out about their interests.

You may also need to develop working relationships with officers dealing with regeneration, employment and training and with links to European Structural Funds (see Chapter 13 *Raising money from Europe*). The government offices for the regions and the regional development agencies have key roles in these areas, and any contacts you can develop will be helpful. However, officers in your local authority may also be able to provide you with advice and direct you as necessary to relevant officers in the regional bodies.

It is worth noting that although many decisions are made by councillors, briefing sessions by council officers can be hugely influential. Assuming that councillors are solely responsible for decision making can lead to missed opportunities – at central government level, there will be many different people behind the decisions that are made.

Establish a relationship

Local authorities are similar to other funders in this guide in that personal relationships count. You need to build your relationship with your local authority as you would any other potential supporter. Particularly if you are a new project, you should not start by asking the local authority for money; you need to work with them in partnership to develop a project and win support.

Before approaching councillors and council officers, it is sensible to find out how much your local council gives for your area of work and the particular projects it supports. This information is readily available in the minutes of council and committee meetings and you may also find it on your local council's website.

It might also help to find out what other councils are doing. If your council is spending very little on voluntary youth organisations, it may be useful to be able to underline this point by making suitable comparisons – though this will probably not help you much in the short term (in that it would be unlikely that the council could increase its budget).

Research

You should get to know the working procedures of your local council. Find out the following.

- What principal responsibilities each tier of local government in your area has, particularly with regard to your own area of activity.
- What each relevant council's stated policies are. If, for example, a council lays strong emphasis on providing educational facilities and services, you may be able to take advantage of this when applying for a grant for an educational component of your work.
- How and when decisions on grants are taken. You need to know both the procedure and the timetable.
- Which organisations the council has funded in the past, and the amounts it has given in individual grants. This more than anything else will give you a picture of the council's general approach and preferences.
- Which councillors and council officers will be involved in the decision to fund you, and which are likely to be sympathetic to your organisation.

Making your case

Once you have identified the councillors and council officers whose support you need, it is advisable to spend time interesting them in your organisation. Invite them to events, which will also be a good opportunity for them to meet the young people in your group and your colleagues. If there are people with local influence in your organisation or who support you in some way, persuade them to talk to some of the key councillors and officials about the value of your work.

It is a good idea to prepare the ground in this way before you make any formal application for a grant, so that you have a fair idea of what will and what will not be acceptable. Make sure that all those responsible for contacting and lobbying councillors are properly briefed: first, on the local importance of the organisation (backed up by figures, analysis, etc.); second, on how your work relates to the policies and priorities of the council; and third, on what the council can do to help. If councillors receive conflicting or muddled statements from a variety of sources, this can do considerable damage to your case.

You may find it difficult to prioritise spending time in meetings or on phone calls with representatives of statutory bodies, but keep in mind that in any community – even in larger urban areas – it's a relatively small number of people who make the majority of decisions across all sectors. These people may often have more than one job title. For example, the chief executives of local businesses, primary care trusts, police and even councillors may also be trustees for charities in the area.

Try to establish relationships to give you access – to be able to advance your cause, find out important information and have a level of influence on decisions where it is appropriate. If you aren't a known quantity, whether on an official or unofficial basis, this will be much more difficult.

Demonstrating the value of your project

What features of your project make it attractive to your local authority? How do any of the following apply to your organisation or project?

- Fits in with local authority priorities (essential)
- Local benefits
- Regional benefits
- Large number of different groups benefit (which ones?)
- Community run; participation of young people
- Innovative approach
- Addresses special needs
- Matching funds raised
- Established track record
- Excellence
- Sound finances
- Includes 'hard to reach' groups

continued...

- Fills a gap or augments local authority service provision
- Number of different bodies/organisations involved (which ones?)
- Established and enthusiastic membership
- Large number of benefits from a small grant (what benefits?)
- Local support
- Good publicity for the local authority
- Value for money
- Other (list)

Particular considerations

Apart from information particular to your council, there are criteria that all councils are likely to use when considering your proposal. You should take these into account at an early stage.

- How well do the work and objectives of your organisation fit in with your council's stated policies and priorities?
- Are there any organisations in the area doing similar work? If there are, do these organisations receive local authority funding? Are there sound reasons why the authority should fund your organisation as well as, or instead of, those it is already funding?
- How successful are you? Is your work of a high calibre? And what outside evidence can you provide to support this? How many people do you serve? How many of them come from the local authority area? Are there other ways in which you can demonstrate local community support, such as membership or local fundraising?
- How well organised are you in terms of financial and administrative control? Are you reliable? Is your work endorsed by way of grants from other official bodies?
- How strongly do the local people feel about you? Would local opposition be strong if you were forced to disband from lack of funds?

Remember, local authorities are like other funders in what they want to know from you:

- What do you want to do?
- Why do you want to do it?
- How will you make it happen?
- Who will be accountable?

- What difference will the work make to the local area?
- What do you want from the local authority?

In other words, they will look to see if you:
- have identified a clear need
- have produced a good and workable plan
- have costed your work
- will be able to measure the value and outcomes of your work.

Think differently

When you meet with people from your local authority, don't talk about funding, talk about collaboration. Council officials don't see themselves as being there to underwrite your core costs year in, year out or even to provide only financial support, and they have their own views on what service provision they want to see in the area. Show how you understand their priorities and concerns and how your work fits into these, rather than expect them to support you to do whatever you want to do.

Media coverage

While you are talking privately to council officers and councillors you should also be directing your efforts at your local media to reinforce your message. Items on local radio and in the local paper about the importance and quality of your work and reviews and interviews in which you outline future plans of benefit to the community should also have an effect on councillors' opinions.

Regular contact

Whatever support you are looking for, you should be talking regularly to council officers and councillors, especially those who are of particular importance to you. Keep them informed of your activities throughout the year, not just when it's grant application time. Establishing relationships shouldn't be just about funding; if it is you will find them more difficult to maintain and you won't be maximising the other potential benefits.

Acknowledgements and personal thanks

Like other funders, local authorities should be thanked for their support and acknowledged appropriately. Local authorities appreciate credit and recognition for their contribution to a project. Tell them how you will publicise their grant and generally help people to view their local authority more positively.

Getting information

The Local Government Association produces some very useful fact sheets about the structures and responsibilities of local authorities, which are available on the web. The funding advice officer in your local council for voluntary service, rural community council or their equivalents should be able to inform you about the committee structures of the council in your area and provide you with contacts and information on funding programmes.

Some final dos and don'ts

Do

- Find out how your local authority works
- Find and contact key local officers
- Build good relationships with local councillors across the political spectrum
- Find out about and understand authority/department priorities
- Think creatively about your project
- Use local media to raise your profile
- Attend meetings regularly
- Be clear and to the point
- Keep well informed about changes in criteria/priorities
- Be persistent
- Budget realistically
- Show 'value for money'
- Find out about application procedures and deadlines
- Plan ahead
- Research fully
- Demonstrate the benefits of your project to the council and its community as well as to your own young people

continued...

Don't

■ Leave talking to councillors and officers until you need money

■ Limit your project to one narrow departmental interest

■ Forget in kind support from your local authority

■ Be modest about what you can offer

■ Let information become out of date

■ Plan in the short term – look to the future

■ Waffle

■ Take local authority support for granted

■ Think that if it has funded you once it will always continue with its support

■ Give up

12 Raising money from government

Introduction

In recent years the voluntary or 'third' sector has been high on the political agenda and consequently government is now a major funder for voluntary organisations. The voluntary sector is currently funded by central government grant programmes totalling £1.4 billion (*The Funders' Almanac 2008*, DSC). There is a range of government funding available for voluntary organisations working with young people, specifically aimed at projects involving or being run by young people or that have a broad scope, making them applicable to youth projects and organisations.

Government funding is an avenue that organisations should explore. However, as this chapter will highlight, it operates in a very different way to other sources of funding detailed in this guide. As always with fundraising, getting money from government begins with being able to access relevant and appropriate funding information, followed by a steely determination to see it through to fruition.

To help organisations approach and hopefully access government funding, this chapter will:

- outline recent developments in government policy and the way this influences funding cycles
- distinguish and identify the different types of funding from government
- suggest ways of accessing support specific to voluntary organisations working in the youth sector.

What does government have to offer?

Types of government funding

The type of funding your organisation applies for will depend very much on its size, capacity, what you require funding for and the level of relationship you are willing to have with government. There are many different relationships and many potential opportunities for funding which bring their different demands and responsibilities.

Funding options

Loan schemes

These are usually low interest and generally repayable over a longer period than a grant. They are to support the increase of an organisation's capacity or the development of social enterprise.

Direct grants

Direct grants are most commonly awarded by central government or its agencies (see below) and can range from a one-off small grant to large grants awarded for up to five years.

Grant in aid

This is given to individual voluntary organisations on an annual review basis and is increasingly characterised as 'strategic funding'.

Contracts

Contracts with government, which occur most extensively at a local authority level.

Areas of government

- **Central** – funding is administered directly from the department or departmental directorate.
- **Agencies** – funding is administered by non-departmental public bodies (NDPBs) or other executive agencies appointed by central government.
- **Regional** – funding is channelled through government offices for the regions (GORs) and regional development agencies (RDAs).
- **Local** – local partnerships of various types and funding distributed by local authorities.

Identifying which departments or agencies are most relevant to your organisation and the work that you do is the first step in approaching funding from central government and NDPBs. Within government, there are likely to be a number of government departments, agencies and public bodies interested in working with your organisation. However, potential funders may not be those most obvious to organisations working with young people, but relevant because you fulfil one of their policy objectives. For example, the Department for Environment, Food and Rural Affairs may have funding programmes to engage young people in environmental conservation.

Some things you should know about government funding

Government funding can be quite complex and unpredictable so it's important to know what to expect. If you are thinking of applying for funding from any of the sources and types of government funding explained above, there are a number of things you need to bear in mind:

- **Funding programmes can change frequently.** In contrast to grant-making charities, which tend to maintain a relatively stable funding 'identity', government funds come and go with shifting 'political winds' (*Funders' Almanac*, page 45 DSC). Criteria and priorities may vary from year to year, or the fund may only be available for a year or two and then disappear or change into something quite different.

- **Different funders and funding programmes associated with government are not 'joined up' and funding is distributed in different ways.** The design of funding programmes varies between and even within departments.

- **Funding announcements are commonly made at very short notice**, and you typically have less than six weeks to put together an application – keeping up to date with government policies and their objectives is a good way to predict announcements and prevent a panic when relevant funding streams occur.

- **For most programmes the number of applicants is far greater than the funding can support.** Typically only between 5 and 20% of applicants will be successful (*The Complete Fundraising Handbook*, page 180 DSC).

- **Because funds are public money, there are usually extensive monitoring and reporting requirements which can be time consuming and difficult to manage**. However, there are smaller grants available which do not have such demanding requirements. The Cabinet Office's Grassroots Grants, for example, is an open programme with minimal reporting requirements (details of these grant programmes are outlined in the 'What's available?' section on page 308).

It's all about objectives

With government funding from any level it is not enough for you to show that your organisation is doing good and important work. You must be able to demonstrate that the work falls within the government department's own strategies and helps it to meet those aims and objectives. The key point is well stated by John Marshall

> *Government grants are primarily designed to meet departmental policy objectives and programme outcomes. These should of course be reflected in the published criteria for grants. Applications are, therefore, expected to demonstrate clearly how they will help departments achieve their objectives. Too many applicants seem to assume that the core work of their organisation is reason enough to secure a government grant. I am afraid that no matter how effective or important the work of your organisation, you need to show how it meets the objectives of the funder.*

> *The Complete Fundraising Handbook*, DSC, page 180

For example, the aims of government grant programmes were refocused in line with the Youth Crime Action Plan (2008). Grants funding from the Youth Sector Development Fund now have 'preventing youth crime and re-offending' as a key thematic focus, and 'supporting families to prevent youth crime' will feature in new criteria being developed for the Children and Young People's Grant and Parenting Fund. Details of these grant programmes are outlined in the 'What's available?' section on page 308. The key point in this is to be able to be prepared to tailor your application around programmes' objectives, without letting them compromise your own.

Policy

As explained in the quote above, funding from government is shaped by its objectives. Therefore, it is important to be alert to changes and developments within government policies and structures. The remits, and sometimes even the names of departments change, new funding programmes will emerge and existing ones alter accordingly. It is important to keep up to date with policy changes, but some key areas to be aware of are outlined in the following section.

Key policy areas and why they are important

The Office of the Third Sector (OTS)

OTS was created at the centre of government in May 2006 as part of the Cabinet Office to drive forward the government's role in supporting the voluntary sector, and bring together sector-related work from across government. OTS has a number of funding streams specifically targeted at the voluntary sector but is also a good way to keep track of changes and developments within government that are relevant to the voluntary sector. The easiest way to do this is to sign up to OTS's newsletter, which you can do on its website, see www.cabinetoffice.gov.uk/third_sector.

Capacitybuilders

Capacitybuilders is a non-departmental public body (NDPB) funded by the OTS. Capacitybuilders exists to help create a more effective third sector by working to improve support for third sector organisations. The resulting national support services opened at the beginning of April 2008 and aim to improve infrastructure of the voluntary and community sector through the following workstreams: campaigning and advocacy; collaboration; equalities and diversity; income generation; leadership and governance; marketing and communications; modernising volunteering; performance management; and responding to social change. For more information see www.capacitybuilders.org.uk.

Futurebuilders

The Futurebuilders' initiative aims to increase the participation of voluntary and community sector organisations in the delivery of public services, primarily through loans and some grant-based finance. The fund focuses on five themes, deemed to be areas of public services in need of improvement: community cohesion, crime, education and learning, health and social care; and support for children and young people. For more information see www.futurebuilders-england.org.uk

The Small Organisation Tender Fund helps finance tendering costs or capacity building work – such as legal costs, advice from procurement specialists, financial expertise and bidding staff costs – to help small organisations win specific public sector contracts.

Grants will be offered on a first come, first served basis for up to 10% of a contract value, up to a maximum of £15,000. Contracts being tendered for must hold a minimum value of £30,000.

For the purposes of the Small Organisation Tender Fund, a 'small organisation' is defined as one with an annual turnover of less than £250,000. Applicants must also have been trading for a minimum of one year.

Futurebuilders England, a consortium of voluntary sector organisations, administered the first phase of the £150 million Futurebuilders Fund following its launch in 2004. The Adventure Capital Fund (ACF) is managing the second phase of the Futurebuilders Fund from 1 April 2008 to 31 March 2011, with an additional £65 million of government funds. The second phase of Futurebuilders will open up a fund to bids from third sector organisations delivering *any* public service.

Key pieces of legislation on youth

DCSF Children's Plan and Every Child Matters Legislation
The Children's Plan was launched in November 2000 to tackle disadvantage among children and young people. The Every Child Matters legislation that followed introduced a ten-year plan from government with the following five main outcomes.

Every Child Matters outcomes:

Being healthy: enjoying good physical and mental health; living a healthy lifestyle.

Staying safe: being protected from harm and neglect; growing up able to look after yourself.

Enjoying and achieving: getting the most out of life; developing skills for adulthood.

Making a positive contribution: giving back to the local community and society; not offending or behaving anti-socially.

Economic wellbeing: overcoming socio-economic disadvantages to achieve full potential in life.

For more information visit the website: www.everychildmatters.gov.uk

---

The most important aspect of this legislation is that it advocated a multi-agency approach and 'joined-up thinking'. In theory, this includes voluntary and community sector organisations in the decision making process as well as being involved in the delivery. How this works in practice will vary depending on your local authority.

Aiming High for Young People

This is 'a ten-year strategy for positive activities'. This document sets out a strategy to transform facilities and support services for young people in England.

Aiming High for Young People: A ten year strategy for positive activities, DCSF 2007 (www.everychildmatters.gov.uk/youthmatters/aiminghigh/)

The Youth Crime Action Plan 2008

In particular, the Action Plan aims to invest in the capacity of third sector organisations to reduce youth crime.

Initiatives include:

Teenage Pregnancy Unit www.everychildmatters.gov.uk/teenagepregnancy

Youth Justice www.everychildmatters.gov.uk/youthjustice

The Respect Task Force www.respect.gov.uk

Children's Fund

Since April 2008, funding has been distributed to local authorities and pooled with other funding to form a new area-based grant for improving a wide range of outcomes, including those for children and young people. The new area-based grant is not ring-fenced, but resources included in it will remain identifiable and transparent.

Distributing funding to local authorities on a non ring-fenced basis gives them the freedom and flexibility to make spending decisions based on the needs and circumstances of their local communities. It is also in line with government's commitment to rationalise funding streams and to deliver services in a more joined-up and integrated way.

www.everychildmatters.gov.uk/strategy/childrensfund/

What's available?

This section gives you an overview of government funding programmes available, to illustrate the variety of funding types to pursue and to point you in the right direction. To remain current and as useful as possible the chapter will outline trends and signpost organisations to possible funding areas for youth projects, rather than acting as a directory of available grant schemes. As mentioned earlier government funding is likely to change with shifting political winds, and although the majority of the grants programmes listed here are likely to be around for the foreseeable future, it is important to keep a tab on changes.

Central government funding

Arguably, the government department with central responsibility for funding youth work is the Department for Children, Schools and Families (DCSF). Other departments, particularly the Department for Innovation, Universities and Skills (DIUS) and the Department for Culture, Media and Sport (DCMS) will also feed into this. Some funding programmes are voluntary sector specific, others will include public sector and sometimes private sector organisations. The Office of the Third Sector at the Cabinet Office offers a range of funding opportunities targeted specifically at the voluntary sector.

Trends in central government funding

- The period funding is offered for can range from one-off grants to grants lasting five years and more. The most common funding length is one to three years. Most funds also open on a yearly or multi-year basis, though this should not be relied upon.

- Applying for government grants is generally a lengthier process than with other grant-giving bodies. Organisations considering applying for government grants should allow sufficient time and resources. For this reason it is essential to get hold of as much information as possible about the grant and read all guidelines thoroughly.

- Applications are now often a two-stage process, with an initial short 'expression of interest' form. This should mean that less time is spent applying for funds for which organisations are ineligible or unsuitable. If the department/administrator approves the project outlined in the first stage, applicants are then invited to submit full bids.

Grant schemes

General

Adventure Capital Fund and Adventure Capital Fund – Business Development Grants

Awarding department: Cabinet Office

The Adventure Capital Fund (ACF) offers a range of investments and support to develop community-based enterprises. The aim of ACF is to fill the investment gap that faces community enterprise organisations, and to increase investment-readiness of community organisations wishing to move to greater sustainability through enterprise. The Business Development Grant is targeted at community enterprises in their early stages of development to improve their investment readiness and sustainability through developing their skills and capacity.

Futurebuilders and Futurebuilders Tender Fund (managed by ACF)

Awarding department: Cabinet Office

The Futurebuilders initiative aims to increase the sector's delivery of public services by providing funding primarily in the form of loans. The idea is that low-interest loans enable the organisation to develop sufficiently to become 'investment ready', meaning that they are able to compete for service delivery contracts from statutory bodies. Futurebuilders is unique in that applicants are not required to fill out an application form. Futurebuilders also offers a Tender Fund of interest-free three-year loans of between £3,000 and £50,000 to community and voluntary sector organisations that need relatively small sums to help them tender successfully for specific public service delivery contracts.

At the end of 2008, Futurebuilders had made £270 million worth of investments, ranging from £300 to £2 million.

Futurebuilders also launched a Small Organisation Tender Fund at the beginning of 2009, offering grants to small third sector organisations that need small sums of money to help them tender successfully for specific public sector contracts. The fund operates on a rolling basis; however, a limited pot of £220,000 is available.

Youth

First Light Movies

Awarding department: Department for Culture, Media and Sport

First Light Movies funds groups of young people aged between 5 and 19 through three funding schemes: the Pilot and Studio Awards and the What's the Big Idea?

award. The Pilot Award offers up to £5,000 for one short film lasting a maximum of five minutes. What's the Big Idea also provides small grants (up to £3,000) for script development projects that team young people with script professionals. The Studio Award offers larger grants, of up to £30,000, for between two and four films. First Light Movies allocates £700,000 of National Lottery funding per year to its funding schemes.

Youth Sector Development Fund – Round 3

Awarding department: Department for Children, Schools and Families

Round 3 of the Youth Sector Development Fund (YSDF) focuses on smaller youth third sector organisations with a turnover of under £1 million, and with a proven track record of delivering positive activities and support to the most disadvantaged young people, particularly on Friday and Saturday nights. DCSF is particularly interested in proposals that have a thematic focus on preventing young people from committing crime or becoming involved in anti social behaviour, gun or gang crime, in line with the Youth Crime Action Plan and wider government strategies on safer communities and cutting crime.

The fund's total fund value is £30 million, with grants of up to £2.5 million (for revenue costs only).

Funding cycle: annual rounds

Contact information: tel: 0845 630 8699; email: ysdf@ecotec.com; website: www.dcsf.gov.uk

Children, Young People and Families Grant Programme

Awarding department: Department for Children, Schools and Families

The Children, Young People and Families Grant Programme is a national grant programme to improve outcomes for children, young people and families (parenting and couple relationships) in England. The programme provides strategic and innovation grants to organisations doing work of national significance that support DCSF's Every Child Matters programme and the DCSF Children's Plan.

Young People's Fund 2: Local Grants

Awarding department: Department for Culture, Media and Sport

The Young People's Fund 2: Local Grants programme aims to put young people in England at the heart of local issues and services that affect their lives *and* to lead on developing the activities and services they want in their local area. The programme is administered by the Big Lottery Fund (BIG) and is available for voluntary and community sector organisations.

v Match Fund

Awarding department: Cabinet Office

v aims to inspire more investment in youth volunteering and help charities to involve young volunteers in their work. v prioritises investing in projects that focus on engaging young people who have never volunteered before, including hard-to-reach and under-represented groups. Through the v Match Fund, v will match up to 100% of new investment from the private sector to fund projects that create volunteering opportunities for 16–25 year olds in England.

Changing Spaces: Access to Nature

Awarding department: Department for Environment, Food and Rural Affairs

Access to Nature funds projects that improve opportunities to access, enjoy and engage with the natural environment, particularly projects encouraging the involvement of young people, older people, black and minority ethnic groups and people with disabilities. Grant funding is available to voluntary and community organisations and statutory bodies across England. Access to Nature is an open grants programme run by Natural England with £25,000,000 funding from BIG's Changing Spaces programme.

Young Advisors Scheme

Awarding department: Communities and Local Government

The Young Advisors Scheme was developed in 2005 to empower young people to have an influence on decision making and services in their communities.

REACH National Role Model Programme

Awarding department: Communities and Local Government

The government has been running a major project to invest in the future of the next generation. REACH aims to make sure that black boys and young black men aspire to, and achieve more. One of the five recommendations of the REACH project is to improve the visibility of positive black male role models.

The Community Spaces Programme

Awarding department: Department of Energy and Climate Change

This programme is targeted at youth groups for youth projects. The aim is to get young people to be fully involved in projects and, where possible, lead projects that are of direct benefit to them (www.direct.gov.uk/en/YoungPeople/ Youthfunds/DG_067006).

Agencies (NDPBs)

As well as central government departments there is a substantial number of public bodies that manages funding programmes relevant to the voluntary sector – the key is to distinguish those that are most relevant and therefore likely to fund your organisation. Like central departments they disburse funds according to their strategies.

The official definition of an NDPB is 'a body which has a role in the process of national government, but is not a government department or part of one, and which accordingly operates to a greater or lesser extent at arm's length from ministers'.

Some examples of NDPBs working with young people:

- **The National Youth Agency** to support youth work developments
- **The Prince's Trust** for youth employment and training opportunities
- **YMCA** for accommodation.

Regional funding

Regional development agencies (RDAs) are financed through a single programme budget (the 'Single Pot'). This pooled budget consists of government departments' funding to RDAs, the majority being supplied by the Communities and Local Government (CLG).

The funding, once allocated, is available to the RDAs to spend as they see fit in order to achieve the regional priorities.

Regional development agencies

EEDA (East of England RDA)
www.eeda.org.uk

East Midlands Development Agency
www.emda.org.uk

London Development Agency
www.lda.gov.uk

One North East (North East of England RDA)
www.onenortheast.co.uk

Northwest RDA
www.nwda.co.uk

SEEDA (South of England RDA)
www.seeda.co.uk

South West RDA
www.southwestrda.org.uk

ADVANTAGE (West Midlands RDA)
www.advantagewm.co.uk

Yorkshire Forward
www.yorkshire-forward.com

Government offices for the regions operate as the voice of central government, through nine offices across England. Government offices should have dedicated voluntary and community sector liaison officers in each region. They manage significant spending programmes on behalf of their sponsor departments, including a number of European funds.

Government offices for the regions

Government Office for the East of England
www.goeast.gov.uk

Government Office for the East Midlands
www.goem.gov.uk

Government Office for London
www.gos.gov.uk/gol

Government Office for the North East
www.go-ne.gov.uk

Government Office for the North West
www.gos.gov.uk/gonw

Government Office for the South East
www.go-se.gov.uk

Government Office for the South West
www.gosw.gov.uk

Government Office for the West Midlands
www.go-wm.gov.uk

Government Office for Yorkshire and the Humber
www.gos.gov.uk/goyh

Local funding

Whilst, as a general rule, central government departments support national work or initiatives with a national significance, and leave the funding of local and community activities to local government, in recent years they have initiated a number of time-limited programmes. Although there are few of them, and they are under-resourced, the application process for these schemes tends to be less complicated.

Community Development Foundation's Grassroots Grants

In August 2008 £130 million of small grants and endowments were made available to strengthen independent grant-making capacity for voluntary groups with an evidenced income of less than £30,000 per annum. This funding is administered by the Community Development Foundation (CDF) and distributed by Local Funders. Applicants are invited to contact their relevant Local Funder for details on applying for the small grants programme. Applications for this fund are accepted on a rolling basis.

For further information, see: www.cdf.org.uk

Local authorities

Nearly all local authorities make grants to the local voluntary and community sector, but each one will organise budgets, administration and support differently according to local conditions and resources.

Most local authorities employ third sector liaison officers (TSLOs) to give advice and support on their funding. The Department for Children, Schools and Families also has a local authority address finder with contact details for each local authority and their director of children's services. By contacting the TSLO or director of children's services for your local authority you should be able to get a good idea of the type of funding available for your youth organisations. Even if this does not result in an immediate funding opportunity, it is important to develop effective relationships with such contacts and other influential figures where feasible.

Local councils for voluntary service (CVS), rural community councils (RCCs) or specialised funding advice agencies should also have contact details and local authority funding information.

The DCSF local authority address finder can be found at www.dcsf.gov.uk/local authorities/index.cfm?action=authority. The www.governmentfunding.org.uk site managed by DSC has a local authority funder finder.

To find your nearest CVS go to the National Association for Voluntary and Community Action www.navca.org.uk.

To find information on RCCs go to www.acre.org.uk and for more information on local authorities see Chapter 11 *Raising money from local authorities.*

Youth Funds

Youth Funds emerged to contribute to a new duty on local authorities to ensure young people can engage in positive activities in their area, targeting high crime areas in particular. There's £173 million available over 2008–11 to create better activities for teenagers in England.

You apply for Youth Funds through your local authority. Some local authorities have set up panels of local teenagers to help choose the best projects. Others are asking all young people in their area what they think the money should be spent on.

Your local authority should have a Youth Funds or Youth Opportunity Funds coordinator.

Youth Opportunity Funds (YOF) are usually awarded to projects and the money can be used to buy equipment.

Youth Capital Fund (YCF) projects tend to be larger than YOF projects, and the fund helps to pay for the buildings and facilities that each project needs, as opposed to the cost of running a project.

Getting information and using websites

For strategy documents and more information
www.thecompact.org.uk
www.everychildmatters.gov.uk
www.skillsactive.com
www.sportengland.org

www.direct.gov.uk
This government information service site provides an index of sites, including departments, councils, NHS Trusts and NDPBs.

www.gnn.gov.uk
This is the government's official news service that contains all press releases from central and regional government as well as NDPBs.

Although the quality and accessibility of information on these websites and the regularity of updates varies, they contain information on government policy and recent press releases.

www.governmentfunding.org.uk

This site, managed by Directory of Social Change, has been developed to help fundraisers navigate the maze of funding available from central and local government. The site contains the following features.

- A searchable database of information on funding from local, regional and national government for the voluntary sector, together with downloadable application forms and guidance. It also provides information on independent grant administrators and regional and European funding.

- A personalised user profile, with the option to save searches and grant information, and receive email alerts on new and updated schemes which match criteria selected by the user.

- A news page containing important news articles from the sector press, with a searchable archive.

- A comprehensive help and advice section which contains general funding help, including an A–Z index of key terms and links to other relevant sites.

- An A–Z section listing 150 outcomes with details of grants schemes it has available.

- Funder ratings compiled by DSC researchers and governmentfunding.org.uk subscribers to let you know what to expect from each of the government funders listed on the website.

Other websites you can use to search for government and other funding opportunities include:

www.info4local.gov.uk
www.open4funding.info
www.grantsonline.org.uk
www.grantnet.com
www.supply2.gov.uk

13 Raising money from Europe

Introduction to European funding

The European Union (EU) provides a huge amount of money for social and economic development, mainly in its 27 member states. These funds go to regional and local government, regional regeneration initiatives, learning and skills councils (CLSCs) and voluntary organisations.

In the field of youth, the European Commission (EC) (see Glossary, page 340) has a double mission: to develop a framework for political cooperation and to manage the Youth in Action programme (see below).

The EU's youth policies aim to meet young people's changing expectations while encouraging them to contribute to society. This work is supported by action in the form of a specific programme for young people called Youth in Action (see page 328).

Getting money from Europe can be a long, slow and painstaking process. There is increasing competition for the available funds, and the programmes, priorities and guidelines are constantly changing. The internet is perhaps the most useful research tool when you are dealing with European funding. There is an enormous amount of information published on the main Europa website – ec.europa.eu – and one of your difficulties will be navigating through it all.

Small groups can find it difficult to complete an application for EU funding because of lack of resources and it is often better resourced organisations that are successful. You might want to consider partnering with another organisation, one with better resources or more experience in making applications to Europe.

This chapter will steer you through the European funding maze by providing an overview, details of the funds available, how to apply, the issues surrounding funding and tips on how to be successful. The glossary on page 340 will help you through the proliferation of departments, organisations, acronyms and jargon.

Each year, the EU agrees its budget. The budget year runs from 1 January to 31 December. When applying for funds you need to keep up to date and make contact as early as possible, ideally a full year in advance. The budget is adopted in December but it will have been under discussion for the whole of the preceding year and so it is never too early to begin your research. However, you will be unable to apply until the official 'invitation to tender' has gone out. Where matching funds are required, you need to make sure that these are committed before you apply.

Overview of EU funding

Grants, funds and programmes by EU policy

- Agriculture
- Audiovisual and media
- Communication
- Competition
- Conference interpretation
- Consumers
- Culture
- Development
- Economic and financial affairs
- Education, training and youth
- Employment and social affairs
- Energy
- Enlargement
- Enterprise
- Environment
- External relations
- External aid
- External trade
- Fisheries
- Fighting fraud
- Freedom, security and justice
- Humanitarian aid
- Human rights
- Information society
- Public health
- Regional policy
- Research and innovation
- Sport
- Statistics
- Transport

Funding is split into three areas:

Structural funds

The most important of these are the European Regional Development Fund (ERDF) and the European Social Fund (ESF), which is of particular interest to voluntary organisations. These funds are controlled by each individual member state government.

Budget line funding

There are 'budget lines' which offer opportunities for voluntary organisations to apply for funding, although eligibility is not necessarily limited to the voluntary sector. These budgets are controlled by officials in Brussels operating within one of the Directorates General (DGs) of the EC.

To an extent, decisions on funding can be influenced by MEPs (Members of the European Parliament) in Strasbourg, who can lobby on your behalf. All applications for budget line funding must have a significant transnational dimension and UK-only projects are rarely considered.

Contract and research funding

This is for specific work which the EC wishes to commission, on behalf of either itself or of another government. It is usually put out to tender and can support research across a range of issues in the areas of health, environment, socio-economic affairs, energy, transport and medicine. There are also opportunities to host EC conferences and events.

The structural funds

There are several structural streams, with funding for the voluntary and community sector available from the ERDF and the ESF. The funds help to deliver the EU's cohesion policy, which aims to narrow the gaps in development and economic performance among the regions and the EU member states.

The Third Sector European Network (TSEN) is the body that brings together the voluntary and community sector support agencies in all nine English regions. These agencies provide technical assistance and encourage the development of voluntary and community sector projects to fulfil the objectives of the structural funds. For further useful information please refer to the National Council for Voluntary Organisations' website: www.ncvo-vol.org.uk/sfp/funding?id=2138.

European Regional Development Fund

The ERDF aims to reduce social and economic disparities between regions of the EU and is therefore only available in certain areas of the UK. It is essentially concerned with business growth and economic regeneration and invests in projects to improve innovation, the environment and infrastructure. Communities and Local Government manages the ERDF in England.

Under the 2007–13 programming period the ERDF, the ESF and the Cohesion Fund (a financial instrument of EU regional policy that aims to help reduce the development inequalities among regions and member states) contribute to three objectives set down by the EU:

- convergence
- regional competitiveness and employment
- European territorial cooperation.

The convergence objective covers regions whose gross domestic product (GDP) per capita is below 75% of the EU average and is aimed at accelerating their economic development. It is financed by the ERDF, the ESF and the Cohesion Fund. The priorities under this objective are human and physical capital, innovation, knowledge society, environment and administrative efficiency. The outermost regions (see Glossary on page 340) benefit from a special ERDF funding.

Outside the convergence regions, the regional competitiveness and employment objective aims at 'strengthening competitiveness and attractiveness, as well as employment, through a two-fold approach. First, development programmes will help regions to anticipate and promote economic change through innovation and the promotion of the knowledge society, entrepreneurship, the protection of the environment and the improvement of their accessibility. Second, more and better jobs will be supported by adapting the workforce and by investing in human resources'.

The European territorial cooperation objective will 'strengthen cross-border cooperation through joint local and regional initiatives, transnational cooperation aiming at integrated territorial development, and interregional cooperation and exchange of experience'.

The ERDF's four main priorities are:

1) promoting innovation and knowledge transfer, including research and development and building links between higher education institutions and businesses

2) stimulating enterprise and supporting successful business, including support for small and medium-sized enterprises and social enterprises

3) ensuring sustainable development, production and consumption, including encouraging take-up of renewable energy and building a better environment

4) building sustainable communities, including support for social enterprise, increasing the attractiveness of deprived areas and improving access to employment and public services.

Since 2000, England has benefited from over £3.4 billion of ERDF investment, with a further £2.5 billion being invested for the 2007–13 round of programmes.

Major projects which have benefited from ERDF investment include the regeneration of the King's Dock in Liverpool (£48 million) and the Eden Project in Cornwall (£12.8 million). Without this investment, these projects and many like them would not have happened.

Who can apply?

ERDF is aimed at economic regeneration projects promoted primarily by the public sector. This involves:

- government departments
- regional development agencies (RDAs)
- local authorities
- further and higher education establishments
- other public bodies
- voluntary sector organisations.

This doesn't exclude the private sector, which promotes and helps to fund high quality projects that meet ERDF objectives. Generally, ERDF grants are not given to profit-making private sector companies, but in certain circumstances the fund can be used to help develop small and medium-sized enterprises (SMEs). Private sector companies are encouraged to present applications in partnership with a public sector body.

How to apply for ERDF

ERDF helps projects which offer substantial benefits that truly meet the needs of the region and wouldn't take place without a grant. To apply for ERDF investment, contact the RDA for your region. The RDA can advise you on the application process, including giving advice on the potential of projects and their eligibility for ERDF funding.

The role of the regional development agencies (RDAs)

The RDAs are responsible for delivering the 2007–13 round of programmes on the ground. They work in partnership with Communities and Local Government and representatives from across the programme area, ensuring the programmes are implemented effectively.

Management of the funds

Communities and Local Government is the designated managing authority for all ERDF structural fund programmes and specific community initiatives in England. The managing authority is the body designated by the member state that will ensure structural fund programmes are implemented and that their activity conforms to EC regulations. The department provides the framework for how ERDF programmes should be delivered, reporting to ministers and the EC. The European Policy and Programmes Division oversees the management of ERDF.

Programme monitoring committees (PMCs) and secretariat

Although the structure and management arrangements vary in detail, each region has a programme monitoring committee and a secretariat to oversee ERDF investment. The monitoring committees are chaired by the regional director of the government office – or in the case of London, the Mayor – and draw their membership from government departments and a wide range of regional partners. These usually include:

- RDAs
- local authorities
- higher and further education institutions
- environmental bodies
- the voluntary and private sectors
- members of the business community.

The committees guide the programme for their region and monitor and assess its implementation.

European Social Fund

As one of the EU's structural funds, ESF seeks to reduce differences in prosperity across the EU and enhance economic and social cohesion. So although ESF funding is spread across the EU, most money goes to those countries and regions where economic development is less advanced.

The ESF supports the EU's goal of increasing employment by giving unemployed and disadvantaged people the training and support they need to enter jobs. By focusing on those most in need of help, it contributes to policies to reduce inequality and build a fairer society. ESF also equips the workforce with the skills needed by business in a competitive global economy.

From 2000 to 2006, the ESF helped over 4 million people in England. In 2007, the EU launched a new round of ESF programmes for the seven years to 2013. The new programme will invest £4.6 billion in 2007–13 of which £2.3 billion will come from the ESF and £2.3 billion will be national funding.

Objectives

The 2007–13 ESF programme has two primary objectives:

- The convergence objective aims to develop areas where the economy is lagging behind the rest of the EU. In England, only Cornwall and the Isles of Scilly benefit from ESF funding under this objective.
- The regional competitiveness and employment objective covers all areas outside the convergence objective areas. The whole of England is covered by this objective, except Cornwall and the Isles of Scilly.

Each region has an allocation of ESF money to fund projects. Allocations are based on regional employment and skills needs – for example, the numbers of people not in work and who do not have good qualifications. The ESF allocations are matched with a similar amount of national funding.

ESF regional allocations 2007 to 2013

Cornwall and the Isles of Scilly	£153 million
Merseyside	£158 million
South Yorkshire	£139 million
East of England	£174 million
East Midlands	£188 million
Gibraltar	£2.6 million
London	£371 million
North East	£180 million
North West (excluding Merseyside)	£254 million
South East	£173 million
South West (excluding Cornwall and the Isles of Scilly)	£109 million
West Midlands	£282 million
Yorkshire and the Humber (excluding South Yorkshire)	£163 million

---

Priorities in the 2007–13 ESF programme

The priorities are designed to focus spending on specific activities and to ensure that it reaches people in most need of support. There are two main priorities in England:

- **Priority 1** is 'extending employment opportunities'. It supports projects to tackle the barriers to work faced by unemployed and disadvantaged people. About £1.2 billion of ESF money is available for this priority.
- **Priority 2** is 'developing a skilled and adaptable workforce'. It supports projects to train people who do not have basic skills and qualifications needed in the workplace. About £670 million of ESF money is available for this priority.

There are similar priorities in the convergence area of Cornwall and the Isles of Scilly, where about £50 million of ESF money is available to tackle barriers to employment, and £80 million of ESF money to improve the skills of the local workforce.

In addition, technical assistance funds are available to finance the preparation, management, monitoring, evaluation, information and control activities of the programmes operations, together with activities to reinforce the administrative capacity for implementing the funds at national and regional levels.

Target groups

In Priority 1 resources are focused on helping people who are unemployed or have become inactive in the labour market. In particular, it focuses on people who are most likely to face disadvantage or discrimination. Key target groups include:

- people with disabilities and health conditions
- lone parents
- people aged over 50
- people from minority ethnic communities
- people without good qualifications
- young people not in education, employment or training.

In Priority 2 resources are focused on people in the workforce who lack basic skills or good qualifications. In particular, it focuses on those who are least likely to receive training. It also supports training for managers and employees in small firms. Priority 2 aims to help people gain relevant skills and qualifications needed for their career progression and for business growth and innovation in the information industry.

Delivery

The Department for Work and Pensions (DWP) has overall responsibility for ESF funds in England. DWP manages the England ESF programme at a national level and liaises with the EC in Brussels. Each region has its own ESF allocation to fund projects to address its regional jobs and skills needs, within the framework of the two priorities in the England ESF programme.

At the regional level, ESF funds are distributed through public agencies such as the LSC and DWP. These agencies are known as 'co-financing organisations (CFOs)'. Their role is to bring together ESF and domestic funding for employment and skills so that ESF complements domestic programmes. The CFOs contract with the organisations or 'providers' that deliver ESF projects on the ground.

How to apply

Any public, private or third sector organisation that is legally formed, and able to deliver ESF provision can apply for funding to a CFO. Individuals and sole traders cannot apply.

CFOs make ESF available through a process of open and competitive tendering. If you are successful you will receive a single stream of funding from the CFO. You do not have to find your own 'match funding' as CFOs are responsible for both the ESF and match funding.

The LSC and DWP are CFOs in every region of England. In some regions, regional development agencies and some local authorities are also CFOs.

ESF Community Grants

Community Grants is a new programme which aims to support small voluntary and community organisations to engage with local communities and deliver a range of skills and employment support activities, through the provision of grants up to £12,000.

The grants aim to support a quality outreach provision, providing an essential stepping stone for unemployed and economically inactive participants to find employment or progress to further learning.

The ESF Community Grants programme builds on the Global Grants programme (known as Fast Forward Grants in London), which was one of the key features of the last regional ESF Objective 3 programme. To find out your region's contact detail for this programme, please visit www.esf.gov.uk/regions/regional_esf_frameworks.asp.

Tips on making applications to Europe

Don't expect clarity

Procedures vary from one office to another and even published guidelines change from time to time. Careful research is well worth the time and effort involved. You should refer to the relevant websites to ensure that your application meets with any changes and thus amend your application accordingly before finalising it.

Match funding is a crucial element to an ESF application

Many organisations fall at the point where they are unable to secure match funding. You should make sure that it is going to be available for your project and find out all the regulations surrounding it from the funder you approach. Make it clear where any co-funding will come from and how much will be available.

Don't be intimidated by the jargon and concepts

Many of the programmes use abstract language and talk about overarching goals such as 'developing a European sense of identity'. This sounds like a grand aim but it could be fulfilled by something as simple as an exchange trip. Make sure you take the time to look at the kind of projects each programme has funded in the past. A list of funded projects is published on an annual basis (usually in June) by each directorate and is available on their websites.

Talk about ideas, not money

Officials are there to develop their programme areas, not yours. You should be prepared to understand the wider picture, discuss your ideas and adapt them to meet their interests as well as yours for those budget lines and programmes where there are no clearly set out guidelines.

Don't be in a hurry

Take a long-term approach. Expect to be talking to officials early in one year in the hope of getting money in the next year. Sometimes it can take far longer. Response times in some departments are very protracted. In other words, plan ahead.

Note and observe all deadlines

Think partnership

This is becoming increasingly important for projects. It takes more time, but adds strength to your application.

continued...

Consider using an expert to help you make your initial approach

There are a number of people based in Brussels and elsewhere who specialise in this sort of work. There are also a number of liaison groups that can advise you, such as the European Citizen Action Service (ECAS) www.ecas-citizens.eu.

Make your proposal succinct and absolutely clear

A well thought through and clearly articulated proposal is much more likely to convince the reader. Make sure you have provided all the accessory information required.

Don't underestimate the red tape

Ensure that you begin nothing before you have a signed contract, and make sure everything is fully documented.

Ask for advice and information from your regional government office or regional development agency

It will coordinate the funding in your area on behalf of the responsible government department (which in turn is coordinating it on behalf of the EU).

It's basic advice . . .

. . . but store your copy application securely and back it up.

Budget line funding

Funding is also accessible to youth groups and organisations through budget line funds, which are distributed directly from the European Commission through Directorates General.

There are currently two ways for youth groups and organisations to access money from these funds: through the designated youth funding stream, the Youth in Action programme, or through schemes held under other Directorates General which have different priorities, but which hold youth in their objectives.

Directorate General and services of the European Commission

In the European Union, the staff of the main institutions (Commission, Council and Parliament) are organised into separate departments, known as Directorates General (DG). Each of these departments is accountable for specific tasks or policy areas. When applying for European funding, it is essential to determine which DG your project best fits under (it may be more than one). The Youth in Action programme falls under the DG of Education and Culture, however there are other programmes that relate to youth in other DGs, which will be mentioned later on in the chapter.

The Youth in Action programme

The Youth in Action programme is a new scheme replacing the former youth programme, 'Support to European Youth Organisations'. It is open to young people aged 15–28 (13 to 30 in some cases) living in the member states and in third countries (see Glossary, page 342), and in particular those living by the New Neighbourhood Policy (see Glossary, page 341).

The main objectives of the Youth in Action programme are to:

- promote young people's active citizenship, particularly European citizenship
- develop solidarity and tolerance amongst young people
- encourage understanding between young people in different countries of different cultures
- contribute to developing the quality of support systems for youth activities and the capabilities of civil society organisations in the youth field
- promote European cooperation in the youth field.

Who can participate?

The Youth in Action programme is open to young people aged 15 to 28 (13 to 30 in some cases) either to participate in, or host, projects. For youth groups, youth workers and organisations, there are certain criteria that your project must adhere to in order to qualify for funding. You must be set up in one of the following descriptions and be legally established in one of the programme or partner countries:

- a non-profit or non-governmental organisation
- a local, regional public body
- an informal group of young people
- a body active at European level in the youth field, having member branches in at least eight programme countries
- an international governmental non-profit organisation
- a profit-making organisation organising an event in the area of youth, sport or culture.

Eligibility

The eligibility of your project will depend largely on which country you are based in. Full details can be obtained from the EC; however, the following list can be used as a rough guide.

- Participants and organisations from programme countries can participate in all Actions (see page 330) of the Youth in Action programme; that is, the 27 member states of the EU, participating countries of the EFTA (see Glossary, page 340), members of the EEA: Iceland, Liechtenstein and Norway and candidate countries for accession to the EU, such as Turkey.
- Participants and organisations from neighbouring partner countries are eligible to participate in Action 2 and sub-Action 3.1.
- Participants and organisations from other partner countries of the world can participate in Action 2 and sub-Action 3.2.

The programme has an overall budget of €885 million for 2007–13, for which priorities of funding within the budget can change from year to year. For instance, 2008 was the European Year of Intercultural Dialogue, so funding during this year was focused around this theme. However, there are some general priorities of the programme which remain constant. These are: the participation of young people; cultural diversity; sport; European citizenship; social inclusion; and combating violence against women.

The sorts of activities the programme will fund include creation of networks, mobility action, teaching, training and exchange of know-how. The type of organisations it will give grants to include local and regional authorities, training centres, federations, agencies, youth groups and organisations.

If you are considering applying for funding from Europe, you must think about whether your project has a significant transnational aspect, as this is the core principle to European funding, and fundamental to the aims of the EU. As you will see from the examples given in the text, projects that have previously been funded have all involved organisations from other programme or partner countries and this is an essential requirement.

Each programme within European Funding will have a broad heading, for example 'Youth in Action', which will then include a number of individual schemes, such as Action 1 – 'Youth for Europe'. These actions are often broken down further into more specific funding streams. For example, Action 3 is broken down into sub-Action 3.1 and sub-Action 3.2. If the Action you wish to apply for funding under requires you to apply through a 'call for proposal' (see the Glossary, page 340), the call will be published in the sub-Action, rather than the larger Action; for example, sub-Action 1.2 Projects and Support Measures.

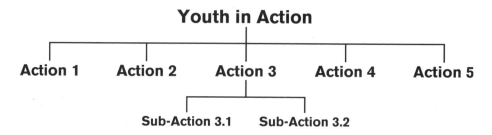

Youth in Action

Action 1: Youth for Europe

Youth for Europe aims to encourage young people to participate in developing the concept of citizenship. It is divided into three sub-Actions:

Sub-Action 1.1

Youth exchanges with partner organisations on a bilateral, trilateral or multilateral level – youth exchanges provide opportunities for young people from different countries to plan and carry out an exchange around a theme of mutual interest.

Sub Action 1.2

Youth initiatives on either a local/regional level or a transnational level – youth initiatives support group projects and the networking of similar projects between different countries.

Sub Action 1.3

Youth democracy projects – young people's involvement in the democratic life of their community on a local, regional, national or international level.

Thematic networking – with the intention of increasing the impact of the Youth in Action programme, a sub-Action may be formed around supporting thematic network projects.

/ Case study \

Project: Kick Out Violence and Racism

Country: France

Grant: €14,462

This project, a youth exchange between football supporters' clubs in Europe, took place in France and involved five organisations, from France, Estonia, Italy, Turkey and Denmark. The project involved young people from disadvantaged backgrounds and aimed to tackle issues such as social inclusion and participation of young people; improving the health of young people through physical and outdoor activities; and anti-discrimination and education through sport. The focus of this project was to enable young people to share ideas and take part in activities around how to tackle racism and violence in football, how to avoid cultural prejudices and learn about communication with people from other countries.

Address: 9 place Jean Jaurès
FR-13005 Marseille
Website: www.ec-network.net
Reference: 262-1.1-FR-2007-2

Action 2: European Voluntary Service

European Voluntary Service (EVS) provides opportunities for young people aged 18 to 30 to volunteer in another country either inside or outside the EU for up to 12 months. Short-term placements are also offered to young people facing disadvantages such as physical or mental disabilities and economic deprivation. Young people taking part in voluntary work with EVS can get involved in a number of activities, such as projects within the care sector, working with children, older people or people with disabilities, with young people in creative settings and in environmental care projects.

> ## Case study
>
> ## Project: Bringing back the joy to life – reintroducing young addicts into society
>
> Country: Bosnia and Herzegovina
>
> **Grant: €6,105**
>
> This project is run by a national youth organisation in Bosnia and aims to improve inter-ethnic dialogue and encourage young people to take an active role in their civil society through participating in decision making processes. The project is based around a local volunteer support service, which provides young people with information on how they can volunteer within their community, whilst dealing with issues such as social inclusion, European citizenship and improving the health of young people through physical and outdoor activities.
>
> Organisation: Asocijacija Graditelji Mira
> Address: BNR 35 BA-88100 Mostar
> Reference: 296-2.0-BA-2007-R2>

Action 3: Youth in the World

Youth in the World offers opportunities for young people from developing countries and young people from the EU member states to take part in skill-share projects. The focus of this action is based primarily on assisting young people from developing partnerships and promoting the exchange of good practice. Within this strand, youth leaders, workers and organisations will be able to apply for networking events, training opportunities and exchanges to help improve the quality of their projects. This Action is divided into two sub-Actions:

Sub-Action 3.1

Cooperation with the neighbouring countries of the EU – this aims to support projects such as youth exchanges and training and networking projects taking place in neighbouring partner countries.

Sub-Action 3.2

Cooperation with other countries of the world – this aims to encourage exchanges and training of young people, youth workers and youth organisations in partner countries. Grant requests relating to this sub-Action can only be submitted in response to specific calls for proposals.

/ Case study \

Project: SK8 4 All – Exploring Skateboard Culture

Country: Macedonia

Grant: €21,208

This project is a youth exchange taking place in Macedonia, involving six organisations from Albania, Bosnia, Herzegovina, Estonia, Italy and the Netherlands. The project aims to explore issues such as social inclusion, participation of young people and cultural diversity and improving the health of young people through sport and physical activity, citizenship and democracy. The exchange is focused on skateboarding as a sport and culture in itself, as well as on the social attitude towards young skateboarders, and aims to support them in their social inclusion and active citizenship.

The project hopes to enable young people to reflect on the role of skateboarding in their society and how they relate to it as young people. The project will also arrange workshops and organise a public event to facilitate these discussions and encourage young people to interact.

Organisation: Council for Prevention of Juvenile Delinquency
Address: Braka Hadzitefovi 28
1430 Kavadarci
Macedónia
Reference: 149-3.1-MK-2007-R1

Action 4: Youth Support Systems

Youth Support Systems has replaced the former 'Support Measures', and provides training and networking opportunities for youth organisations and youth workers. This action has been designed to assist organisations that are already working within the youth sector at a European level and is divided into the following eight sub-Actions.

- Support of youth organisations already active in Europe
- The European Youth Forum
- Training and networking for active organisations
- Innovation and quality
- Information

- Partnerships
- Support for the structures
- Activities that add value to the programme

Case study

Project: African Youth Foundation (AYF)

Country: Germany

Grant: €25,550

African Youth Foundation is a non-profit organisation based in Bonn, working with young African people in the Diaspora and in Africa, as well as Europeans of African descent. The foundation runs projects that aim to provide young people with necessary life skills. It is especially active in the field of vocational training through running workshops, seminars and training courses and providing financial and pastoral support to young people involved in education and entrepreneurship. The foundation also offers opportunities for young people to become involved in its management.

Address: Bonner Talweg 330
DE-53129 Bonn
Germany
Website: www.ayf.de
Reference: 2007-027

Action 5: Support for European Cooperation in the Youth Field

This is a new strand which seeks to promote the sharing of good practice and communication between youth policymakers and administrations at all levels. This action will facilitate structured forums, seminars and networking events for policy and decision makers to discuss the ideas of good practice. This Action is divided into three sub-Actions:

Sub-Action 5.1

Meetings of young people and those responsible for youth policy – supporting cooperation, seminars and communication between young people and those active in the field of youth, including youth workers and youth policymakers.

Sub-Action 5.2

Support for activities to bring about better knowledge of the youth field.

Sub-Action 5.3

Cooperation with international organisations.

Case study

Project: European Youth Congress 'It's Your Turn!'

Country: UK

Grant: €46,877

Founded in 1982, Peace Child International has member branches in 38 European states, with its mission being to 'empower young people' to address the global challenges facing their generation. The aim of this project is to organise a transnational meeting for European youth leaders to examine good practice in the management of youth-led community improvement projects. It covers the themes of social inclusion, participation, cultural diversity and European citizenship and provided an input for the Year of Intercultural Dialogue in 2008. The project is managed by 20 organisations in 28 countries, of which nine, from Austria, France, Hungary, Serbia, Slovenia and the UK, are formally included as partners.

Organisation: Peace Child International
Address: The White House, 46 High Street
Buntingford, Hertfordshire SG9 9AH
United Kingdom
Reference: 001-5.1-UK-2007-R1

For further information refer to the Youth in Action website: ec.europa.eu/youth/youth-in-action-programme/doc126_en.htm.

Other programmes

It is also possible for youth groups and organisations to obtain funding through other programmes that aren't specifically targeted at youth but that have it within their objectives. Examples include:

Programme: Lifelong Learning Programme
DG: Education and Culture
Duration: 2007–13
Website: ec.europa.eu/education/index_en.htm

Summary: Supports projects that foster interchange, mobility and cooperation between education and training systems in the EU.

Programme: Daphne III (Fight against Violence)
DG: Justice, Freedom and Security
Duration: 2007– 13
Website: ec.europa.eu/justice_home/funding/daphne3/funding_daphne3_en.htm

Summary: Grants for protective measures against all forms of violence and support for victims and groups at risk: children, women and young people.

Programme: Life +
DG: Environment
Duration: 2007–13
Website: ec.europa.eu/environment/life/funding/lifeplus.htm

Summary: Funding for the development of environmental policies and community projects.

How to access the budget lines

Read the handbook on grant management
Since 1999, all DGs must meet the minimum standard set by the *Vade-mecum on Grant Management*. The purpose of this document is to provide a clear reference guide for all those involved in grants at any stage of their process, whether it be drawing up, proposing or evaluating programmes or processing individual applications. The document was produced in 1998 and has not been updated since; however, it still holds useful and relevant information (see website: ec.europa.eu/justice_home/funding/expired/guidelines/2002/vademecum_subv_2000_en.pdf).

Research thoroughly
Find out as much information as you can about which budget lines, programmes and actions will connect to your project. The internet is an invaluable research tool when dealing with Europe, with an enormous amount of information available on the main Europa website. Lists of current grants, previous grants and projects that have already been funded are also available through the

336

individual DG websites, such as education, training and youth (website address at end of chapter). You may also find it useful to get in touch with other organisations that are applying for funding, or that have already received funding, to learn from their experiences.

Make contact

Once you have identified a budget line or lines, make initial contact with the relevant DG (in the case of the Youth in Action programme this would be education and culture), or the Education, Audiovisual and Culture Executive Agency (EACEA), by telephone, fax or email; any of these methods is acceptable during initial stages. Establish whether your project fits in with the conditions of the programme by asking for written conditions and criteria. You can also ask for application deadlines and information on how soon after the deadline a decision might be made. The 'call for proposals' is published in the Official Journal of the EU, however by that time, there may only be a few months left in which to submit an application. For this reason, it is important to find out which calls for proposals are in the pipeline so that you can prepare a draft in advance.

At this stage, you may decide whether you want to submit a firm application or a brief outline of your proposal. Firm proposals are more appropriate if you are applying to a large funding programme with tight restrictions. If this is not the case, it is acceptable to submit an outline of your proposal that you can discuss with the relevant officials, whom you may be able to meet in either Brussels or the UK. This can be arranged at a relatively low cost and can give you the chance to explain your ideas fully and find out their priorities and any special requirements. Although this may seem like a far-fetched idea, it is in fact common practice; officials are accustomed to being seen in their offices and are happy to discuss potential applications.

After you have discussed your ideas and obtained all the relevant information, you will then be required to submit a formal application. At this stage, you may encounter difficulties, as it can take over a year for a decision, by which time your need may have altered. Officials are aware of this issue and if you are in contact with them, they will usually tell you about the latest deadlines.

Lobby

It may be worthwhile lobbying MEPs, if you can find one who takes an interest in your project. Although they don't have any authority over the budget, their interest alone can be a powerful influence over officials. This should be approached with caution however, as lobbying can be viewed by officials as interference.

Applying to the Youth in Action programme

The Youth in Action programme is managed by the EACEA, which is responsible for the complete life cycle of these projects, from evaluating grant proposals to monitoring projects in their development.

There are a number of ways to apply for funding; you can apply directly to the executive agency or it may be possible to apply to a national agency. These agencies have set deadlines which will change from year, so you should refer to the Youth in Action website, 'How to participate', for current information (see web address on page 335).

After your application is approved

Once you have agreement from the appropriate DG to support your project, you will be asked to sign a contract with the EC with a number of conditions. Possibly the most difficult are the financial reporting requirements, which are especially complicated as they need to be done both in sterling and in euro. You should always get professional advice about the problems of fluctuating exchange rates, which can leave you with either less or more money to spend than you had planned for. Also make sure that you only charge for expenses that were included in your original project budget. If changes to this become necessary, get agreement from the EC first; you do not want to be put in the position of having to refund money. Finally, it may appear obvious, but it is extremely important that you submit your report and evaluation on time and in the required format, particularly if you expect to be applying for EU funding again.

If your application is not approved

As with other sources of funding, the DGs receive more applications than they can accept, so failure need not mean that your project was completely unsuitable. You can ask for feedback, for information about successful applications, and for the percentage of successful applicants. You may be able to revise your proposal and try again under a different heading or under the same heading the following year.

Issues around European funding

Contract funding

European funding is usually contract funding, not grant funding. If your project application is approved, you must do what you said in the application. If you use the money for activity not detailed in the application form you may be deemed to be in breach of contract and will have to pay back any European monies claimed.

Co-financing

European funds rarely pay 100% of the costs of running a given project. The money given to top up the European money is known as match funding or co-financing. Until recently, it has been the responsibility of organisations to secure match funding from another source in order to obtain European funding. However, the majority of ESF funding in England is now distributed in a system known as co-financing. Under co-financing GORs distribute ESF funding via a variety of intermediary bodies, such as LSCs, Jobcentre Plus, Connexions Partnerships, Business Link, RDAs and some local authorities. These organisations are responsible for finding the match funding which they then combine with their ESF allocations to create a single funding stream.

A European dimension

Many of the budget line funds are conditional on you working in partnership with like-minded organisations in other member states. In most cases you will be expected to name these transnational partners in your application. The implication is that you should build relationships with like-minded organisations across Europe even before you consider submitting a proposal. Go to conferences, use email, and develop contacts by joining any relevant European networks and liaison groups. If you do not have a transnational partner, you can also ask officials of the relevant DG to help you find one.

Delays in decision making and payments

Applications can take a long time to process. For budget line funds this can be as long as a year. For ESF funds a delay of three months is not unusual. You are strongly advised not to start your project until formal approval has been received. Different European funding streams have different payment systems. The relevant guidance notes should give you details. However, be aware that the reality does not always follow the theory. Payments may be delayed for a number of reasons, the most common being that the claimant organisation has not provided all the required information.

Glossary

Call for proposal

This is an invitation for candidates to submit their proposals for action. They are published on the DG websites and also in the Official Journal of the European Union.

Candidate countries

Candidate countries are those which have been granted candidate status and are undergoing accession negotiations to join the EU. Current candidate countries are Turkey, Croatia and Macedonia, which were all granted candidate status in 2005.

Directorate General (DG)

The Directorates are essentially the government departments of the EU. They are each headed by a director general and are responsible for a specific area of European policy.

EACEA

The Education, Audiovisual and Culture Executive Agency (EACEA) is based in Brussels and works with the Directorate General of Education and Culture to manage the Youth in Action programme. Its website can be used as the main point of reference when applying to this programme, as it is used to publish calls for proposals.

EEA

The European Economic Area (EEA) was created in 1994 to allow countries of the EFTA (see below) to participate in the European single market without joining the EU. The contracting countries to this agreement are three of the four members of the EFTA: Iceland, Lichtenstein and Norway, and the 27 member states of the EU.

EFTA

The European Free Trade Association (EFTA) is an intergovernmental organisation created to promote free trade and economic integration to benefit its four member states: Iceland, Liechtenstein, Norway and Switzerland.

ENGO

European non-governmental organisation. For example, a body active at European level in the youth field.

Europa

Europa is the name of the EU's website and its address can be found in the contacts section at the end of this chapter. It has a huge range of information and guidance available on all aspects of the EU's activity. To navigate to the area on grant funding from the main page go to Services then Grants and then choose the relevant area. You can also view the programmes by going to the relevant DG website.

European Commission (EC)

The EC is a politically independent body based in Brussels, responsible for upholding the interest of the EU as a whole. It carries out the day-to-day running of the EU, including preparing legislation, overseeing the budget and implementing the decisions of the Parliament and Council. There are currently 27 Commissioners (one for each member state), who are supported by approximately 25,000 European civil servants organised under different departments (the Directorates General).

Intergovernmental organisations

An intergovernmental organisation is an organisation made up of sovereign states, such as the European Union and the United Nations.

Member states

Member states are the 27 countries which acceded to the EU since its inception in 1951. These countries are: Austria, Belgium, Bulgaria, Cyprus, Czech Republic, Denmark, Estonia, Finland, France, Germany, Greece, Hungary, Ireland, Italy, Latvia, Lithuania, Luxembourg, Malta, Netherlands, Poland, Portugal, Romania, Slovakia, Slovenia, Spain, Sweden, United Kingdom.

New Neighbourhood Policy

The European Neighbourhood Policy was developed in 2004 in order to strengthen stability and security in the EU during the accession of new countries and to counteract any division between the widening EU and its border countries.

The New Neighbourhood Policy applies to countries that are immediate neighbours of the EU by land or sea: Algeria, Armenia, Azerbaijan, Belarus, Egypt, Georgia, Israel, Jordan, Lebanon, Libya, Moldova, Morocco, Occupied Palestine Territories, Syria, Tunisia and Ukraine. Although Russia falls into this category geographically, it is covered by a different policy.

Official Journal of the EU

The Official Journal of the EU is a periodical published every working day in all official languages of the EU. It includes information on legislation, notices and a supplement for public procurement and can be accessed online at the following website: www.eur-lex.europa.eu/JOIndex.do.

Outermost regions

There are seven outermost regions: Guadeloupe, French Guiana, Martinique, and Réunion (the four French overseas departments), the Canaries (Spain), and the Azores and Madeira (Portugal). These regions are distinguished by their low population density and considerable distance from mainline Europe. Their specific location makes them European bridgeheads for fostering trade with their non-EU neighbours, most of which are less developed countries.

Programme countries and neighbouring partner countries

Programme countries are the 27 countries of the original EU accession (see Member states on page 341).

Partner countries are broken down into four categories: Neighbouring Partner Countries, South East Europe and Caucasus, Mediterranean Partner Countries and Other Countries of the World.

Technical Assistance Office

Technical Assistance Office is a term that was previously used for the Education, Audiovisual and Culture Executive Agency.

Third countries

Third countries is a term given to all other country-relationships to the EU, outside the 27 member states. This includes all of the neighbouring partner countries.

The Youth in Action youth glossary can be found at http://eacea.ec.europa.eu/youth/tools/glossary_en.

14 Youth organisations and charitable status

It is generally accepted that most grant-giving organisations, statutory bodies and the public are much more likely to give to charities which are registered. This is because they are subject to regulation by the Charity Commission (the Commission).

The rules regarding charity registration have changed. From April 2007, charities with a gross annual income exceeding £5,000 that are not legally excepted or exempt from registration are required by law to register. Gross income means all the money the organisation has received in a financial year from all sources.

Many youth organisations are required to register as charities. There are benefits to being a registered charity, but it can also bring restrictions. This chapter looks at the pros and cons of being a charity, which organisations should be registered and how to go about this.

What are the benefits of being a charity?

The main advantages are that charities:

- can claim relief from tax on most income or gains and on profits from some activities
- can also claim tax repayments on income received on which tax has already been paid, including Gift Aid donations from individuals
- can take advantage of some special VAT exemptions
- will receive a mandatory 80% of business rate relief on premises, which can be increased to 100% at the discretion of the local authority

- that are VAT registered may be able to reclaim some of the VAT they are charged from Her Majesty's Revenue & Customs (HMRC)
- are often able to raise funds from the public, grant-making trusts and local government more easily than non-charitable bodies
- can seek advice and get information, including free publications, from the Commission
- can formally represent and help to meet the needs of the community
- are able to give the public the assurance that they are being monitored and advised by the Commission.

What are the disadvantages of being a charity?

There are restrictions on what charities can do, both in terms of their work, and the ways in which they can operate:

- A charity must have exclusively charitable aims. Some organisations may carry out their aims by a range of activities, some charitable, some not. To become a charity, this type of organisation would have to stop its non-charitable activities. (The non-charitable activities can, of course, continue if carried on by a separate non-charitable organisation.) You will need to consider carefully if becoming a charity will severely restrict your planned activities. If so, charity registration may not be right for your organisation.
- There are limits to the extent of political or campaigning activities which a charity can take on.
- Strict rules apply to trading by charities.
- Trustees (i.e. the body of people administering and managing the charity) must not benefit from their position beyond what is allowed by law and is in the best interests of the charity.
- Charity trustees have signicant responsibilities and potential liabilities.
- Financial benefits from the charity which a trustee manages are not permissable unless they are specifically authorised by the governing document of the charity or by the Commission. Financial benefits include salaries, services and the awarding of business contracts to a trustee's own business from the charity. Similar problems arise where the spouse, relative or partner of a trustee receives such benefits. Trustees are, however, entitled to be reimbursed for reasonable out-of-pocket expenses, such as train fares to trustee meetings.

- Trustees need to avoid any situation where their personal interests conflict with their duties as trustees.
- Charity law imposes certain financial reporting obligations; these vary with the size of the charity.

What is a charity?

A body is a charity if it is established for exclusively charitable purposes and for the benefit of the public.

A charity's purposes are usually expressed in the objects clause of its governing document, for example, trust deed, constitution, memorandum and articles of association or rules.

The minimum requirement for registration is that a charity must have an annual income of more than £5,000. Organisations with an annual income not exceeding £5,000 from all sources will be able to seek voluntary registration when the part of the Charities Act 2006 that permits this comes into effect – information on this will be publicised on the Commission's website – www.charity–commission.gov.uk.

What are charitable purposes?

'Charitable purposes' are those set out in the Charities Act 2006:

1) the prevention or relief of poverty
2) the advancement of education
3) the advancement of religion
4) the advancement of health or the saving of lives
5) the advancement of citizenship or community development
6) the advancement of the arts, culture, heritage or science
7) the advancement of amateur sport
8) the advancement of human rights, conflict resolution or reconciliation or the promotion of religious or racial harmony or equality and diversity
9) the advancement of environmental protection or improvement
10) the relief of those in need, by reason of youth, age, ill-health, disability, financial hardship or other disadvantage
11) the advancement of animal welfare

12) the promotion of the efficiency of the armed forces of the Crown or of the police, fire and rescue services or ambulance services

13) other purposes recognised as charitable under the existing law and any new purposes which are similar to another prescribed purpose.

Educational charities

Many youth organisations have educational objects. These are some of the areas they may cover.

- Formal education in schools and colleges.
- Scholarship funds.
- Vocational training and work experience.
- Sports organisations for young people, provided there is open access and training for all members.
- Arts organisations for young people such as youth theatre groups or bands.

To be an educational charity there must be some element of study or training and the subject must be of some educational worth. A young people's chess club has been held to be charitable, but a tiddlywinks club would be unlikely to qualify. Many youth clubs have been registered with objects to educate young people to develop their skills so as to develop their full potential as members of society.

Recreational charities

The Recreational Charities Act 1958 specifically included the provision of facilities for recreation 'or other leisure time occupation in the interest of social welfare' as being charitable. *This is provided that* the organisation is established for the public at large or for any disadvantaged group (which includes young people) and is altruistic in nature, and the facilities provided are set up to meet certain social needs.

The organisation also needs to be for a sufficient section of the public (see 'Assessing the public benefit of organisations applying to register as charities' on page 349. Other criteria apply and reference should be made to the Commission to determine whether the organisation is charitable. Many youth clubs and organisations involved in outdoor activities will come within the Act.

Other charitable purposes

Youth organisations may also come within several other charitable purposes. Church groups or religious youth organisations for example may be charitable under the advancement of religion. Organisations coming under the prevention or relief of poverty would include those giving direct financial assistance or legal advice or providing housing to financially disadvantaged young people.

Some non-charitable aims that are often presumed to be charitable

The following are examples of organisations or aims often assumed to be charitable, but which in fact are not.

- Individual sports clubs set up to benefit their members or promote excellence (as distinct from sports facilities open for everyone or provided for specific groups of people, such as young people, or as a method of promoting healthy recreation).

- The promotion of political or propagandist aims, or the promotion of a particular point of view (for more details please refer to booklet CC9, available on the Charity Commission's website).

- Aims that include arrangements where people running the organisation get significant personal benefit.

- Raising funds for other charities where the organisers do not have any say over how the funds are spent.

- Aims that promote friendship or international friendship, such as town twinning associations.

Appeals for funds

Fundraising is not a charitable object, it is simply an activity which can be undertaken to help achieve a charitable purpose. That purpose must fall within the charity's objects.

There are complex rules about fundraising and you may need to take professional advice. In the first instance you should refer to the Commission's booklet on fundraising – CC20, obtainable from the website.

The following points are considered good practice.

- Great care should be taken over the wording of a written appeal asking for money from the public. Organisations should make sure the aims for which the charity intends to use the money are accurately described.

- The record of a speech or broadcast may be regarded as evidence of the aims of an appeal. The organisers of that appeal cannot alter its aims to something not consistent with the terms under which donors were invited to contribute. Care should be given to the wording of any spoken appeal.

- If you want to raise money for a charity's general purposes, you must make this clear and avoid any suggestion that the money will be used for a more specific purpose.

- If an appeal is for a specific purpose, such as paying for or restoring a building, you should state what will happen to the money if either not enough, or too much, is raised.

See also Chapter 6 *Fundraising for projects.*

Public benefit

Under the Charities Act 2006, the Commission is required to issue guidance on public benefit. Statutory guidance on this is contained in the Commission's publication 'Charities and Public Benefit'. Anyone thinking of setting up and registering a new charity should familiarise themselves with this guidance and refer to the supplementary guidance on the public benefit of specific types of charity.

What is meant by 'the public benefit requirement'?

The public benefit requirement means that to be a charity, an organisation must be able to demonstrate that it is set up for aims that are charitable, and that its aims are, and will be, carried out for the public benefit. This applies to each of an organisation's aims; a charity cannot have some aims that are for the public benefit and some that are not.

Two key principles must be met in order to show that an organisation's aims are for the public benefit. Within each principle there are some important factors that must be considered in all cases. These are:

Principle 1: There must be an identifiable benefit or benefits

- It must be clear what the benefits are.
- The benefits must be related to the aims.
- Benefits must be balanced against any detriment or harm.

Principle 2: Benefit must be to the public, or a section of the public

- The beneficiaries must be appropriate to the aims.
- Where benefit is to a section of the public, the opportunity to benefit must not be unreasonably restricted by:
  - geographical or other restrictions or
  - ability to pay any fees charged.

- People in poverty must not be excluded from the opportunity to benefit.
- Any private benefits must be incidental.

Charity trustees' public benefit duties

Charity trustees have the following public benefit duties. They must:

- ensure that they carry out their charity's aims for the public benefit
- have regard to guidance the Commission publishes on public benefit (when they exercise any powers or duties where that may be relevant)
- report on their charity's public benefit in their trustees' annual report.

Anyone applying to register their organisation needs to understand that the charity trustees must be aware of, and fulfil, their statutory duties with regard to public benefit and public benefit reporting. This requirement is a continuing duty for charity trustees throughout the life of the charity; it is not just a requirement at registration.

Assessing the public benefit of organisations applying to register as charities

When considering whether an organisation's aims are for the public benefit, the Commission may assess its activities in order to:

- clarify its aims (i.e. understand the meaning and scope of the words used in its objects)
- decide whether those aims are charitable (i.e. that the aims fall within the descriptions of charitable purposes in the Charities Act 2006)
- ensure that the aims are or will or may be carried out for the public benefit.

In the case of an organisation applying to register as a charity, the Commission can consider relevant factual background information, such as asking for evidence of its current or proposed activities, in order to decide whether its aims are charitable and for the public benefit. Where it is not clear, the Commission will ask the organisation to provide further evidence. If the Commission is not satisfied that the public benefit requirement will be met, it may refuse registration, or may ask the applicant to amend the organisation's objects or activities to ensure it will meet the public benefit requirement before registration can proceed.

No organisation can be charitable if:

- its aims are illegal or could be said to further illegal aims under the law of England and Wales; or

- it is set up for the personal benefit of:
  - its trustees
  - its employees (other than in the case of relieving poverty – for example, there would normally be no reason why a firm or business should not operate a benevolent fund for its staff limited to the purpose of relieving poverty); or
  - other specific individuals; or
- it is created for political aims.

Different legal structures – governing documents

The governing document means any formal document which establishes a charity and which sets out its purposes and how it is to be administered. It may be a trust deed, constitution, memorandum and articles of association, will, conveyance, Royal Charter, Charity Commission Scheme or a simple set of rules.

A charity's governing document should contain information about:

- its registered name and any working name
- what it is set up to do (objects)
- how it will do those things (powers)
- who will run it (charity trustees)
- how the trustees will run it, including administrative provisions for meetings and proceedings, voting and financial procedures
- what happens if changes to the administrative and/or other provisions need to be made – except in the case of a charitable company, where company law makes provision (amendment provision)
- what happens if it wishes or needs to wind up (dissolution provision).

The governing document (formally referred to as the 'govening instrument'), is the charity trustees' 'instruction manual', as well as a legal document by which the charity is administered and managed. Charity trustees should refer to it regularly to remind themselves of the charity's purposes and how it should be run. Trustees and senior members of staff should be given a full copy of the governing document on appointment.

When questions arise over the running of the charity or a particular problem needs addressing, reference should be made to the governing document. You will often find that the document covers the point raised. Even if it does not, it is a useful first point of reference and should guide you in the right direction for your next steps.

The document should be clear and as simple as legal requirements allow. The Commission publishes model documents. If yours is not a model and you have found it difficult to follow, you should contact the Commission for advice on whether you can simplify it, perhaps by adopting a more straightforward document, or by amending your existing one. In some cases, e.g. where the organisation is run by a Charity Commission Scheme, the process of changing it will be more complicated and it may not be possible to make the provisions of your document any less complex, but you should ask the Commission's advice.

Main types of governing document

There are three main types of governing document:

- constitution or rules
- trust deed
- memorandum and articles of association.

The Commission provides model documents free of charge, which contain administrative provisions suitable for each type of organisation. However, it is still necessary to insert the objects of the organisation and complete information, and to consider the suitability of the provisions generally to the individual circumstances of the organisation. The models are available on the Commission's website or by calling Charity Commission Direct on 0845 300 0218.

Where there is an umbrella body, it will expect a level of affiliation from the local charity. This means that it wishes to be approached by individual groups that intend to establish a charity under its umbrella, rather than local groups applying directly to the Commission for registration.

There are many types of youth clubs and there does not seem to be one central umbrella body to which they are all affiliated. Some are more religious than others and some, for example, have particular sports at the centre of what they wish to achieve.

If you are, or are considering becoming, a member of the National Association of Clubs for Young People you should contact the Association for the regional constituent's contact details and discuss this issue with them. If you decide to become a member you should make full use of the advice and guidance offered by the regional and/or national office. Refer to the next page for your regional office's contact details.

The Charity Law Association (CLA) also produces suitable model governing documents but a charge is made. To order copies of these email the CLA administrator on admin@charitylawassociation.org.uk.

Charitable incorporated organisations (CIOs)

Many trustees of unincorporated charities feel they require the protection of incorporation and, in the past, they have opted for their charity 'adopting' a new structure to become a charitable company limited by guarantee. In this way, their liability becomes limited (with strict provisos concerning negligence and fraud). The charitable company is however subject to both charity and company law and the impact of this on a former non-incorporated charity requires more expertise, time and resources.

The purpose of the CIO is to provide a legal framework for charities which seek the protection and practicality of incorporation but without having to meet the regulatory and reporting requirements of both company and charity law.

Following the 2006 Act, the Commission has prepared draft documents for two specific types of organisation, although at the time of writing (March 2009) these had not yet been published:

- a charity which would formerly have operated under a constitution and which has a membership – referred to as the 'Association' model
- a charity which would formerly have been governed by a will, trust deed or declaration of trust and which would have been referred to as a trust and whose body of members is not distinct from its charity trustees – referred to as the 'Foundation' model.

The new CIO will not be suitable for all charities and for many, the legal requirements will be considered still too onerous for the size of their organisation – they will remain as unincorporated organisations. However, the CIO does provide a legal framework within which many medium-sized organisations can work and grow.

The model documents are perhaps more wordy than most would have hoped, the idea behind them being to simplify, but they need to include provisions which would affect companies, unincorporated organisations and those which have come about simply because of the new structure.

Charity trustees should take some time to consider which form of governing document they choose, taking into consideration the nature of their work and the provisions they will need to run it both at the start and as it develops. They should also avoid taking on provisions that are too much for their capacity and resources.

How do you register as a charity?

In order to be registered as a charity, the Charity Commission must be satisfied that your objects are charitable. It will also want evidence of how you intend to operate within those objects and what your activities are and that they don't conflict with your stated purposes, and it will also check that your governing document is appropriate for your charity. The procedure is as follows:

1) Write to or telephone the Charity Commission for a copy of its charity registration pack. This includes information on setting up a charity and guidance booklets as well as an application form. The application pack is very useful and you should read the guidance and information carefully and follow the procedures outlined. Tell the Commission if you intend to use an agreed or approved model constitution, as a special application form will be available for these cases and, everything else being acceptable, it should quicken the process.

2) Establish your organisation either by executing and stamping the trust deed, adopting the constitution at a members' meeting or incorporating the company.

3) Send all the required documentation (listed in the pack) to the Commission for consideration.

4) If all the documentation and the information you provide on your activities is acceptable, the charity will be registered and you will receive written confirmation and your charity registration number. If not, the Commission may call for additional information or require amendments to the governing document. If the Commission considers that your activities and purposes are charitable but the wording of your document does not reflect this and precludes the organisation from registration, it will do all that it can to help and advise you. If it considers that your activities and purposes are not exclusively charitable (even if your stated purposes are), it will give you reasons for rejecting your application.

- If you are a branch or a local group of a national organisation you should first approach your national body, which will usually have an approved model constitution that has been agreed with the Charity Commission.

- For a sports charity for young people (up to university age) contact the Central Council for Physical Recreation, Burwood House, 14–16 Caxton Street, London SW1H 0QT. Tel: 020 7976 3900; fax: 020 7976 3901; email: info@ccpr.org.uk; website: www.ccpr.org.uk.

- For a youth club contact the National Association of Clubs for Young People, 371 Kennington Lane, London SE11 5QY. Tel: 020 7793 0787; email: office@clubsforyoungpeople.org.uk; website: www.clubsforyoungpeople.org. uk.

- For a model trust deed, constitution or memorandum and articles of association contact the Commission or the Charity Law Association – see *Useful contacts and sources of information* on page 371. These models do not include objects clauses.

15 Tax and tax benefits

There is a legal requirement to pay taxes due regardless of status, (i.e. whether a charity, company, other organisation or individual) and whether or not we are asked to by HM Revenue & Customs (HMRC). Although tax issues can be highly complex, the penalties, if we get them wrong, can be severe and not knowing or understanding the law is not considered an excuse by HMRC.

You might need to take specialist advice, especially at an early stage. For example, if you are planning a major fundraising campaign, you may go over the VAT threshold for the first time. This will affect not just that particular appeal but all your other activities as well. Or if you organise an event that generates a surplus, the profit may be taxed (usually to corporation tax) and there is the chance that either VAT will need to be levied on the price charged or VAT incurred in putting on an event will not be recoverable.

On a positive note, there are some tax benefits available to UK charities, for example, tax relief on income and gains, and on profits from *some* activities, as well as claiming tax back on income received on which tax has already been paid, for example on bank interest and Gift Aid donations.

In order for your charity to benefit from the tax benefits available, you must be recognised by HMRC as 'a charity for tax purposes' (this is a different process than registering as a charity with the Charity Commission or the Office of the Scottish Regulator).

HMRC has a very informative and helpful website which includes a guide on how to apply for recognition as a charity for tax and Gift Aid purposes – www.hmrc.gov.uk/charities – and you should refer to this in the first instance.

It is not possible to cover all aspects of tax issues in relation to charitable youth organisations in this one chapter. Here we offer an overview of the following subjects.

- Tax advantages
- Corporation tax

- Exemptions from corporation tax – trading income
- VAT
- Charity lotteries
- Gift aid
- Payroll giving
- PAYE
- Donation vouchers

Tax advantages

Registered charities:

- do not normally have to pay income/corporation tax (in the case of some types of income), capital gains tax, or stamp duty, and gifts to charities are free of inheritance tax
- pay no more than 20% of normal business rates on the buildings which they use and occupy to further their charitable aims
- can get special VAT treatment in some circumstances
- can reclaim tax made on tax-effective donations (gift aid).

Corporation tax

Corporation tax is a tax on the trading profits of companies and other business organisations (including charities).

Even though the profit is only a surplus to be retained by the charity, in some cases it is still subject to tax.

Charity exemptions from corporation tax – trading income

Trading income is a term used to describe activities which involve the provision of goods or services to customers on a commercial basis (as opposed to donated income and investment income). When deciding whether a trade exists, it is of no relevance to HMRC that you do not intend to make a profit or that you intend profits to be used only for charitable purposes.

Trading is not itself a charitable purpose, but charities can and do trade, either to fulfil a charitable purpose or simply to raise funds.

Any profits your charity generates from trading activities are taxable but a range of tax exemptions is available depending on the nature of your trading activities.

Your charity may be able to benefit from one or more of the three main reliefs available to reduce or exempt tax on the profits from trading activities. These are:

- a primary purpose trading exemption
- an exemption for trades conducted mainly by charitable beneficiaries
- a small trading exemption.

Primary purpose trading exemption

In order to discover what the primary purposes of your charity are, look at the objects clause in the governing document (the trust deed, memorandum & articles of association, constitution etc.).

If your charity's trading activities are carried out in the course of meeting your primary purpose (your objects) then this is known as primary purpose trading.

The profits from primary purpose trading are exempt from corporation tax (or income tax in the case of charitable trusts). This exemption from tax is only available if the profits are applied solely to the purposes of the charity. However, the sales that have given rise to those profits will be regarded as a business activity for the purposes of determining liability for VAT.

Examples

Where youth projects are concerned an example might be running courses designed to improve the conditions of life of young people and to assist in their spiritual, moral and physical development. The provision of such courses for a fee would count as primary purpose trading and would be exempt. This is because the activities are fulfilling the objects of the charity.

If the primary purpose of your charity is the advancement of education you can claim a primary purpose trading exemption on profits from the sale of goods or services that advance education, for example, school fees or university top-up fees. Any profits from trading activities that do not advance education will not qualify; for example, the sale of general conference facilities on your premises – this is not advancing education, it is merely a fundraising activity.

Basically, if you are thinking of trading (i.e. charging for any service) get advice from HMRC before you start, rather than just hope that the trade will qualify for exemption from tax.

Activities ancillary to the primary purpose trade

Some activities that are not strictly primary purpose trading but which could not exist without the primary purpose trade, can also be exempted, as 'activities ancillary to the primary purpose trade'.

Example

A college providing places at a crèche for the children of students in return for payment.

An exemption for trades conducted mainly by charitable beneficiaries

If the work in connection with your trading activities is mainly carried out by beneficiaries of your charity then the profits generated can be exempt from tax as long as those profits are used solely for the charity's charitable purposes. For example, the sale of goods made by people with disabilities (as part of their therapy or training) and then sold to the public would be exempt.

However, be very careful to work out exactly who are the beneficiaries of the charity. For example, a charity may be established to relieve older people and carry out that purpose by providing gardening services to them. If the work is carried out by young people the fees charged will not be exempt under this heading because the work is not carried out by the beneficiaries of the charity. Consulting the objects clause of your charity's governing document is the starting point.

Workers do not need to be exclusively charitable beneficiaries; other workers acting in a supervisory or voluntary capacity are acceptable so long as charitable beneficiaries do most of the work.

PAYE (see page 367) and National Minimum Wage rules must still be applied to any paid employees (including those who are charitable beneficiaries).

The small trading exemption

This exemption can be claimed against the profits from any trading activities that are not otherwise exempt and where the trading turnover falls within certain limits.

These limits are set in relation to the turnover from small trading in comparison with the overall income of your charity (including income from this trade) and are subject to change in the future.

The following advice is provided by HMRC and is current at the time of writing (March 2009). However, as with all tax matters, figures need to be calculated using up-to-date information, so you should refer to HMRC's website when assessing your income for tax purposes.

From April 2000 there is a statutory exemption for the profits of 'small trading' carried on by a charity that are not otherwise already exempt. Before charities consider whether this particular exemption applies, they may first want to consider whether the Extra Statutory Concession (ESC C4) for fundraising events applies. [Please refer to this sub-heading on page 362].

How does the small trading exemption apply?
The small trading exemption applies to the profits of all trading activities that are not already exempt from tax, provided:

- *the total turnover from all of the activities does not exceed the annual turnover limit, or*
- *if the total turnover exceeds the annual turnover limit, the charity had a reasonable expectation that it would not do so, and*
- *the profits are used solely for the purposes of the charity.*

The small trading exemption does not apply to VAT.

Calculation of the annual turnover limit
The annual turnover limit is:

- *£5,000, or*
- *if the turnover is greater than £5,000, 25 % of the charity's total incoming resources, subject to an overall upper limit of £50,000.*

This table illustrates the application of these rules:

Total incoming resources of the charity	Maximum permitted turnover
Under £20,000	£5,000
£20,001 to £200,000	25% of charity's total incoming resources
Over £200,000	£50,000

For the purpose of this limit, 'total incoming resources' means the total receipts of the charity for the year from all sources (grants, donations, investment income, all trading receipts, etc), calculated in accordance with normal charity accounting rules (whether the income would otherwise be taxable or not).

Examples

Example 1

A charity sells Christmas cards to raise funds. This trading is not primary purpose nor does it fall to be considered under ESC C4 because it is not raising income from a fundraising event.

- Assume this is the only taxable trading activity.
- The turnover from the Christmas cards amount to £4,500 in the year.
- Any profits will be exempt from tax, because the turnover does not exceed £5,000.

Example 2

- A charity has a turnover from non-primary purpose trading of £40,000 for the year.
- Its total incoming resources for the year are £160,000 (including the £40,000 turnover).
- Profits will be exempt from tax because the turnover from the non-exempt trading does not exceed either:
  - 25% of the total incoming resources (£160,000 @ 25% = £40,000), or
  - the overall upper limit of £50,000.

Example 3

- A charity has turnover from non-primary purpose trading of £40,000 for the year.
- Its total incoming resources only amounted to £150,000.
- The £40,000 turnover exceeds the annual turnover limit (£150,000 @ 25%= £37500).
- However, the profits on sales may still be exempt from tax for this year if the charity had a reasonable expectation at the start of the year that the turnover would not exceed the limit.

Example 4

- A charity has turnover of £60,000 for the year.
- Its total incoming resources only amounted to £150,000.
- The turnover exceeds the overall upper limit of £50,000.
- The profits on sales may still be exempt from tax for this year if the charity had a reasonable expectation at the start of the year that the turnover would not exceed that limit.

The reasonable expectation test

If the total turnover of taxable trading does exceed the limits, profits may still be exempt if the charity can show that, at the start of the relevant accounting period, it was reasonable for it to expect that the turnover would not exceed the limit. This might be because:

- *the charity expected the turnover to be lower than it turned out to be, or*

- *the charity expected that its total incoming resources would be higher than they turned out to be.*

HMRC Charities will consider any evidence the charity may have to satisfy the reasonable expectation test.

Example:

- *the charity may have carried on the activity for a number of years and may therefore be able to show that the turnover increased unexpectedly compared with earlier years*

- *the charity might have started carrying out the trading activity during the year in question and might be able to show that the turnover was higher than it forecasted*

- *the charity's total incoming resources might be lower than it forecast, for example, because the charity did not receive a grant for which it had budgeted.*

The type of evidence needed to demonstrate the levels of turnover and incoming resources which were expected might include:

- *minutes of meetings at which such matters were discussed*

- *copies of cash flow forecasts*

- *business plans and previous years' accounts.*

If the charity expects to be regularly trading at or around the small trading exemption limits, it might be better for the charity to consider using a trading subsidiary company.

For further guidance see HMRC's website: www.hmrc.gov.uk.

This information is taken from: www.hmrc.gov.uk/charities/guidance-notes/annex4/sectionb.htm#19.

Extra Statutory Concession ESC C4

You can also take advantage of 'Extra Statutory Concession C4' if your trading activities are connected only with fundraising events:

> *Certain events arranged by voluntary organisations or charities for the purpose of raising funds for charity may fall within the definition of 'trade' in Section 832 ICTA 1988, with the result that any profits will be liable to income tax or corporation tax. However, tax will not be charged on such profits provided:*
>
> *1)   the event is of a kind which falls within the exemption from VAT under Group 12 of Schedule 9 to the VAT Act 1994 and*
>
> *2)   the profits are transferred to charities or otherwise applied for charitable purposes.*

The fact that an activity is exempt from VAT, and that any profit will not be taxed, does not necessarily mean that charities can undertake the activity directly rather than through a trading company.

To get tax relief for trading activities not covered by these exemptions, your charity may also want to consider conducting all or part of its trading activities from a subsidiary trading company and transferring any profits back to the charity as a corporate gift aid donation.

Further information about the direct tax treatment of trades carried on by charities can be found on HMRC's website.

VAT

VAT law uses the concept of 'business', which has a broad definition. As a general rule, if your charity is making a charge for an activity then it is in business for VAT purposes. Its charitable status has no bearing on whether you are in business for VAT purposes. Once registered for VAT your charity will be subject to the normal VAT requirements of any other business.

If your charity is carrying on a business activity you need to consider whether that activity is taxable or exempt from VAT. If your charity is engaged in taxable business activities you are subject to VAT registration thresholds in the same way as any other business.

In certain cases the charity will need to register for VAT and charge VAT on what it sells. VAT registration is compulsory if your total trading income (across all funds and projects) exceeds the current VAT registration level, and penalties will be charged if your charity doesn't register for VAT as soon as required. In calculating the total trading income you can exclude sales which, if you were VAT registered, would be VAT exempt.

If your charity's income is more than £67,000 (2008/09 figure), work out how much of this is trading income. This means being very clear whether funding agreements are grants or contracts. Then deduct items that would be VAT exempt.

You will find information on exempt goods and services at www.hmrc.gov.uk/vat/reclaim-exempt.htm#1. Items that are exempt from VAT include:

- insurance, finance and credit
- education and training
- fundraising events by charities
- subscriptions to membership organisations
- selling, leasing and letting of commercial land and buildings – but this exemption can be waived.

Exempt supplies are not taxable for VAT, so you do not include sales of exempt goods or services in your taxable turnover for VAT purposes. If you buy exempt items, there is no VAT to reclaim.

If the total comes to more than about £60,000, you will need to watch the position carefully. If it goes over the threshold you must register for VAT within a month. Note that all income, primary purpose and trading for fundraising counts for the VAT threshold.

If you do this calculation and realise that your charity went over the VAT threshold some time ago, but you haven't registered, then a 'retrospective registration' will be needed. In other words, on the form VAT1, where you give the date from which the charity needs to be registered, this may be several years in the past. This can give rise to complex issues such as the need to re-invoice past work or, if this is not possible, previous income may have to be treated as VAT inclusive – which could prove to be very expensive. The charity may have to submit retrospective VAT returns and repay the VAT amount due. The charity would also be liable to VAT penalties unless the trustees could persuade HMRC that they had a 'reasonable excuse' for not realising the position at the time. In these circumstances you would need specialist help.

However, in some cases, charities making a retrospective registration where they are able to re-invoice work (for example, to a local authority) have found they are able to reclaim substantial VAT on past expenditure, which more than covers the cost of professional help. However, the level of monitoring trading income should be such that the organisation should not get into this position.

If you conclude that you do not need to register, you can ignore VAT issues in relation to income, but in that case you should remember to allow for all expenditure at prices including VAT. (If a charity has some trading income, but is below the threshold, it is possible to register for VAT voluntarily but there are few cases where it would be advantageous to do so. Voluntary registration is worth considering where most or all of the sales would be zero-rated, for example, if the charity derives substantial income from charity shops selling donated goods, or from sales of books and publications).

VAT registration is done through the relevant HMRC VAT registration office for your area, by completing and returning form VAT1. Charities that do have to register for VAT are usually VAT partially exempt because the grants and donations side is non-VATable, which makes the VAT issues more complex.

Where an organisation is VAT registered, it must charge VAT at the appropriate rate on everything sold. The implications of VAT depend on your customer, in some cases this is an added financial burden, in others they may be able to reclaim the VAT.

Once you register, you will have to charge VAT in the future on all full rated supplies at the standard rate (for example on catering) and do a quarterly VAT return to HMRC. The good news is that you can 'offset' some VAT you have to pay against the VAT you charge. The other point to note is that you may well have a range of activities, some of which may be exempt from VAT, some full rated and some outside the scope. In any case, you will probably need a VAT specialist to help you, at least in the early stages.

When planning your fundraising, it is worth thinking about the VAT situation. If you are planning major building alterations, is there a way of recovering some or all of the VAT? Will your fundraising mean you go over the VAT threshold anyway? Is there a way around this (such as organising payments so that you do not receive more than the limit for VAT-able income in any one financial year)?

For more information or advice on any of these matters please see the detailed guidance notes on the HMRC website, www.hmrc.gov.uk/charities. 'CWL4' is an excellent leaflet produced by HMRC and also available from its website.

Brief guidance on the VAT issues relating to admission charges for cultural charities is available on the Charity Commission website on www.charity commission.gov.uk.

Charity lotteries

Tax exemption for profits from charity lotteries

There are detailed statutory regulations about the conduct of charity lotteries including accounts, age restrictions, the maximum price of tickets, the application of resulting profits and the amounts which may be paid out in prizes and deducted for expenses. You are advised to consult the appropriate local authority, the Gambling Commission and HMRC for further information and advice.

Generally, profits from lotteries organised by charities for fundraising purposes are exempt from tax as long as all current statutory requirements and both the following conditions are met:

- the lottery is promoted and conducted with a lottery operating licence
- all the proceeds are used for the charitable purposes of the charity.

For detailed information on tax and charity lotteries please refer to the following websites:
www.hmrc.gov.uk/CHARITIES/tax/trading/exemptions.htm#5
www.gamblingcommission.gov.uk/Client/detail.asp?ContentId=259

Contact details for the Gambling Commission and HMRC are given in *Useful contacts and sources of information* on page 371.

Gift Aid

Gift Aid is a scheme to encourage individuals and businesses to donate more money to charity.

Under the scheme, UK charities can claim back the basic rate tax already paid on gifts of money received from individuals who pay or have paid UK tax.

The scheme also allows UK companies to make gifts of money to charity before any tax is deducted.

Key requirements of the Gift Aid Scheme:

- Gift Aid only applies to donations of money.
- Gift Aid donations from individuals must be supported by a valid 'Gift Aid declaration'.
- You can give donors modest tokens of appreciation (called 'benefits') in order to acknowledge a gift but there are strict limits on their value.
- Your charity must keep adequate records to support any claims for Gift Aid repayments and of any benefits provided to donors.
- Donations and/or tax repayments received through the Gift Aid scheme must only be used for charitable purposes.
- Donations that give a right of admission to view a charity's property and some other particular types of donation must follow special rules to qualify for Gift Aid.

For further information and useful examples of gift aid, please refer to HRMC's website, www.hmrc.gov.uk/charities/gift_aid/index.htm.

Payroll giving

Payroll giving is a unique way for people to give regularly to charity. It allows employees, or occupational pensioners, to give money to any UK charity directly from their pay, before tax is deducted. This means that it costs the donor less and charities get more. It offers a regular flow of income and the money can be used as core funding.

Payroll giving also provides an opportunity to educate donors and potential donors. Unless donors wish to remain anonymous, you can send them regular newsletters about your charity's input into the community, so they see that their gifts are valuable, thus helping to reinforce their decision to choose your organisation. Equally, if your charity is helping a company to promote the scheme, it is a unique opportunity to talk to a captive audience.

Payroll giving provides unique access to corporate networking. The opportunity is also there for you to get to know your donors.

/ Case study \

Success story
Save the Children

Save the Children is the UK's leading international children's charity working to create a better world for children. It works in 70 countries, including the UK, helping the world's most disadvantaged children.

Save the Children introduced its payroll giving scheme in 1987 and, after steady growth, 20 years later, almost 13,000 employees from 1,329 organisations will contribute £900,000 to support its vital work. The long-term commitment of payroll givers enables Save the Children to plan its continuing work with children, their families and communities, more effectively.

Payroll giving is extremely cost effective to administer. For the employer, it is also easy to administer after the initial set-up and often organisations support their employees by matching their donations or by paying the small administration fee. For the employee, payroll giving is a tax effective way to commit funds to Save the Children, or other charities, on a regular basis.

Save the Children promotes payroll giving direct to its corporate supporters. In addition, it has worked successfully with two professional fundraising organisations, Sharing the Caring and Charity Link, to reach a wider audience. Save the Children receives donations from a wide range of companies, from those with less than 100 staff to major organisations employing over 100,000.

Save the Children's payroll givers are kept informed about the charity's important work with children via Payroll Giving News, which also contains information about tax rate changes and charitable giving.

For additional guidance about payroll giving, promotional materials and useful links visit www.payrollgivingcentre.org.uk, operated by the Institute of Fundraising.

PAYE

PAYE (Pay As You Earn) is the system that HMRC uses to collect income tax and national insurance contributions (NICs) from employees' pay as they earn it; this includes the directors of limited companies.

If you employ and pay staff, you will have to deduct tax and NICs from your employees' pay each pay period and pay Employer's Class 1 NICs if they earn above a certain threshold. You pay these amounts to HMRC monthly or quarterly and need to send the correct amount on time or you may be charged interest.

Employers' responsibility for PAYE

As an employer you have a legal obligation to operate PAYE on the payments you make to your employees if their earnings reach the national insurance lower earnings limit (LEL). You use the employee's tax code and national insurance category letter to work out how much income tax and NICs to deduct from their pay and how much Employer's Class 1 NICs you owe on their earnings. You must send the correct amount on time each month, although you may be able to send the amounts due every quarter if your average monthly payments are likely to be less than £1,500. For further details of the current LEL, the date for online and postal payments and whether you can send payments quarterly, please refer to HMRC's website.

What payments does PAYE apply to?

PAYE is applied to all the payments that an employee receives as a result of working for you, including:

- salary and wages
- overtime, shift pay and tips – unless these are paid directly to your employee or they come out of an independent tronc (an arrangement for the pooling and distribution to employees of tips, gratuities and/or service charges in the hotel and catering trade)
- bonuses and commission
- certain expenses allowances paid in cash
- statutory sick pay
- statutory maternity, paternity or adoption pay
- lump sum and compensation payments – such as redundancy payments – unless they're exempt from tax
- non-cash items such as vouchers, shares or premium bonds – you apply PAYE to the cash value of such items.

To check the current PAYE and NIC rates and limits please refer to the HMRC website, which includes a link to the current information.

PAYE on expenses and benefits

Employees are also taxed through PAYE on benefits in kind, such as a company car, medical insurance and other benefits. As an employer you will have to pay Class 1A NICs on some benefits. However you don't pay these contributions under the PAYE system – you do so separately at the year end.

PAYE is also applied to any expenses allowances that you pay to your employees – unless they are covered by a dispensation. A dispensation allows you to make the payments free of tax and NICs and can cut out a lot of form filling and other paperwork.

Other deductions under PAYE

As well as deducting income tax and NICs from your employees' pay each pay period, you might also use the PAYE system to deduct other items, such as:

- student loan repayments
- employees' pension contributions
- payments under an attachment of earnings order
- repayment of a loan you've made to an employee.

Pay statements

You are required to give each of your employees a pay statement – or payslip – at or before the time that you pay them. This can be in either paper or electronic format but it must show certain items, including each employee's gross pay (before tax), any deductions and the net amount payable after the deductions have been made. If you don't give your employees an itemised payslip they could complain to an employment tribunal.

At the end of each tax year you must give employees a summary of their pay and deductions on form P60. This must be in paper format.

Getting started with PAYE

When you pay your employees for the first time you must check whether you need to operate PAYE and register as an employer with HMRC. You can register as an employer by email or by calling the New Employer Helpline on 0845 60 70 143.

You can also contact your local HMRC Customer Advice Team for free confidential advice or to find out about workshops and presentations to help you with PAYE and payroll.

For more detailed information on the topics listed above, key dates, current rates and limits, forms and useful links to other guidance, please visit www.hmrc.gov.uk/paye/intro-basics.

CAF and other vouchers

If someone gives you a donation using a Charities Aid Foundation (CAF) voucher – or another charity voucher – you cannot reclaim any tax on these. This is because the donor has already made a gift aid donation to CAF and CAF has then reclaimed the tax. Tax cannot be reclaimed twice.

Conclusion

You need to make sure that you get the payment of taxes right. HMRC will not be swayed by the fact that your committee is made up of willing volunteers who did not know the law – if tax is due you will have to pay it. It should also be stressed that it is vital to keep up to date with any changes; amendments often happen with little publicity and the onus is on you to be aware of all the current information. This chapter should have alerted you to the main areas of possible concern. The message is that if you are not sure, refer to HMRC at an early stage and if necessary get specialist advice.

Useful contacts and sources of information

Here are some sources of information and advice, many of which are referred to in the chapters of the guide. The list is in alphabetical order and a brief description of the organisations is given, with information taken from their websites.

Arts Council England

Arts Council England is the national development agency for the arts in England, distributing public money from government and the National Lottery.

14 Great Peter Street
London SW1P 3NQ

Tel: 0845 300 6200
Fax: 020 7973 6590
Textphone: 020 7973 6564
Email: enquiries@artscouncil.org.uk
Website: www.artscouncil.org.uk

BBC Children in Need

'Our mission is to positively change the lives of disadvantaged children and young people in the UK. Our vision is a society where each and every child and young person is supported to realise their potential.'

If you're applying for a grant or need advice on any aspect of fundraising for BBC Children in Need, get in touch with your local office (details below).

For general enquiries, please use the form online or call 0345 609 0015.

National offices

England and general helpline

BBC Children in Need Appeal
PO Box 1000
London W12 7WJ

Tel: 020 8576 7788

Scotland

BBC Children in Need Appeal
BBC Scotland
G10, 40 Pacific Drive
Glasgow G51 1DA

Tel: 0141 422 6111

Northern Ireland

BBC Children in Need Appeal
Broadcasting House
Ormeau Avenue
Belfast BT2 8HQ

Tel: 028 9033 8221

Wales

BBC Children in Need Appeal
Broadcasting House
Llandaff
Cardiff CF5 2YQ

Tel: 029 2032 2383

Regional offices

North – Newcastle

BBC Children in Need Appeal
Broadcasting Centre
Barrack Road
Newcastle NE99 2NE

Tel: 0191 232 1313

North – Manchester

BBC Children in Need Appeal
Room 2010

New Broadcasting House
Oxford Road
Manchester M60 1SJ

Tel: 0161 244 3439

North – Leeds

BBC Children in Need Appeal
BBC Broadcasting Centre
2 St Peter's Square
Leeds LS9 8AH

Tel: 0113 224 7155

Central – Norwich

BBC Children in Need Appeal
BBC East
The Forum
Norwich NR2 1BH

Tel: 01603 284 774

Central – Nottingham

BBC Children in Need Appeal
BBC Nottingham
London Road
Nottingham NG2 4UU

Tel: 01159 021851

Central – Birmingham

BBC Children in Need Appeal
Level 10, BBC Birmingham
The Mailbox
Birmingham B1 1RF

Tel: 0121 567 6707

South and West – Bristol

BBC Children in Need Appeal
Broadcasting House
Whiteladies Road
Bristol BS8 2LR

Tel: 0117 974 6600

South and West – Plymouth

BBC Children in Need Appeal
Broadcasting House
Seymour Road
Mannamead
Plymouth PL3 5BD

Tel: 01752 234588

London and South East

BBC Children in Need Appeal
Room 735, South East Block
Bush House
Strand
London WC2B 4PA

Tel: 020 7557 0389
Email for all enquiries:
pudsey@bbc.co.uk
Website: www.bbc.co.uk/pudsey

Big Lottery Fund (BIG)

'We are committed to bringing real improvements to communities, and to the lives of people most in need.'

1 Plough Place
London EC4A 1DE

Tel: 020 7211 1800
Textphone: 0845 039 0204
Fax: 020 7211 1750
Website: www.biglotteryfund.org.uk

For funding information or general enquiries call the BIG advice line on 0845 4 10 20 30 or email general.enquiries@biglotteryfund.org.uk.

Strategic grants office

4th floor
Pearl Assurance House
Friar Lane
Nottingham NG1 6BT

Telephone: 0115 934 2950
Textphone: 0115 934 2951

Fax: 0115 934 2952
Email: strategicgrants@biglotteryfund.org.uk

Northern Ireland office

For funding information or general enquiries call the BIG advice line on 028 9055 1455.

1 Cromac Quay
Cromac Wood
Belfast BT7 2JD

Telephone: 028 9055 1455
Textphone: 028 9055 1431
Fax: 028 9055 1444

Scotland office

For funding information or general enquiries call the BIG advice line on 0870 2 40 23 91 or email enquiries.scotland@biglotteryfund.org.uk.

1 Atlantic Quay
1 Robertson Street
Glasgow G2 8JB

Telephone: 0141 242 1400
Textphone: 0141 242 1500
Fax: 0141 242 1401

Wales offices

For funding information or general enquiries call the BIG advice line on 01686 611 700 or email enquiries.wales@biglotteryfund.org.uk.

Newtown office

2nd Floor
Ladywell House
Newtown
Powys SY16 1JB
Telephone: 01686 611700
Textphone: 01686 610205
Fax: 01686 621534

Cardiff office

6th Floor
1 Kingsway
Cardiff CF10 3JN

Telephone: 029 2067 8200
Textphone: 0845 602 1659
Fax: 029 2066 7275

England regional offices

East Midlands

For funding information or general enquiries call the BIG advice line on 0845 4 10 20 30 or email enquiries.em@biglotteryfund.org.uk.

4th Floor
Pearl Assurance House
Friar Lane
Nottingham NG1 6BT
Telephone: 0115 872 2950
Fax: 0115 872 2990

West Midlands

For funding information or general enquiries call the BIG advice line on 0845 4 10 20 30 or email enquiries.wm@biglotteryfund.org.uk.

Big Lottery Fund, Birmingham Centre
Apex House
3 Embassy Drive
Edgbaston
Birmingham B15 1TR

Telephone: 0121 345 7700
Textphone: 0121 345 7666
Fax: 0121 345 8888

East of England

For funding information or general enquiries call the BIG advice line on 0845 4 10 20 30. For information about events that are happening in the East of England region email regionevents.ea@biglotteryfund.org.uk, or contact:

Big Lottery Fund
2nd Floor
Elizabeth House
1 High Street
Chesterton
Cambridge CB4 1YW

Telephone: 01223 449000
Textphone: 01223 352041
Fax: 01223 312628

London

For funding information or general enquiries call the BIG advice line on 0845 4 10 20 30 or email general.enquiries@biglotteryfund.org.uk.

For information about the work of the London team, contact:

The London regional office
5th Floor
1 Plough Place
London EC4A 1DE

Telephone: 020 7842 4000
Textphone: 0845 039 0204
Fax: 020 7842 4010

North East

For funding information or general enquiries call the BIG advice line on 0845 4 10 20 30 or email enquiries.ne@biglotteryfund.org.uk.

2 St James Gate
Newcastle upon Tyne NE1 4BE

Telephone: 0191 376 1600
Textphone: 0191 376 1776
Fax: 0191 376 1661

North West

For funding information or general enquiries call the BIG advice line on 0845 4 10 20 30 or email general.enquiries@biglotteryfund.org.uk.

There is no separate email address for the North West

Big Lottery Fund
10th Floor
York House
York Street
Manchester M2 3BB

Telephone: 0161 261 4600
Textphone: 0161 261 4647
Fax: 0161 261 4646

South East

For funding information or general enquiries call the BIG advice line on 0845 4 10 20 30. For more information on events in the South East email southeastevents@biglotteryfund.org.uk.

4th Floor
Dominion House
Woodbridge Road
Guildford
Surrey GU1 4BN

Telephone: 01483 462900
Textphone: 01483 568764
Fax: 01483 569764

South West

For funding information or general enquiries call the BIG advice line on 0845 4 10 20 30 or email general.enquiries@biglotteryfund.org.uk.

Beaufort House
51 New North Road
Exeter EX4 4EQ

Telephone: 01392 849700
Textphone: 01392 490633
Fax: 01392 491134

Yorkshire and the Humber

For funding information or general enquiries call the BIG advice line on 0845 4 10 20 30 or email enquiries.yh@biglotteryfund.org.uk.

3rd floor Carlton Tower
34 St Pauls Street
Leeds LS1 2AT
Telephone: 0113 224 5301
Textphone: 0113 245 4104
Fax: 0113 244 0363

BRE Trust

The BRE Trust (formerly the Foundation for the Built Environment) is a charitable company whose objectives are, through research and education, to advance knowledge, innovation and communication in all matters concerning the built environment for public benefit.

Room 5 Building 1
Bucknalls Lane
Garston
Watford
Herts WD25 9XX

Tel: 01923 664598
Fax: 01923 664089
Email: burdettj@bretrust.org.uk
www.bretrust.org.uk

British Youth Council

'All young people across the UK will have a say and be heard.'

The British Youth Council (BYC) is led by young people, for young people, aged 26 and under, across the UK. It provides training and volunteering and campaigning activity, both locally and globally.

The Mezzanine 2
Downstream Building
1 London Bridge SE1 9BG

Tel: 0845 458 1489
Fax: 0845 458 1847
Email facility available online
Website: www.byc.org.uk

Business in the Community (BitC)

'Business in the Community inspires, engages, supports and challenges companies to continually improve the impact they have on society and the environment through their responsible business programme, sometimes referred to as corporate social responsibility (CSR).'

BitC works through four areas: community, environment, marketplace and workplace. It has more than 850 companies in membership and represents one in five of the UK private sector workforce; it also convenes a network of global partners.

137 Shepherdess Walk
London N1 7RQ

Tel: 020 7566 8650
Email: information@bitc.org.uk
Website: www.bitc.org.uk

Charities Aid Foundation (CAF)

CAF's mission is: 'An integrated customer-focused organisation for donors and charities that stimulates giving, social investment and the effective use of funds.'

25 Kings Hill Avenue
Kings Hill
West Malling
Kent ME19 4TA

Tel: 01732 520 000
Fax: 01732 520 001
Email: enquiries@cafonline.org
Website: www.cafonline.org

Charity Commission for England and Wales (the Commission)

'Mission

The Charity Commission is the independent regulator for charitable activity

- enabling charities to maximise their impact
- ensuring compliance with legal obligations
- encouraging innovation and effectiveness
- championing the public interest in charity to promote the public's trust and confidence'

The Charity Commission has four offices:

London: Harmsworth House, 13–15 Bouverie Street, London EC4Y 8DP
Liverpool: 12 Princes Dock, Princes Parade, Liverpool L3 1DE
Taunton: Woodfield House, Tangier, Taunton, Somerset TA1 4BL
Newport: 8th Floor, Clarence House, Clarence Place, Newport NP19 7AA

The Commission provides an online knowledge base for the most frequently asked questions raised by customers and this is continually updated – go to www.charity-commission.gov.uk.

Email: enquiries@charitycommission.gsi.gov.uk.

If you experience difficulties accessing the online facility you should call 0845 300 0197.

If you would rather speak to an advisor you can call Charity Commission Direct – see below. You can write to the Commission at:

Charity Commission Direct

PO Box 1227
Liverpool L69 3UG

Tel: 0845 3000 218

Staff are available to take calls between 8.00am–8.00pm from Monday to Friday and 9.00am–1.00pm on Saturdays (except national holidays).

There is also a Textbox service on 0845 3000 219 for hearing impaired callers.

The centralised fax number is: 0151 703 1555

A comprehensive range of guidance documents is available to download from the Commission's website: www.charity-commission.gov.uk.

The Commission advises that it is not always necessary to seek legal advice for issues you need clarifying and it is advisable to contact the Commission in the first instance.

If you do need legal advice, make sure you find a solicitor who specialises in charity law.

Information about suitable solicitors is available from the Charity Law Association – details given below.

Charity Law Association

'The Charity Law Association was established at the end of 1992 with the aim of enabling those who advise on or use charity law to meet together, to exchange ideas and intelligence and to use their experience and expertise for the benefit of the charity sector.

'To ensure that it is free to promote any changes to charity law which appear to its members, based on their expertise in the field, to be necessary or desirable the Association is not itself a charity.

'The Association works closely with the Charity Commission and is now consulted by government and others in connection with charity law issues.

'The Association currently has over 850 members, including many of the country's largest charities and most leading charity lawyers.'

10 Tavistock Close
Rainham
Kent ME8 9HR

Email: admin@charitylawassociation.org.uk
Website: www.charitylawassociation.org.uk

Comic Relief

'Comic Relief's vision is a just world free from poverty.'

Comic Relief was set up in 1985 by comedians who wanted to do something to help others. It now has two major fundraising campaigns: Red Nose Day and Sport Relief.

Comic Relief UK
5th Floor
89 Albert Embankment
London SE1 7TP

Telephone: 020 7820 5555
Fax: 020 7820 5500
Minicom: 020 7820 5579
General enquiries info@comicrelief.org.uk
Website: www.comicrelief.com

Community Foundation Network (CFN)

'Community Foundation Network represents the community foundation movement in the UK. Our aim is to help clients create lasting value from their local giving through the network of community foundations.

'Community foundations are charities located across the UK dedicated to strengthening local communities, creating opportunities and tackling issues of disadvantage and exclusion. Community foundations target grants that make a genuine difference to the lives of local people. They manage funds donated by individuals and organisations, building endowment and acting as the vital link between donors and local needs, connecting people with causes, and enabling clients to achieve far more than they could ever by themselves.'

Details of all local community foundations can be found on the network's website – www.communityfoundations.org.uk.

Community Foundation Network
Arena House
66–68 Pentonville Road
London N1 9HS

Tel: 020 7713 9326
Fax: 020 7713 9327
Email: network@communityfoundations.org.uk

Companies House

Main office

Companies House
Crown Way
Maindy
Cardiff CF14 3UZ

Edinburgh

Companies House
37 Castle Terrace
Edinburgh EH1 2EB

London

Companies House Executive Agency
21 Bloomsbury Street
London WC1B 3XD

Tel: 0303 1234 500
Minicom: 029 2038 1245
Email: enquiries@companies-house.gov.uk
Website: www.companieshouse.gov.uk

Council for Environmental Education (CEE)

'The Council for Environmental Education (CEE) is a national membership body for organisations and individuals in England committed to environmental education and education for sustainable development.

'CEE works with and for its membership to develop policy, enhance practice and enable members to work more effectively together.'

Its website gives details of CEE's work, member organisations and current news. The information centre provides access to CEE's database on events, training, funding and learning resources.

94 London Street
Reading RG1 4SJ

Tel: 0118 950 2550
Fax: 0118 959 1955
Website: www.cee.org.uk

Department for Culture, Media and Sport (DCMS)

This government department aims 'to improve the quality of life for all through cultural and sporting activities, to support the pursuit of excellence and to champion the tourism, creative and leisure industries'.

Department for Culture Media and Sport
2–4 Cockspur Street
London SW1Y 5DH

Tel: 020 7211 6200 (open 9.30am–4.30pm) Monday to Friday

Email: enquiries@culture.gov.uk
Website: www.culture.gov.uk

Directory of Social Change (DSC)

'Directory of Social Change (DSC) is an independent charity with a vision of an independent voluntary sector at the heart of social change. We achieve this by providing essential information and training to the voluntary sector to enable charities to achieve their mission.

'Our independent status and well respected research means we can challenge and create debate around government policy, trust funding, and other issues which threaten the independence of smaller charities. We are in touch with over 20,000 charities annually through our conferences and training on fundraising, management, organisational and personal development, communication, finance and law.

'We also publish a wide variety of resources for charities, including our well-known UK fundraising guides, directories and websites. We were started in 1974 and our 45 staff are based in London and Liverpool.

'Our mission is to be an agent connecting givers, influencers and service deliverers.

'We believe that the activities of voluntary and community organisations are crucial, both to the causes they serve and the social environment in which they operate.'

24 Stephenson Way
London NW1 2DP

384

Tel: 08450 77 77 07
Fax: 020 7391 4804
Email: enquiries@dsc.org.uk
Website: www.dsc.org.uk

For publications that may be useful to readers of this guide, please see DSC publications at the end of this section.

Europe in the UK – Information Network

The website for this network brings together contact details for organisations in the UK regions, from local authorities to universities, business support agencies to libraries, who find it useful to work together on European issues to serve the needs of their customers more effectively. You can find full details of the Europe Direct drop-in centres which are spread throughout the UK and are designed to help members of the public get basic information about what the EU does and how it works.

The site also aims to raise awareness of how the European Union affects the UK and to demonstrate how its citizens can both benefit from, and influence, what happens at a European level.

The website gives details of where in your area one can find out more about Europe, whether you want to know about funding initiatives, comparative statistics or up-to-date information on EU decisions.

Website: www.europe.org.uk

European Union – Education, Audiovisual and Culture Executive Agency

The Education, Audiovisual and Culture Executive Agency (EACEA) is a public body of the European Commission operational since January 2006.

The role of EACEA is to manage European funding opportunities and networks in the fields of education and training, citizenship, youth, audiovisual and culture.

The Agency's mandate covers a variety of Europe and worldwide opportunities for organisations, professionals and individuals, at all ages and stages of life. Seven key community programmes have been partly or fully delegated to the EACEA: Lifelong Learning, Erasmus Mundus, Tempus, Culture, **Youth in Action***, Europe for Citizens and Media, as well as several international Cooperation Agreements in the field of higher education.

*The Youth Unit
Education, Audiovisual, and Culture Executive Agency
Unit P6: Youth
BOUR 01/01
Avenue du Bourget 1
B-1140 Brussels

Youth Helpdesk–(general information, accreditation, insurance, visa support, crisis management):
Tel: +32 2 29 68724
Fax: +32 2 29 21330
Email: youthhelpdesk@ec.europa.eu

General Executive Agency information tel: +32 2 29 75615
General email: eacea-info@ec.europa.eu

European Youth Parliament

The European Youth Parliament (EYP) is an educational foundation that aims to build on the potential of young people through the strengthening of skills such as communication, teambuilding, trust, understanding and working with others from very different backgrounds. It also seeks to offer young people across Europe the opportunity to become active citizens by participating in one of its events. The EYP is active in over 33 countries across Europe with local, regional, national and international events.

EYPUK
39 Woodcote Avenue
St Nicolas Park
Nuneaton
Warwickshire
CV11 6DE

Contact: Marcus Pollard – chairperson
Email: Marcus.pollard@eypalumni.org
Email (media): media@eypuk.org
Website: www.eypuk.org

European Youth Portal

'The European Youth Portal is an initiative of the European Commission. It has been suggested by the Commission's White Paper *A new impetus for European Youth.* Its aim is to give as many young people as possible quick and easy access to relevant youth related information on Europe. The ultimate objective of the portal is to enhance young people's participation in public life and to contribute to their active citizenship. The target group is young people between 15 and 25 years of age. In addition, the portal will cater for the needs of those working with young people.'

European Commission
Directorate-General for Education and Culture
Youth unit
VM 2 5/7
B-1049 Brussels
email: EAC-PORTAL-YOUTH@cec.eu.int

Gambling Commission

The Gambling Commission was established in October 2005 taking over the role previously played by the Gaming Board for Great Britain in regulating casinos, bingo, gaming machines and lotteries.

The Gambling Commission has responsibility for the regulation of betting and remote gambling; helping to protect children and vulnerable people from being harmed or exploited by gambling; and for advising local and central government on issues related to gambling.

The Gambling Commission is not responsible for regulating spread betting or the National Lottery, which are the responsibility of the Financial Services Authority and the National Lottery Commission, respectively.

The Gambling Commission is a non-departmental public body, sponsored by the Department for Culture, Media and Sport and is funded mainly by licence fees from the gambling industry.

Victoria Square House
Victoria Square
Birmingham B2 4BP

Tel: 0121 230 6666
Fax: 0121 230 6720
info@gamblingcommission.gov.uk
Website: www.gamblingcommission.gov.uk

Heritage Lottery Fund (HLF)

This non-governmental public body gives grants to a wide range of projects involving the local, regional and national heritage of the UK. It distributes a share of the money raised by the National Lottery for good causes.

Tel: 020 7591 6000
Fax: 020 7591 6271
Email: enquire@hlf.org.uk
Website: www.hlf.org.uk

HM Revenue & Customs (HMRC)

'HM Revenue & Customs (HMRC) was formed in April 2005, following the merger of the Inland Revenue and HM Customs and Excise Departments. We are here to ensure the correct tax is paid at the right time, whether this relates to payment of taxes received by the department or entitlement to benefits paid.'

St John's House
Merton Road
Bootle L69 9BB

Tel: 0845 302 0203
Email: charities@inlandrevenue.gov.uk
Website: www.hmrc.gov.uk/charities

Institute of Fundraising

'The Institute of Fundraising is the professional body that represents fundraisers in the UK. Our mission is to support fundraisers, through leadership, representation, standard setting and education, to deliver excellent fundraising. At the core of the Institute lies membership and we currently have 4,600 individual members and 270 organisational members.'

Park Place
12 Lawn Lane
London SW8 1UD

Main switchboard: 020 7840 1000
Tax-effective giving helpline: 0845 458 4586
Fax: 020 7840 1001
Email facility online
Website: institute-of-fundraising.org.uk

London Voluntary Service Council (LVSC)

'LVSC's vision is for the voluntary and community sector to play a fully empowered and effective role in the diverse life of London. LVSC brings London voluntary and community sector organisations together to learn and share best practice and to create a coordinated voice to influence policymakers. We provide policy briefings, up-to-date information on management and funding, advice and support for voluntary and community groups, topical e-bulletins and short courses for those working in the sector.'

356 Holloway Road
London N7 6PA

Tel: 020 7700 8107
Email: lvsc@lvsc.org
Website: www.lvsc.org.uk

National Association of Clubs for Young People (CYP)

CYP is a UK-wide network of clubs, services, projects and activities providing support for young people in their local communities.

371 Kennington Lane
London SE11 5QY

Tel: 020 7793 0787
Fax: 020 7820 9815
Email: office@clubsforyoungpeople.org.uk
Website: www.clubsforyoungpeople.org.uk

National Council for Voluntary Youth Services (NCVYS)

'Established in 1936, the National Council for Voluntary Youth Services is a diverse and growing network of over 180 national organisations and regional and local networks.

'Our mission is to ensure the development and recognition of a vibrant, sound and diverse voluntary and community sector that involves, empowers and meets the needs of all young people.'

Third Floor
Lancaster House
33 Islington High Street
London N1 9LH

Tel: 020 7278 1041
Fax: 020 7833 2491
Email: mail@ncvys.org.uk
Website: www.ncvys.org.uk

National Council for Voluntary Organisations

'NCVO believes passionately in the voluntary and community sector. This is a sector with the power to transform the lives of people and communities for the better.

'Vision

NCVO's vision is of a society in which people are inspired to make a positive difference to their communities.

'Mission

A vibrant voluntary and community sector deserves a strong voice and the best support. NCVO aims to be that support and voice.'

Regent's Wharf
8 All Saint's Street
London N1 9RL

Tel: 020 7713 6161
Helpdesk: 0800 2 798 798
Email: ncvo@ncvo-vol.org.uk
Website: www.ncvo-vol.org.uk

National Endowment for Science, Technology and the Arts (NESTA)

NESTA is not primarily a grant-making organisation and does not fund charities, but it does work in partnership with those that are delivering programmes on NESTA's behalf.

'We invest in early-stage companies, inform and shape policy, and deliver practical programmes that inspire others to solve the big challenges of the future'.

1 Plough Place
London EC4A 1DE

Tel: 020 7438 2500
Fax: 020 7438 2501
Email: information@nesta.org.uk
Website: www.nesta.org.uk

The National Youth Agency (NYA)

'Our mission: supporting young people to achieve their full potential The NYA works with organisations and services to improve the life chances of young people and also works directly with young people themselves to develop their voice and influence in shaping policy and securing social justice. The NYA is an independent organisation, with its own board of trustees, responding to and influencing local and national government policy, representing the rights and needs of young people and promoting best youth work practice'.

Eastgate House
19–23 Humberstone Road
Leicester LE5 3GJ

Tel: 0116 242 7350
Fax: 0116 242 7444
Email: nya@nya.org.uk
General enquiries: dutydesk@nya.org.uk
Website: www.nya.org.uk

Olympic Lottery Distributor

The Olympic Lottery Distributor is an independent body set up by Parliament and uses money raised by the National Lottery to fund the delivery of the infrastructure for the London 2012 Olympic and Paralympic Games and their legacy.

1 Plough Place
London EC4A 1DE

Tel: 020 7880 2012
Email: info@olympiclottery2012.org.uk
Website: www.olympiclotterydistributor.org.uk

OpenOffice.org

OpenOffice.org is an open-source office software suite for wordprocessing, spreadsheets, presentations, graphics and databases. It is available in different languages and works on all common computers. It can be downloaded and used completely free of charge for any purpose.

Email: users@openoffice.org – *Please note that all mail sent to openoffice.org is in the public domain.*

Website: www.openoffice.org

Payroll Giving Centre

The Payroll Giving Centre website is hosted by the Institute of Fundraising. The website is an independent resource centre for Payroll Giving, and includes information on Payroll Giving, the Payroll Giving Quality Mark and the National Payroll Giving Excellence Awards. The Payroll Giving Centre is funded by government and administered and promoted by the Institute of Fundraising.

Payroll Giving Centre
PO Box 52709
London EC3P 3WX

Tel: 0845 602 6786
Email: info@payrollgivingcentre.org.uk
Website: www.payrollgivingcentre.org.uk

Royal Society of Wildlife Trusts (RSWT)

The RSWT is a registered charity, established to promote conservation and manage environmental funds.

Although a charity in its own right, RSWT also operates as an umbrella group for the 47 local wildlife trusts that have been formed across the UK, helping to coordinate their activities and campaigning at a UK level.

The RSWT Grants Unit manages several funds, administering nearly £20 million a year in grants to support local, regional and national environmental projects, carried out by charities and not-for-profit organisations.

The Kiln
Waterside
Mather Road
Newark
Nottinghamshire NG24 1WT

Tel: 01636 677711
Fax: 01636 670001
Email: grants@rswt.org
Website: www.rswt.org

School Councils UK

'School Councils UK is an independent charity which promotes and facilitates effective structures for pupil participation in every school. Our vision is of young people as decision-makers, stakeholders and partners in their schools and communities.'

108–110 Camden High Street
London NW1 0LU

Tel: 0845 456 9428/020 7482 8910
Fax: 0845 456 9429
Email: info@schoolcouncils.org
Website: www.schoolcouncils.org

Sport England

'Sport England is the government agency responsible for developing a world-class community sport system.'

3rd Floor Victoria House
Bloomsbury Square
London WC1B 4SE

Tel: 020 7273 1551
Fax: 020 7383 5740
Tel: 08458 508 508 for general advice and fund details.
Email: info@sportengland.org
Website: www.sportengland.org

Third Sector Magazine

Third Sector is one of the largest publications aimed at the voluntary and not-for-profit sector. It currently has a readership of around 80,000 and is available as a printed magazine and online e-magazine. It also holds conferences and events in its efforts to bring the third sector together.

Haymarket Professional Publications
174 Hammersmith Road
London W6 7JP

Tel: 020 8267 4652
Email: thirdsector@haymarket.com
Website: www.thirdsector.co.uk

UK Film Council

'The UK Film Council is the government-backed lead agency for film in the UK ensuring that the economic, cultural and educational aspects of film are effectively represented at home and abroad.'

10 Little Portland Street
London W1W 7JG

Tel: 020 7861 7861
Fax: 020 7861 7862

Email: info@ukfilmcouncil.org.uk
Website: www.ukfilmcouncil.org.uk

UK Sport

'UK Sport is responsible for managing and distributing public investment and is a statutory distributor of funds raised by the National Lottery. It works in partnership with the home country sports councils and other agencies to lead sport in the UK to world-class success.'

40 Bernard Street
London WC1N 1ST

Tel: 020 7211 5100
Fax 020 7211 5246
Email: info@uksport.gov.uk
Website: www.uksport.gov.uk

UK Youth

'UK Youth is the leading national youth work charity supporting over 750,000 young people, helping them to raise their aspirations, realise their potential and have their achievements recognised via non-formal, accredited education programmes and activities.'

Avon Tyrrell
Bransgore
Hampshire BH23 8EE

Tel: 01425 672347
Fax: 01425 679108
Email: info@ukyouth.org
Website: www.ukyouth.org

UK Youth Parliament

The UK Youth Parliament (UKYP) enables young people to use their energy and passion to change the world for the better. Run by young people for young people, UKYP provides opportunities for 11–18 year olds to use their voice in creative ways to bring about social change.

UK Youth Parliament
15 Clerkenwell Green
London EC1R 0DP

Tel: 020 7553 9890
Fax: 020 7843 6310
Email: info@ukyouthparliament.org.uk
Website: www.ukyouthparliament.org.uk

YouthBank UK (YB-UK)

'YouthBank is a new and innovative UK-wide grant-making initiative run by young people for young people. Local YouthBanks provide small grants to projects led by young people, of benefit to the community and that also benefit the young people taking part. YouthBank is unique in that it is young people themselves who make decisions about how local YouthBanks are managed and run and, through a board of young people, also direct the UK-wide programme.'

Eastgate House
19–23 Humberstone Road
Leicester LE5 3GJ

Tel: 0116 242 7446
Email: youthbank@nya.org.uk
Website: www.youthbank.org.uk

Youth Justice Board (YJB)

The Youth Justice Board for England and Wales is an executive non-departmental public body. The 12 board members are appointed by the Secretary of State for Justice. The YJB works to prevent offending and reoffending by children and young people under the age of 18, and to ensure that custody for them is safe and secure and addresses the causes of their offending behaviour.

Head office:
11 Carteret Street
London SW1H 9DL

Tel: 020 7271 3033
Fax: 020 7271 3030
Email: enquiries@yjb.gov.uk
Website: www.yjb.gov.uk

DSC publications

Publications that may help readers of this guide include the following DSC publications:

The Charity Treasurer's Handbook, Gareth G Morgan

The Complete Fundraising Handbook, Nina Botting Herbst & Michael Norton

Directory of Grant-making Trusts, Alan French, Sarah Johnston, Denise Lillya, John Smyth & Tom Traynor

A Guide to the Major Trusts Volumes 1 and 2, Tom Traynor, Denise Lillya, Alan French & John Smith

The Guide to UK Company Giving, John Smyth

A Practical Guide to VAT for Charities and Voluntary Organisations, Kate Sayer & Alastair Hardman, published in association with Sayer Vincent

The Sports Funding Guide, Tom Traynor & Denise Lillya

Voluntary but not Amateur, Ruth Hayes & Jacki Reason

A free publications catalogue can be viewed or printed from the DSC website www.dsc.org.uk or ordered by calling 08450 77 77 07. DSC publishes a range of fundraising guides.

DSC also runs an extensive programme of training courses, seminars and conferences. For a copy of the latest training guide, contact the training department on 08450 77 77 07, email training@ dsc.org.uk or visit the DSC website: www.dsc.org.uk.

Alphabetical index of funders